Pushing the Boundaries

A Personal Account of Recovery from Stroke

Pushing the Boundaries

A Personal Account of Recovery from Stroke

as observed by
David Guthrie
in his role as a reluctant carer

Dartas

Books

© David Guthrie, 2017

Published by Dartas Books

A CIP catalogue record for this book is available from the British Library.

ISBN 978-0-9955820-0-2

Book layout and cover design by Clare Brayshaw

Cover picture: December 2012, after Rita had completed about 15 months of South African Therapy. The photo is from Noordhoek Ridge looking south-west over the Atlantic coast of the Cape Peninsula. In the background are Chapman's Peak and Noordhoek Beach.

Prepared and printed by:

York Publishing Services Ltd
64 Hallfield Road
Layerthorpe
York YO31 7ZQ

Tel: 01904 431213

Website: www.yps-publishing.co.uk

Contents

Part 2

Recovery – How it Happened

October 2010 to April 2013

Part 3

Recovery – and Why it Happened

January 2011 to the Summer of 2015

Preface

Would you like a new job? Something you can begin immediately, possibly almost overnight? Work you have never done before and with a real challenge? No training is necessary. Surprisingly perhaps, thousands of people achieve this objective every year. All it needs is for your spouse, partner, or someone close to you to become a victim of a severe stroke. My wife Rita suffered a life-threatening stroke and I had a change of job.

At the time the dreaded word "stroke" suddenly arrived to fill my life, I knew little about the effects it could have on people – both those who suffered a stroke and others who had to care for them. Nor had I ever had dealings with social service organisations and I was lucky enough to have consulted a doctor only rarely. My knowledge of how these big care and health organisations worked, and under what rules, was close to zero.

In April 2008, Rita suffered a severe stroke that changed both our lives as we knew them, suddenly and effectively, without warning. During the next six years or so our lives were successively defined by four facts. The first was that the stroke was life-threatening; I was told there was a high probability that she would not live. She did survive the operations to her brain, but was left with multiple physical and cognitive disabilities. The second fact was that, after making little progress towards recovery during two years at home in the UK, in the summer of 2010, Rita was assessed as having no ability to recover, due mainly to severe cognitive and memory problems. She was effectively written off by the health and care authorities so far as recovery was concerned. I was told her interests would be best served in a care home. The third fact was that, in October 2010, in the seaside town of Fish Hoek, near Cape Town in South Africa, Rita began an intensive rehabilitation therapy programme that was straight-forward, effective and inexpensive. The fourth fact was that, by April 2013, Rita was cured of all disabilities other than a poor short-term memory. She no longer needed therapy or care – she was once again as physically fit as any lady of 74 could expect to be – and we both had our lives back.

I have written this story around these four facts from the point of view of an amateur, full-time carer. It is the story of how one person, who happened to be my wife, made a most unusual and almost complete recovery from a severe stroke. It is a story that is inevitably anecdotal, my wife being a sample of one. Anecdotal histories such as this are commonly viewed in scientific circles as of little value – what is almost inevitably asked for is a well set-up, double-blind project carried out on a large enough sample of people to provide mathematically significant results. An anecdotal history can never provide such results as these. But it is, I believe, able to provide potentially useful insights into what is going on during stroke treatment and rehabilitation; perhaps act as a guide to new, and maybe underused, areas of therapy that should be investigated.

So the story is seen purely from my carer's point of view – as a factual record of what happened to Rita and me, including our responses to these events. I made many mistakes, mostly from ignorance of what might be the best action to take; sometimes from deep frustration at the close to impossible jobs that family carers take on despite lack of support, because they see it as their responsibility – which it probably is.

Readers will find that I am critical of the services provided by UK health and care authorities. This criticism is restricted to the narrow field of stroke rehabilitation therapy which, in our region of the country anyway, seemed to me to be inadequate. I regret having to write about bad service from health authorities, but that fact was central to this story. (On the infrequent occasions when Rita and I have had need of a doctor for other reasons, the service has always been good). When compared with the excellent therapy given to Rita in South Africa, so easily accessed and so exactly what was needed, those rehabilitation services available to us in the UK were shown as often poor, sometimes non-existent, and certainly difficult to access. Readers can come to their own view on those I have described and may disagree with my assessment, being detached from the circumstances which, for me, were desperately difficult. I have recorded it all as I experienced it.

Ultimately, my success in finding a cure in South Africa for Rita's disabilities persuaded me that a proportion of badly disabled UK stroke survivors may be capable of making a much better recovery than they commonly do. What it comes down to is that a disabled survivor has only two options when discharged home from hospital: to recover to a greater or lesser extent, or to learn to live with their disabilities. The latter is the default option. Unless the determination to get better exists – which must be supported by professional rehabilitation (ideally on a time-unlimited basis, which we found difficult to access in the UK) – then good care, however loving and attentive, will at best do no more than provide a comfortable life of dependence. My reasons for this view are explained in Part 3.

Rita's recovery emphasised two reasons why it is so important not to give up and accept a life of care and dependence. The first reason is ethical. If a good recovery can be achieved, then everyone concerned enjoys a better quality of life. If recovery is a possible outcome, it is unethical not to give people who are prepared to work for it the support and professional treatment they need. The second reason is financial. Care for the severely disabled is expensive. If stroke survivors can recover sufficiently well that they can take care of all their own needs again, as Rita succeeded in doing, then large sums otherwise spent on care homes can be avoided.

Perhaps the biggest single reason for recording Rita's history is this. I have assembled a substantial amount of circumstantial evidence to suggest that a proportion of badly disabled survivors *do have* the innate ability to recover, but that ability is rarely realised, mainly because most stroke victims do not receive the therapy needed. But those ideas are all covered in Part 3. Now return to where I am going with Part 1.

A serious stroke, the cause of this book's existence, is not a disease but an injury. Strokes happen without warning – or without any warning easily identified by those who know, at best, little about the condition. Not only does the victim suffer a sudden life-changing event, so do those who have to take on the task of determining what must be done next and, usually, for a long time thereafter.

I fell within this group of "amateur" carers, as do so many others. In writing this account, I am making the assumption that a high proportion of other carers-to-be have a similar background to mine insofar as – when stroke suddenly happens – they have little knowledge of what stroke is, how it should be treated or what support and treatment is available from local health and care services. The nature of stroke is unusual in that its outcome can be spread across a wide range of different symptoms (usually seen as disabilities because that is what they are), any combination of which may be displayed by the victim (eg, *partial paralysis, tiredness, poor mobility, speech impediment, changes in personality, irrational behaviour, incontinence and several more*). Ideally, the best treatment for each stroke survivor should therefore be planned to suit his or her individual mix of disabilities. This, of course, calls for an initial careful assessment of all that person's problems, whatever they may be. This understanding then provides the basis for the individual treatment programme. It follows that the best treatment for any stroke survivor is more personal and more complex than for an illness having what might be regarded as "standard" symptoms, treatable in much the same way for all patients.

During the nine weeks Rita was held in hospital, I decided my aim should be to help her recover her former life so far as was possible. If that proved an impossible target, then at least she would have had sufficient treatment to establish that fact, before any important decision was made concerning her future care.

This was a fine aim, much easier to decide on than to put into practice, due largely to my ignorance of the whole subject of stroke and its rehabilitation. For example:

- I was ignorant of what a stroke is and what damage it can do to a brain.

- I badly underestimated the difficulty in caring for someone with irrational behaviour.

- I underestimated the difficulty of providing full-time care, 24/7, pretty well on my own.

- I naively expected that Rita would be given treatment that represented best practice.

- I did not understand the important difference between care and rehabilitation.

- I was unaware of the rules applied by health services and social services when assessing what care and treatment should be provided for badly disabled patients.

- I was unaware of the long time it would take me to discover what *is* best practice for the treatment of stroke.

– and so on.

I had a great deal to learn and too much to do.

Had I known what I know now, when Rita was discharged from hospital in June 2008 to my untrained care at home, I would have done many things differently and made far fewer mistakes. But I didn't know, and things went very wrong in several directions that were not entirely my fault – or anyone else's – but due more to my ignorance and frustration. By the summer of 2010, relationships between me and the "powers that be" had deteriorated badly, Rita's recovery was very limited. At that time she was assessed as having no capacity for recovery; her social worker advised placing her in a care home as being "in her best interests". I was angry at this – not because I knew better, but because her ability, or lack of ability, to recover had only been speculated upon, not proven. So my original aim was, at that time, not fulfilled.

So, Part 1 describes how we reached that impasse in 2010, with no one in our local health and care professions then willing to support further treatment for Rita. Intertwined with this story is my long struggle to discover what in fact *is* best practice treatment that will help seriously disabled stroke survivors, why bad strokes are seen as so difficult to treat successfully, and why it takes so long.

The difficulty I had in finding this vital information was a mystery. It wasn't altogether my incompetence because I know of no one else who found it either, other than from long-term experience. However, it can be difficult to find a source document when you are unaware that it even exists. The ones I found most useful are listed in Appendix D. By the time I had discovered these documents and understood what best practice was, we were too far down the road to have it implemented, belatedly, for Rita.

With hindsight, I do wonder why it took me so long to pick up that Rita was just not getting the treatment that best practice prescribed, but there was much else going on and I had several "battles" occurring simultaneously. In answer to the question "What is Part 1 about?", it describes two voyages of discovery, firstly, how difficult it can be to look after a seriously disabled patient when the necessary support described by authoritative documents is not provided and, secondly, how long it took me to find those documents that should, in all conscience, be made available to carers of seriously disabled stroke survivors.

There is a small administrative point that needs explaining, to avoid later confusion, due to a complication that has developed in the names in our family. Rita and I have three children, in order of appearance Gary, Duncan and Susan. Gary is married to Sheilagh and they live in France. Duncan's wife is also Susan and I will use that name when referring to our daughter-in-law. They live not far from Cambridge. As our daughter is always called Sue by her friends, whenever referring to our daughter I will call her Sue. She lives with her partner Cass in Birmingham.

There is also the carer organisation that gave us so much help in Fish Hoek, that goes by the rather ungainly title of the Fish Hoek Home Nursing Services Trust. Just for brevity, I will refer to them throughout the book as Fish Hoek Home Nursing, or even FHHN. The details of this organisation are shown at the end of the References section.

As a last point for this preface, I do say with some pride that I *was* right about being determined to get the best treatment for Rita because she *was* capable of recovery, despite authoritative prognoses to the contrary in 2010. She did, in the end, get rid of all her disabilities except a poor short-term memory (and that was much improved). That success was achieved by taking her to Cape Town, South Africa, as described in Parts 2 and 3. And "No", it should most definitely not be necessary to go to the seaside town of Fish Hoek for the required treatment, as I also explain. Though the Cape Peninsula is a great place to spend some time during the UK winter!

Prologue

Mid April to 5 May 2008

The days were lengthening and becoming warmer, time to look forward to spring and summer and say goodbye to winter's coughs and sneezes, but some bug or other seemed to have affected Rita. My wife had a reputation in the family for never being ill, but for several days she had complained of a slight headache when waking. These didn't last long and after an hour or so she claimed to be fine, but it was something unusual. A friend commented, "Oh, yes, I had that last week. I'm sure it's a virus going round".

Anyway, by the end of the week she claimed to feel better, so perhaps she had got over it. Sunday 20 April was a fresh breezy day with patches of sun. Rita was on the rota for reading the lesson at church at 10.00 am which gave her time to return home and prepare Sunday lunch for our younger son Duncan, wife Susan and two children, who were coming over for the afternoon. But again she had woken with a headache, rather worse this time. I was quite concerned at this recurrence and twice offered to read the lesson for her, but after breakfast she claimed to be fine. I didn't join her at the service as there were a few tidying up jobs I had lined up that would take a couple of hours before our visitors arrived.

By 11.30, all the work was finished and I was thinking it was time Rita appeared; she must be talking to someone. I began pottering outside and then I heard the phone.

"This is the care home along the road from you. Does your wife drive a blue car?"

"Yes, she does."

"I'm afraid she has had an accident just outside here; she is all right but can you come over?"

"Yes, of course. Is the car driveable?"

"No, it isn't. It looks like a write-off, but your wife doesn't seem to be injured."

I phoned a taxi company who promised to be with me within five minutes. What on earth was Rita doing in the next village? She should have been coming straight home and must have driven directly passed our house. What had caused her to do that? The police then rang from the scene of the accident and I said I was going straight there.

"Does your wife suffer from confusion?"

"No, certainly not."

"All right. I'll see you when you can get here."

The taxi dropped me on the S-bend opposite the village church where the wall had been demolished at least three times during the previous ten years by vehicles not making it round the two bends. Rita had demolished it again; our car was buried in scattered stone and brick. Rita was still sitting in the driver's seat but was conscious and appeared to be uninjured, although the front of the car was pushed back and the door panels were scored by stone. She was surrounded by deflated airbags. It was her voice that appalled me. It sounded just like my mother's voice, shortly before she died, when suffering from severe dementia. But Rita recognised me and she had obviously been able to give one of the staff of the care home, whose wall it was, our phone number. The traffic policeman handed me her handbag.

"Has she had anything to drink this morning?"

"No, certainly not. She's just been to church and should have been on her way home."

"I have witnesses to your wife's driving. They say she looked to be drunk and was weaving along the road. I'm told she brushed two cars on the way along the village High Street."

The policeman had already ascertained that the car was taxed and insured and that Rita had no points on her licence. I knew for a certainty that she had had no alcohol, so I left it there. It was easy enough to prove that fact later, if necessary.

The ambulance was another half an hour; it came from near the hospital although there was a small ambulance station only three miles away. A paramedic had arrived independently and was already attending to Rita. He said he could find no injury other than a cut lip, though her voice was deteriorating and she was sounding more and more confused. Eventually she was slid carefully across the car, out of the passenger door and into the ambulance. All four doors of the car still opened and closed as they should which, considering the damage done to the front of the car and the door panels, said a great deal for the body strength of that model of Honda Civic.

I travelled in the ambulance to the nearest hospital with an A&E department. Rita was put straight into a bed, but it was an hour and a half before a doctor came to see her. Meanwhile, in my uptight and emotional state, uniformed staff just seemed to carry bits of paper around and busy themselves at a bank of computer terminals in the centre of the ward. How could this be more important than seeing to Rita, I thought? After half an hour, most of the staff grouped themselves a couple of beds away from Rita and had a meeting, which I learned was a "changeover". While that was going on, Rita was violently sick. No one took any notice of this. I asked if there were any cloths or sick trays available and had a nearby cupboard silently pointed at, plus irritated glances at having their meeting interrupted.

When the duty doctor arrived, it took him only a few minutes to decide that a CT scan was needed. Being Sunday, the machine was not operating and there was another delay while a technician was called in and the machine started up. By this time, Duncan and family had arrived at the hospital in response to a phone call.

The doctor showed me the scans on a terminal.

"You see those white splodges? That's blood in your wife's brain. She's had a haemorrhage," he said. "There is nothing we can do here, she must go to a hospital with a neurosurgical department. I'll see what is available." He was soon back.

"The nearest neurological surgical unit is 30 miles away, but it is the best place to be and luckily they have a bed at the moment. However, they have to see the scan first. I'll send it over electronically."

It wasn't long before a message from the hospital said the haemorrhage was bad enough for them to accept Rita as a patient. She was loaded into an ambulance and, after some discussion, I was allowed to travel in it with her. There was a further 15-minute delay while the scan was transferred to a CD, a higher resolution image to work with than the low resolution one sent electronically, but then we were on our way. Duncan said he would come too and follow the ambulance, but at the first set of traffic lights, the siren and blue flashing lights were switched on and the ambulance drove straight through red, leaving Duncan stranded. He found his way, of course. My main memory of the journey was discomfort. I had expected a smooth ride but we were bounced and shaken all the way down a dual carriageway and swung round corners once we left it.

Rita disappeared into the hospital, barely conscious. I sat in a waiting area near reception where Duncan joined me. Not long after, our daughter Sue arrived, having driven down from Birmingham. I have no idea how long it was before we were led down long corridors to join a group of serious-faced surgeons dressed in what appeared to be theatre garments. The senior consultant told us the facts they had determined.

"Your wife has suffered a severe brain haemorrhage," he said. "It has bled into the right frontal lobe which is the decision-making area of the brain. She has done well still to be with us. We must operate to seal the bleeding. This is a dangerous operation, but if we don't do it, without any doubt your wife will die. With your written permission, we shall operate this evening."

I don't remember all the statistics that were reeled off, but recollect being told that 30% of patients do not survive that operation. Whether we were told it then or the next day, I'm not sure now, but the operation involved opening a blood vessel in the groin, pushing a tube up into her brain and, somehow, locating it close to the damaged blood vessel. Then small platinum coils are pushed through the tube and, in a way I fail to understand, these seal the leakage of blood. Whatever. I signed the form giving the neurosurgeons permission to operate on my wife.

Back near the hospital entrance we had another long wait. Eventually the message came – Rita had survived the operation and was in intensive care.

"She is physically stable so far as we can tell and we'll run tests in the morning," we were told. "Do you want to stay here overnight?" I was asked. "We can provide you with a bed."

I decided to go back home with Duncan and Sue. Rita was apparently not in immediate danger now. I had no spare clothes or night things, of course, and the next day I could bring some things for Rita.

The next few days are largely a blur. Not surprisingly, at this time I had not begun a diary to record each day. I travelled over to the hospital for the visiting hours every afternoon, and sometimes killed a few hours in the local town before returning for another two hours in the evening. On the day following the accident, Monday, there was a shorter meeting with the senior doctors. The results of the tests run on Rita that morning were as good as could be expected; she remained in intensive care in the neuro ward, but could be visited. I wish now I had taken a photograph of her there. She had no recollection at all of being in hospital, nor of the several months, maybe even years, prior to the accident. For the first few days she did almost nothing but sleep. Her eyes just opened occasionally and she smiled. We tried reading to her, and talking, but it seemed to make no difference to her level of consciousness. I tried to count all the machines and instruments that were attached to her. I got to 15, but am not sure that was the correct total. Most seemed to be monitoring various functions, but several were pumping medicines and one was supplying liquid food. She was receiving one-to-one nursing 24 hours a day and the nurses were brilliant; cheerful, expert and willing to answer any questions we had. The most alarming thing was the surprisingly large glass bottle attached to a plastic tube coming from a hole drilled in Rita's left temple and filling steadily with pink liquid. She was suffering from hydrocephalus, pressure on the brain caused by excess fluid production by the damaged organ. This liquid should be "gin clear", we were told. The pink colour was caused by blood still flushing away. Without this drain, pressure would have built up within my wife's skull, she would have fallen into a coma and soon died.

The doctors had a difficult balancing act to perform. Rita's blood pressure should not be too high or it might cause further leakage from the damaged blood vessel. On the other hand, the hydrocephalus was causing increased pressure on the brain which could restrict blood flow, resulting in even more damage than had been caused already by the haemorrhage. So, the slow feed of drug controlling Rita's blood pressure was constantly adjusted to keep her systolic blood pressure some way above normal, but with a firm upper limit that the nurses were monitoring constantly.

The hydrocephalus lasted a long time. After about a week it was found that the drain – the hole through Rita's temple – was leaking. This was serious because it could result in infection getting through the skull, leading to meningitis. So, back to the operating theatre, where that drain was blocked and another was drilled though Rita's right temple. Eventually, the fluid did run clear, but it still ran and the doctors were concerned at the length of time the drain was in place; the risk of infection was increasing all the time. Rita was regularly "challenged" by the simple expedient of raising the collection vessel from its normal position just below head height, where the fluid would drain into it, to just above this to provide a resistance to flow. Would the pressure in Rita's head build as a result of this? Yes it did, shown by Rita beginning to fall into a coma, whereupon the bottle was lowered again and she woke up! The decision was made that the drain had been in place as long as could be risked and that a shunt must be installed. This is an internal drain, a plastic pipe inserted internally from the brain cavity into the neck in order to continue to remove excess fluid and prevent pressure building up after the external drain was removed.

Rita was returned to the operating theatre that evening. When I phoned just after the time when I had been told the operation would be finished, I was informed it had not, after all, taken place.

"Why not?" I asked.

"I don't know the reason."

Of course I assumed the worst – that Rita was too ill to undergo the operation, or something had gone wrong. It was several hours of worry before the message came that more tests had been done while in the operating theatre and a revised decision made that the hydrocephalus could be treated with drugs, not an operation.

While all the above was going on, Rita's blood sodium level fell below a safe value – and I began to see why so many parameters had to be monitored. I was told of several other problems that might arise, but none had so far. A low blood sodium level is a fault known to occur quite often following brain haemorrhage; what caused it was a question I didn't ask. But it had been looked for and, when found, the procedure to correct it was implemented. Two or three days later, to my relief, her sodium level was back to within the safe range.

Although Rita's physical condition was improving with the intensive treatment, her brain needed sleep and more sleep. Much of the time I was with her she just slept. She might open her eyes on my arrival, smile gently, and then drop into another deep sleep. On occasion it was impossible to wake her. The nurses said we should wake her from time to time to ensure she was not in a coma. So, when she refused to waken, of course I worried. However the nurses came, checked a number of the monitors and said everything was OK, she just needed sleep.

At other times she would seem bright, giving almost her usual smile when we arrived and was willing to talk a little although she remembered nothing of what had happened and, in fact, had little recollection of anything at all. The neurosurgeon warned me that it was common for personalities to change following such a traumatic event, but I was naively confident that Rita would always be the Rita I knew.

Approaching two weeks into intensive care, Rita remained awake when challenged by the drain bottle. The liquid oozing from her head was now completely clear and the flow rate was low enough for the surgeons to be satisfied that the hydrocephalus was under control. It was safe to remove the drain from her skull. Soon after that she was designated as physically stable, her bed was needed for another patient and she was moved to a recovery ward on the floor above. This was the start of the long road to getting better, a far longer and more difficult road than I ever anticipated. Rita's life, such as it was going to be, had been saved by the extraordinary skill of the surgeons, nurses and doctors and at a high cost to the NHS. Little was I aware of the problems I was soon to grapple with.

Part 1

If You're Going to Have a Stroke, Don't Have it Here!

April 2008 to September 2010

1

5 May to 23 June 2008

Recovery in Hospital

Rita was moved into the recovery ward, having a pleasant view across trees, on the floor above the intensive care unit. This was around 5 May I think, I had still not begun keeping a daily journal at that time. My recollection of the next ten days is dim. Visits each day were for a couple of hours, plus the two hours round trip, longer than it should have been as Rita had chosen a time to be ill when roadworks had slowed traffic dramatically on part of the journey, whatever the time of day. My memory is of a cheerful, if sleepy, Rita who really wanted to do nothing but rest, but would rouse herself a little on our behalf from time to time.

It must have been around Wednesday 14 May that Rita was assessed as being physically stable and strong enough to be returned to our local hospital as soon as a bed could be made available there. A little later, I was told that she should be transferred during the afternoon of Friday that week. The actual time of arrival became closer to 9.00 pm and, when I went in to see her next day, she was pretty tired from the journey, wanting to rest and again sleeping most of the time I was there. Rita was in a ward of the hospital wing where I knew all the neurological and stroke patients were treated. She was in a small bay of six beds and seemed comfortable, though she was next to a large lady with a desperately bad chest who called to the nurses for help so frequently that she was almost totally ignored.

On Sunday, Rita was sitting in a chair by the bed when I went in, seeming much brighter and speaking clearly, though with no short-term memory of events over the past few years so far as I could determine. Being the weekend, there were no doctors available to speak to and no information on whether Rita's condition had been assessed in any way.

My naivety displayed itself because it was only on this visit that I thought to ask what speciality department this was.

"Oh, Respiratory," I was told.

"Shouldn't she be in the Stroke Unit? There's nothing wrong with her breathing or her lungs; she has had a major stroke."

"You'll have to speak to the consultant for the Respiratory Unit about that."

Rita had now been seen by a physiotherapist, though not the occupational therapists (OTs). I asked to see the consultant, but he was not available, it being Sunday. Nor was he there on Monday.

On Tuesday, Rita was now having one physiotherapy session each day, though the OTs had yet to put in an appearance. She was eating normal food, if very slowly. The consultant would see me at the end of his round later in the afternoon. He didn't. By the time I enquired as to his whereabouts, he had already left the hospital.

On Wednesday, I said I must speak to the consultant and would stay after visiting hours if necessary until he was free. Rita was bright and cheerful and interested in trying to do a simple crossword puzzle which she managed quite well, with me reading out the clues. At 5.30, I met the doctor, who was very pleasant and apologised for not seeing me earlier. I asked why Rita, following a subarachnoid haemorrhage, had been placed in the Respiratory Unit.

"They usually seem to be put in here," he said.

"Wouldn't she be better in the Stroke Unit?"

"That seems sensible. I'll see the consultant for the Stroke Unit in the morning. No treatment programme has been set so far – she has a long way to go."

The next day, Rita was still in the same ward, waiting for an available bed in the Stroke Unit. This was expected to be later in the afternoon, but she was eventually moved at 10.00 pm. So, six days after leaving the neurological unit, Rita arrived in the hospital Stroke Unit, another six-bedded bay.

On the morning of the Friday, I went to a "carers' meeting", organised monthly by a local charity, Headway. Meeting several other carers (not that I was one yet, in practice anyway) was both surprising and shocking. Several appeared to be looking after relatives who had suffered a serious head injury, with consequent personality changes leading to aggression in some cases and apparent selfishness in most. This must be desperately difficult. Most seemed to be doing their best with little support and found a couple of hours talking with people in similar straits to be therapeutic. The lady sitting next to me said, "You just have to get on with it, you know". Perhaps *we* were lucky as Rita had shown no signs of aggression, but I knew then little of what was to come.

When I visited that afternoon, Rita was looking tired again after the late night transfer and was sleepy throughout my visit. She had been seen by the stroke consultant and the physios, though the consultant was not available to see me. Nor was I able to meet the Nurse Consultant for Stroke Services, whom I had been told was very helpful. She was on leave for a week.

Visits over the next week or two soon developed a pattern. Rita was sometimes bright, other times sleepy. She always welcomed family and friends who came to visit but quite cleverly skirted round the fact she didn't remember friends' names. She enjoyed being read to and tried to play card and board games, but these were not a success. She needed a lot of prompting, couldn't keep to her turn and played other people's cards, counters or dominos. I tried her on mental arithmetic and the results were odd. Her simple addition and subtraction were hopelessly bad, but it took her only a few seconds to divide 96 by 6 and square 13 correctly. She had spells of fantasising; one afternoon she said she had spent the morning delivering babies. I now had a new granddaughter!

On 28 May, two weeks after Rita had arrived in the hospital, I had my first and only discussion with the stroke consultant, which lasted about 20 minutes. He told me that Rita was medically stable from a physical viewpoint and everything was within normal ranges. She was taking a little paracetamol, plus a pill to keep her blood pressure normal and another to control a slight fungal infection. Her memory was a worry. His aim now would be to assess the improvement attained over the next three weeks which should enable new goals to be set and an assessment made for Rita to return home soon after.

The day after that, I was invited to a multidisciplinary team meeting, comprising physios, OTs and senior nurses, so far as I can remember. They asked me what the stroke consultant had said to me the day before – they couldn't read his writing! They assured me that Rita was constantly being assessed. They were concerned about her memory, not asking to use the lavatory and her poor mobility (no mention of any liability to fall). They thought recovery would take a long time. What we (her visitors and I) were doing was "brilliant" and ideal for her – reading to her, dominos, crosswords and other simple games.

The next day, Rita was struggling with a crossword when I went in. She could read the clues without difficulty and answer some of them, but was totally incapable of locating the position on the grid where the answer should be written. The answers were scrawled anywhere across the paper. We tried a card game, Spite and Malice, but it was too much. Rita needed a lot of prompting, put cards in the wrong place, wouldn't follow suit and kept playing my cards – not a success. So I read a couple of chapters from the *No. 1 Ladies' Detective Agency*, which she enjoyed, and we tried a 35-piece Winnie-the-Pooh jigsaw puzzle. This was much too involved. (Later, when back home, we found doing even a six-piece jigsaw was impossible; she could not match pieces either by shape or colour, nor recognise the corner pieces.) Generally, she seemed a little more tired than the previous day.

Activities during the first week of June continued in a similar vein, with Rita showing signs of improvement. She was beginning to want to dress herself, though needed prompting and help. The occupational therapists (OTs) and physios were working steadily with her and I watched some exercises being done. Rita obviously enjoyed these and tried hard.

A few days later, I joined another team meeting. The main outcomes were that continence was still a concern, especially her lack of awareness during the night. Rita was liable to do unexpected and, to us, irrational things. One day, she decided to strip all the bedclothes from an old lady on the other side of the ward "because they needed washing". A home visit was confirmed for 16 June, it being thought that she was nearly ready for discharge, and a provisional discharge date of 23 June was set. I was told there would be lots of help and support available when she came home (there wasn't). I specifically asked whether Rita was singly or doubly incontinent. They looked at each other, looked at their notes, and said there was no indication that she was doubly incontinent and I could assume she was not. (This was incorrect.)

Mid-morning on Monday 16 June, an OT in the Stroke Unit arrived at our house with Rita and an assistant. They let Rita guide them around the house, which she did quite confidently. The OT identified the places where she thought grab handles should be provided, plus a gate at the top of the stairs. She would arrange for a raised toilet seat with handles. I would need to request supplies of incontinence pads through our GP. The daily carers would be arranged by Social Services. I also have a note saying that she suggested physiotherapy would be arranged through the Social Services too. This must have been a misunderstanding somewhere.

A few days later, I collected Rita from the hospital to spend five hours at home. We had coffee; Rita wanted a nap before and after lunch; we walked round the house and garden. I'm not sure we learnt a great deal.

Back at the hospital, a social worker was waiting to discuss arrangements for taking Rita home the following Monday. She had arranged for the "re-enablement team" to provide visits daily; the carers would also do simple rehabilitation work with Rita – making drinks, peeling vegetables and suchlike. This service would be free for up to six weeks, after which they would recommend further longer-term provision. She would arrange for various alarms to be fitted in the house (which turned out to be ineffective).

The day after, 20 June, Rita seemed more tired than usual. We walked to the pond in the hospital grounds, but slowly, with regular reminders for Rita to lengthen her stride, but it quickly reverted to a shuffle. This tiredness and poor mobility continued over the next few days. After a bad episode of walking, I located the stroke consultant who also checked her and spoke to a physio. They had noticed an increase in the shuffling gait, but did not seem to think she was as much worse as I found her.

A few days earlier, and unknown to me, the social worker had written an 11-page assessment of Rita's status. Large parts were not completed, some because I was not involved and should have been to provide the information. Since each page was headed in red, *"Bring this document with you if you need to attend hospital"*, I should clearly have been given a copy, but was not. I discovered later – a year later! – that page eight defined the services that should have been put in place for Rita's return home – but were not – and that she should not be discharged until they were in place – but she was. When, much later, I obtained a copy of this document I viewed it as extraordinary that an assessment of Rita's status could be written without my knowledge when clearly I should have been involved. That social worker left her job at the hospital a week after Rita was discharged, moving to work in the next county, she told us. We haven't seen her again and were allocated a new social worker. There was no passing of information between the two.

2

Irrational Behaviour

It is one thing to visit your disabled spouse for a couple of hours in hospital once a day, but quite another to take them home and be responsible for attending to all their needs.

When in hospital and out of your sight, someone else has washed, dressed and fed them, dealt with the idiosyncrasies caused by the brain trauma, prepared them for visitors and then put them to bed at the end of the day. That has taken nurses working shifts around the clock, albeit with other patients to look after as well. Once the patient arrives home, the disabilities become all too evident and it is the main carer's responsibility – yours (maybe) and mine – to deal with them all.

There are two broad categories of disability: physical and cognitive. Physical disabilities are easier to recognise, if not necessarily easier to deal with. Luckily, Rita did not suffer from the quite common problem of an inability to swallow food and was able to feed herself, if slowly and only when given regular prompting. She did suffer from poor mobility and posture, lack of balance, a weak left side and – contrary to what I had been told by hospital staff – she was very definitely doubly incontinent. It quickly became apparent that she was liable to fall over without warning, something else I had not been aware of before she arrived home.

Cognitive disabilities can be harder to understand, difficult to identify in some instances and very difficult to deal with because you don't expect the person you have known for years to suddenly have a changed personality, to behave in ways that are most unlike their former self and can be completely irrational. I found the subtlety of some cognitive problems took longer to correct than the physical ones, once we eventually reached the stage of working towards Rita's recovery more than two years later. Cognitive problems are often hidden to those who only visit occasionally. I have been told by many carers of their frustration when friends and acquaintances have commented, "Jack looks fine. Does he really need looking after? Surely, he will be back at work soon?"

As with most stroke survivors who have come through a severe trauma, Rita's brain worked very slowly and she tired quickly. She did not become aggressive or throw things about, but she was self-centred with no interest in the needs of others; most unlike her former self. In fact, she had no real interest in anything and could spend hours at a time doing no more than sit in a chair inspecting her fingernails.

It was irrational behaviour that was most difficult to understand and cope with, particularly with respect to her incontinence. Rita would never indicate when she might need the toilet, but would pull down her pants, pull off the continence pad and do whatever was necessary on the floor of whichever room she happened to be in. Perversely, she would wait until I was out of the room before doing this. When I remonstrated with her, asked her to tell me when she needed the loo, she just giggled and said it didn't matter. Of course, I tried to take her to a toilet every two hours or thereabouts and so prevent the whole house from being used as a loo, but those occasions could be fraught as well. Quite often she would refuse to sit on the toilet and would keep her body rigidly straight until she had peed on the floor. A variant of this was to sit on the toilet, then suddenly stand upright and pee on her clothes and the floor. This was all so frustrating as I had plenty of other things to do without all the extra washing.

One time I discovered her in the kitchen, having defecated on the floor and now trying to clean herself. I whisked her into the bathroom and got her into clean clothes, then realised I hadn't seen the continence pad she had been wearing. By this time there was a strange smell in the house, quickly located as coming from the oven where the soiled pad was cooking at 200 °C.

Cooking meals could be a fraught business. Rita regarded the kitchen as her preserve and would come in while I was preparing a meal, switch hobs on or off, or move pans of boiling water from the hob to a worktop, with an obvious risk of scalds. She would become angry when I stopped her doing this and it really needed two people to handle the situation, one to distract Rita and one to continue preparing the meal.

This leads into a related subject of eyesight, and the perception of what has been seen. It was probably two years before I really understood what was happening here, but now is a good opportunity to explain it because, had I understood it or been told about it sooner, a number of problems would have been avoided.

Rita had worn contact lenses for about 40 years before her stroke, but clearly couldn't continue to do so as they needed to be taken out every night. So, a visit to the optician was arranged, just a few weeks after Rita came home, to replace the contact lenses with spectacles. With a good deal of patience, the optician managed to check Rita's eyesight and said, unsurprisingly, that her eyes were much the same as on the previous test. So, we picked up a pair of spectacles a week later and I knew Rita now was able to see well. What I did not understand was that she had great difficulty interpreting what she was looking at and recognising what it meant.

We should have realised there was a difficulty when in the hospital. Next to Rita's bed in the six-bed bay was the loo, with both the word "toilet" and a picture of a lavatory on the door. Rita occasionally said she wanted a loo and headed off out of the ward until we pointed to the door and asked her:

"What does that say?"

"Oh, toilet," she said, and changed direction.

Back at home we had the strange arrangement of a ground-floor bathroom leading off the main living room. So, of course, a large TOILET sign was pinned to the door. This Rita ignored completely until it was pointed out to her. The same applied to a whiteboard that I fixed to the living room wall to note down plans for each day, so Rita wouldn't have to keep asking me what we were doing. She could read it perfectly well when asked to, but otherwise ignored it completely – even when she wanted to know what we planned for the day, she never thought to consult it.

Three years later, when she was being taught to walk again by carers in South Africa, the carers had to hold her hand to prevent her falling down kerbs or tripping over them, or walking in dog mess, or colliding with other obstacles. It was very strange. She could see these obstacles perfectly well, but the potential hazard did not register and she appeared not to realise that action needed to taken. It was actually more serious than that because she treated cars in the same way. Left to her own devices, she would wander down the middle of a road, totally ignoring the traffic.

Overcoming this specific disability, that seemed an inability to perceive meaning in what she could see, was one of the last cognitive disabilities to be corrected (apart from her very poor short-term memory).

3

Back in Our Own Home

On Tuesday morning, 24 June, I drove over to the hospital. Rita was sitting by the bed with her possessions beside her, but without any paperwork other than a Medical Discharge Summary that I did not find particularly enlightening. There was no paperwork concerning rehabilitative treatment arranged for when she was home, nor was there a copy of the assessment written by the social worker, of which I had no knowledge, and so did not ask about it. Had I known what was in that assessment, I would have asked for several changes to the patient discharge procedure. As it stood, we were off to a worse start than I had anticipated.

[Eventually, in July 2009, just over a year later, I was sent a copy of the assessment. The social worker had completed part of this 11-page document in Rita's company, despite noting that "Mrs Guthrie has difficulty in expressing herself fully due to cognitive impairment". The only clear statement Rita is reported to have made was that "she wished to go home". The social worker commented that, "Mrs Guthrie would require intensive ongoing support and assistance within her own home if this is to be successful. … It is essential to the discharge that Mrs Guthrie receives assessment and ongoing support from community health services, eg, continence specialist nurse, GP and OT/Physio input". Under a heading, Outcome if needs are not met, the social worker added that Mrs Guthrie will not be discharged from acute hospital setting without appropriate support – which would include possible admission to residential placement. Most of the document was left incomplete.]

At the time I collected Rita from hospital, I was unaware of all of the above. I merely asked the senior nurse if she could let me have some continence pads and she gave me a bag with about a dozen, sufficient, she said, to last a few days, plus two minutes of instruction on how to fit them as they were really very easy, which was true. I should see the Continence Service for more.

We were both excited and Rita seemed really pleased to be going home. I was glad to have no more trailing off to hospital almost every day, as I had done for the past nine weeks. I hoped, and expected, that Rita would blossom from the experience of living back in her own home again. I could not have been more wrong. She was glad to be home, but her incontinence and severe cognitive dysfunction got in the way of setting up our lives together again. Clearly, visiting her in hospital did not allow an accurate judgement to be made of her real condition when someone else had got her cleaned and dressed and fed, and put her to bed again at the end of the day. I had never seen her when really tired in the evening and I believed the nurses when they told me she could manage the toilet on her own (ignoring the evidence of the piles of soiled clothes I had been taking home to wash).

If I had been given access to one person allocated to help get Rita settled at home with the services she needed, and able to give me a little training on handling severe disability, it would have saved a huge amount of stress, time and several misunderstandings. This is a need recognised by the *National Stroke Strategy*, but I did not discover this helpful document for more than a year. As it was, I had two groups of people involved; the NHS for treatment and Social Services for care. Far from giving advice, several health and care professionals, who visited us at home, told me they were not permitted to advise carers. This is not only extraordinary, but so stupid because advice is exactly what a new carer in my situation needed. Apparently, their instructions were to give me a number of options from which I had to choose one that best suited our circumstances – something I was quite incapable of doing then, having too little understanding of Rita's mental and physical states.

So I learnt the hard way, by experience. I discovered Rita was liable to fall without warning, usually when I was not close by. She just lay where she fell, making no attempt to get back on her feet or even to call for help. Before her discharge from hospital, I had no idea that she was liable to fall over.

I discovered her cognitive dysfunction was serious and, combined with her almost non-existent short-term memory, this meant that it was useless to give her instructions – I could ask her to stay on the toilet while I went to fetch a clean pad, towel or whatever, but she would forget what I had said immediately I left the room. This meant that it was not safe to leave Rita on her own for more than, say, ten minutes, because she might do anything. One other example of many: on the morning of 1 July, I left Rita slowly topping and tailing gooseberries in the kitchen while I went outside for exactly seven minutes. On my return, she had vanished from the kitchen. I found she had climbed the stairs on her own and was in the guest bedroom with her pants down and a soiled pad on the floor.

It quickly became clear that for me to take care of Rita on my own did not provide a safe environment for her; nor for me for that matter. She was going to hurt herself or do some damage, probably sooner rather than later. The fact that four carers came in each day did not affect this conclusion. They were rarely with us for more than 10 – at most 15 – minutes at a time, neither were they doing any of the rehabilitation exercises that had been discussed beforehand. Rita was too cognitively disabled and nothing of consequence could be achieved in the short time allowed. What was just as important, the carers were not trained therapists.

So what to do about it? At my request, managers from the domiciliary services agency came to discuss the situation. They agreed that the daily carers they provided were not giving the service Rita needed. They suggested a new banister rail and more grab handles but had no other suggestions. The district nurse, whom we saw no more than a few times, was very positive and emphasised the need to get a good programme for curing the incontinence from the nurse who was due to visit eight days after Rita's discharge from hospital. That suggestion was being much too hopeful and unrealistic.

Our daughter, Sue, was driving down from Birmingham nearly every weekend, a 280-mile round trip. Our daughter-in-law, Susan, called in nearly every day from 17 miles away. Both had young children and this help could not continue.

In addition to these difficulties, the situation with Rita's incontinence was deteriorating. The pads given to me at the hospital lasted a few days only and they would give me no more. I bought the ones that seemed closest to the Tena "Flex" used by the hospital from Boots and the district nurse kindly gave me some more she had found in her office. None of these were effective and leaked regularly. Fortunately, our practical daughter-in-law decided we should have Kylie sheets to protect the bed and purchased three. These were excellent and, during the more than three years that Rita was incontinent, they did not once fail to protect the mattress from urine or worse. Why had not one of the hospital staff or local doctors suggested these should be used?

Although we had carers calling four times each day – and they were helpful, cheerful and charming ladies – almost invariably they came at the wrong times. When Rita soiled a pad, I had to change it immediately and not wait for the next carer to attend to it. Quite apart from the unpleasantness of waiting, Rita would try to clean herself if I didn't do it, and the mess would be far worse. As a result, during one week soon after Rita was back home, I cleaned up after 15 soiled pads and the carers did not attend to a single one. Regularly, the carers arrived to find a dry pad, so regarded the visit as a waste of time, which it was. Apart from the showering and dressing each morning, the system was not working as intended. If I had been given a copy of the assessment prepared by the social worker we met in the hospital, I would have known that everything needed to handle Rita's incontinence should have been resolved *before* she was discharged home. At last, the continence nurse visited Rita for the first time on 2 July.

She had a helpful attitude and asked a lot of questions. She explained that I was doing most things in the wrong way. What a surprise – since no one had given me any training or guidance! She specified the type of pads that could be provided by the Continence Service. We would be supplied with continence pads every four months; Rita was allowed three each day and one each night. The Tena 'Flex' could not be provided – they were too expensive – but plain pads that fitted between Rita's legs and were held in place by net pants would be fine.

She also thought Rita had a urinary infection and took a sample of urine for analysis.

This nurse was one of the few professionals we met who was willing to give advice. She suggested Rita should drink 1850 ml of water each day, a curiously precise quantity. Day pads should be used until full, even when slightly wet when first examined. Rita should have a sleep on her bed each afternoon, this would help keep her ankles from swelling, and her night pad should be put on at midnight. The nurse would order bulk supplies of pads that should be with us the next Monday, in five days' time.

Within a few days, this advice given by the continence nurse began to unravel. There was no way Rita was going to drink almost two litres each day. Her method for drinking now was to sip all drinks. Every drink lasted a long time and she needed constant reminders "not to forget the drink". She could not be left with a drink by her, it got knocked over, or Rita fell asleep while holding a mug, with obvious consequences. The best she ever did in a day was 1550 ml and was more usually in the range 1100 to 1300 ml.

The nurse's suggestion that pads should be changed at midnight was a dreadful idea, one that might have worked in a hospital environment, but not at home. Rita was hard asleep and objected very strongly to being woken and dragged to the bathroom for a pad change. She was most uncooperative. Handling an uncooperative baby is one thing, dealing with an uncooperative adult is another matter entirely. Besides that, I was fast asleep at midnight too (I had tried staying up till that time, but was so exhausted by ten o'clock that I could stay awake no longer). Once I was wide awake again, having struggled with an obstinate Rita, I couldn't get back to sleep for a long time. So that was a suggestion that bit the dust very quickly.

I discovered with experience that the day pads were OK if checked often, but were overwhelmed fairly frequently with the volume of liquid. The night pads that the nurse said would be suitable were hopeless at retaining the urine and excrement.

The pads were big flaps and did not fit closely enough, even when encased in strong knickers, or even in waterproof ones that I bought later from Boots. There was a wet bed and wet nightie, or worse, every morning. The Continence Service had provided us with a four-month supply of pads; the fact they were not suitable was irrelevant, apparently. During a phone call soon after the delivery of the bulk supply, they refused to do anything to help until the time for a re-order arrived. Within a few days I had found an online source of the Tena "Flex" pads (as used in the hospital) and I bought our own, so resolving the issue for a while. (*My apologies for spending so much time on this unpleasant subject, but when double incontinence is not handled adequately it does become a major issue. It is also in danger of becoming a health issue, especially with Rita's cognitive problems that could result in any room in the house being used as a lavatory.*)

During the week leading up to 11 July, Rita's behaviour had been becoming more difficult and she did not seem well. I called in at the surgery to ask if they had heard from the continence nurse about the urine sample she had taken nine days before. They hadn't. I called the Continence Service; the nurse we had seen was out but called back later. She had "just" received the results – Rita had a urinary infection (meaning that nine days previously when the sample was taken she had an infection; probably it was now worse). By this time it was 4.00 pm. I asked her to fax the results to the surgery, then rang our GP to ask if he could rush through a prescription. He was very good and arranged for me to pick up some antibiotics at 6.00 pm. Very quickly Rita's behaviour improved – to a degree.

Reverting to the health and safety aspect of me alone looking after Rita, on the afternoon of the day the continence nurse came, I thought it was time to speak to the new social worker who had been allocated to us (who I will call Amy – not her real name) and who had not been in contact. Odd as it may seem, we never did meet Amy. I explained on the phone what was happening and asked if she had any suggestions. She asked whether we wanted Rita to go into a residential care home, because that was one possibility. I said we both wanted Rita to live at home as long as possible, so was a live-in carer practical? Amy said that would be expensive, around £700 per week. I commented that I didn't think we could afford that for more than a short period and would have to think about it. Half an hour later, Amy rang back, sounding enthusiastic. She had spoken to her manager who said they were prepared to offer £400 per week towards the cost if I found the balance. That was a good offer that I had not been expecting. She said there would have to be a financial assessment of Rita's assets, "But not to worry about that, the offer was not dependent on the outcome".

I asked if she could recommend an agency. No, she was not allowed to recommend, but she named one that had a good reputation and there was another locally that I could look at.

I should, of course, have queried this offer a bit harder, and asked for confirmation in writing, but it was what I wanted to hear. At that time, no one had given me any information on who paid for what. I assumed, naively, based on what Amy had told me, that managers had the authority to award grants to justifiable cases. Two days later, I rang Amy again to ask if there was a time limit on this offer.

"No," she said. "It will continue as long as it is needed."

Well, I was happy to find £300 per week for at least a few months to get us out of a serious hole and I spoke to the two agencies to see what they could offer.

Both seemed well set up and competent. I chose the one that told me they could provide a carer two or three days after I had made a decision and she had just the person available, one of their best carers with lots of experience. We had to accept that we had no choice on who came, that decision was made by the agency. "Camelia", our new live-in carer, was delivered to our door on Friday 11 July. This was 19 days after Rita's discharge from hospital and a lot of water had flowed under the bridge since then.

4

11 July to 22 August

The Next Six Weeks

The agency manager delivered Camelia to us at around 2.30 pm. Camelia was a Ghanaian lady of comfortable proportions with a big smile and an even bigger suitcase. The first task concerned this suitcase; it was closed with a padlock and Camelia had omitted to bring the key with her. With little optimism, I fetched my small hacksaw, expecting to make little impression on a hardened steel shackle. Fortunately it was not hardened steel and two minutes were sufficient to destroy the padlock and gain access.

Camelia and Rita began to get to know each other while the manager explained the arrangements that would apply. The agency carers did not have days off during the week. They were allowed two hours free time each day and were not expected to carry out routine chores at night, but would be available to help with emergencies, should any occur. We should make our own diet available to her and she would normally join us for meals, but if she decided not to eat with us she would be responsible for finding her own food. She would also assist with normal household chores – and that was about it. So, she would be with us for the next six weeks without a break, but then was planning to take a week's holiday with her family.

We quickly developed a routine centred around Rita's needs. Rita and Camelia spent much of the day together, outside whenever possible as Rita has always preferred being out of doors. They usually walked to the top of the garden and sat on the little grassy area, away from the noise of the road. It will be a lot harder in the winter when the weather will preclude sitting outside. I shall need to find some other way of giving Rita an interest and quiet stimulation.

Rita's walking was variable from day to day. A good day made me too optimistic, then we had a bad one when she shuffled along and wanted to hang onto whoever was with her. She would walk with a marked lean to the right (although it was her left side that was weaker) and she sat with a pronounced lean the same way, finishing by lying in an uncomfortable sideways position on her chair and needing to be hauled upright again. When tired she was often stubborn and irrational.

Camelia showed a lot of patience and didn't mind working at Rita's speed while dressing in the mornings. It frequently took 90 minutes, sometimes up to two hours, before Rita was showered, dressed and had finished breakfast.

Camelia professed to be perfectly happy to be woken at midnight every night to change Rita's pads. She showed a lot of perseverance in continuing to use the rubbishy continence pads provided by the Continence Service, experimenting with different ways of fitting them, but eventually accepted the fact that they were effectively useless and we switched to 24-hour use of the Tena "Flex" pads I still purchased regularly online. These worked much better and the cost was more than outweighed by the reduced washing and cleaning that the others entailed.

I took Rita out in the car two or three times a week for short outings while Camelia was having her break and tried to give her short walks to improve her mobility. Sometimes she walked well, other times her legs gave way before we had gone any distance. We attempted a stroll around a tiny country churchyard on one afternoon, no more than 150 yards for the round tour, but halfway round Rita collapsed onto me and I had almost to carry her back to the car.

One day when Rita was walking well, we went to the pillar box, 400 yards down the road. Rita made it back to the house, but only just. She had to hang onto the gatepost while I opened the door. A few days later, when she was again looking strong, I tried it once more, but this time Rita's legs totally gave up before we were home and she collapsed onto the ground. A passing driver saw we were in trouble, stopped and very kindly helped me support Rita for the 50 yards back to the house. I could not have managed her on my own.

One of the hardest things to accept was Rita's irrationality and stubbornness, especially when she was tired. For a person who had always been very active, helpful, regarded as never ill and full of common sense, her behaviour was often difficult to understand or tolerate. Occasionally, she was able to peel potatoes and carrots, slowly and not too effectively, but I think she may have been subconsciously upset at others taking over her kitchen. Our daughter, Sue, was cooking one weekend and had plates warming in the top oven. Rita walked into the kitchen and took them out. Sue put them back, saying they needed to warm, but out they came again. Rita eventually became angry and Camelia had to distract her and take her elsewhere. Similarly, when I was cooking and had potatoes and vegetables boiling in pans on the hob, Rita walked in and lifted the boiling pans onto the worktop. She could not be persuaded to leave them alone, quickly became angry again and, without Camelia to take charge of her, it could have developed into a potentially dangerous situation with boiling water being moved around.

The toileting times were frequently fraught during these few weeks. At that time, Rita could not undress herself properly and certainly could not get dressed again. But, as mentioned earlier, it happened all too often that, when undressed, she refused to sit on the toilet and did a pee while standing, wetting the floor and her clothes. Had she sat down sensibly, it would have saved a lot of washing and cleaning. She *never* went to the toilet or a bathroom on her own, but continued to choose anywhere in the house to either pee or pass a bowel movement. She seemed to wait until nobody was in the room before deciding on her own toilet area. You would think that, just by chance, she would pick the toilet door to go through occasionally, but it never happened, despite the large TOILET sign fixed on the door itself.

Two weeks later, we saw our GP about arranging a consultation at the urinary department at the local hospital, in the hope they could give some help in overcoming Rita's incontinence. An appointment was made for 16 September. I asked the GP whether he could suggest any other action we could take to assist Rita's rehabilitation, but he said, "No, I cannot think of anything".

"Could any other member of the practice help?"

"No, I don't think so."

A few days later, he phoned us at home and said, after discussion with his colleagues, it had been suggested that oxybutynin tablets should help to relax the bladder and he would have a prescription ready for collection the next day.

A great day on 4 August! We had a visit from an NHS physiotherapist, the first since Rita left hospital six weeks earlier (though we had yet to see an occupational therapist). She concentrated on Rita's poor posture, gave advice on a safer way of helping her upstairs and getting in and out of bed and the car, and left a list of daily exercises. These Camelia incorporated into the getting-up routine, to be done on the bed after showering but before dressing. This was fine for a while, but after a week Rita refused point blank to do any exercising. The physio returned on the 20th for another session, announcing at the end of the hour that she was now retiring and we would not see her again. She said that no replacement had been appointed and, in her opinion, was doubtful whether one would be. So that was a remarkably short programme of physiotherapy and completely contrary to the recommendations of the *National Stroke Strategy*, a document still unknown to me.

On the 12 August, Rita and I had an appointment at the hospital with the Nurse Consultant for Stroke Services, the nominal six-week review after discharge from hospital. Her letter prior to the meeting said it was to "discuss how you are progressing, any concerns you may have and to re-evaluate your needs if necessary". A seven-page Stroke Impact Scale questionnaire was enclosed for Rita to complete, which she was quite incapable of doing, of course. So, Camelia and I completed that and I included with it a current status report on Rita. In this I said that, in my view, Rita should have had consultants guiding us regarding overcoming the incontinence and on rehabilitation from the cognitive dysfunction; and that these should have been in place at the date of discharge from hospital.

The meeting lasted 75 minutes. The nurse seemed helpful and gave the impression she would like to do everything she could to assist, but was constrained by lack of resources, especially the fact that, although that hospital is the nearest to our home, it and our home were actually in different primary care trust (PCT) areas. This meant that she could not offer help to us directly. Provision of help for Rita would be the responsibility of the PCT in whose region we lived and with which we had had no real contact, apart from through the GP. I asked if she could recommend a rehabilitation clinic that Rita could attend. She said rehabilitation facilities in our locality were particularly poor and she did not know of any, though she did think it would be worthwhile contacting the private charity, Success After Stroke (SAS), that operated in a town some miles from where we lived.

Following the review, she wrote a summary letter, dated 27 August, saying that any help would depend on an appropriate report from the review meeting with the neurosurgeon, to be held at the neurosurgical unit at a date in September still to be set, and, in effect, if lots of people liaised with lots of other people everything should be all right. No one did anything as a result of this and, so far as I remember, we did not hear from the nurse consultant again until May 2010. Nothing practical that might help Rita resulted from the meeting; we certainly never got near to having a consultant, or anyone else, appointed to guide Rita's rehabilitation.

But my mind was rather taken off sorting this out by developments with the Social Services. At the beginning of August, I had paid another cheque for around £2800 to the carer agency for Camelia's services for the next four weeks and was getting decidedly edgy about the £400 per week promised by Amy, the social worker who had still not visited us. Up to that point, she had never met Rita, so I made an appointment with her to meet us for the first time on 13 August, about seven weeks after Amy had nominally been made responsible for Rita. A call came from her office, that morning, cancelling the appointment because she had phoned in ill. By the Friday there had been no further message, so I called again. Not there, but I left a message for her to call urgently. On Monday 18 still no call from her so I rang back in the afternoon. She was "training" and unavailable, but would call back. By the next afternoon, Tuesday, she had not done so. I rang once more and this time she picked up the phone. On my query concerning the promised £400 per week, Amy stated categorically that she had never promised this payment; that any payment was dependent on the financial assessment and, as I had chosen not to disclose Rita's finances, any cost was down to us. They had rules they had to follow; she had been doing this job for a long time and would never have promised £400 per week. She added a few other confrontational comments. There was no suggestion that there might have been a misunderstanding and perhaps it would be best to meet and try to sort out what could be done for Rita. The strong inference was that, so far as this social worker was concerned, there had been a misunderstanding and it was entirely mine. I was absolutely furious but managed to put the phone down while I cooled down and decided on the best course of action given this information.

Later on the Tuesday, I decided to apply for a carers' assessment. This had been suggested by several people, including Headway, as being a facility offered to carers that should prove helpful. I had not gone ahead earlier because the leaflet I had been given had not explained exactly the purpose of the assessment, only implied that it was a "good thing" to do and carers had a "right" to a free assessment of their needs. Anyway, I rang the number provided, said I was interested in an assessment and asked if they could explain its purposes to me. The girl told me that the assessor either called or telephoned, asked a series of questions … Yes, I interrupted, that is what happens. What I wanted to know was the purpose to be achieved; how might I benefit? She seemed not to understand the question and said she would put me through to someone who could help. Guess who? Amy, the social worker came on the line. After both of us expressing surprise, I explained the purpose of the call. Yes, their office did carry out assessments for carers and I suggested a meeting here – it was more than time we had one and it might be an opportunity to resolve the matter of the part-payment for Camelia's services. We settled on 10.00 am on Thursday, in two days' time, when Amy would visit us at home.

It was a busy time. On searching the Internet, I had found UKABIF (the UK Acquired Brain Injury Forum) and emailed them with a brief summary of Rita's problems and asked if they could recommend anything. I had an immediate reply that told me of two clinics in the adjoining county and added that there was a rehabilitation clinic, specifically for head injuries, based in the same town as our local hospital. I rang both clinics and found they were day-care centres; one had an age limit of 65 and the other required referral from a GP resident in that county, which our GP, of course, was not. Those two options bit the dust immediately. I spoke to a clinician at the rehabilitation clinic and that sounded to be a possibility, so I made an appointment for Rita and me to visit on 26 August. I then phoned the nurse consultant at the hospital and asked why she had not suggested this clinic. She said that they specialised in severely disruptive clients and she didn't think it was appropriate for Rita.

Thursday morning 21 August, the day arranged for our meeting at home with Amy, I had a phone call from her at 9.30 am. She had been thinking about it, she said, and had decided to refer things to another team – of which I had never heard and now don't remember the name – and they would contact me soon.

"We have an appointment in half an hour," I pointed out.

"But I've asked another team to take over."

"So you are not coming this morning?" I asked.

"No."

I really lost my cool at that and was rather impolite, whereupon Amy prissily announced she was "terminating the conversation" and put the phone down. I promptly rang back and was put through to a more senior social worker who seemed to pick up the situation quickly. After a short conversation, he suggested it might be a good idea if he arranged for a different social worker to take over. I agreed this would be a very good idea and he said he thought it would be a young lady, whom I will call Margaret, and she would phone me within a few days. He would also ask the aforementioned "team" to call me today. (No one ever did.)

It was at the end of this week that Camelia's first six weeks would be completed and she was having a week's holiday. Strangely, she had been appearing rather morose for a few days, rather than excited at the thought of seeing her family again. This had reached the stage that, on Wednesday, she had eaten no lunch and no dinner, but stayed in her room. I asked if anything was the matter.

"No," she said. "I'm fine."

But it was said without the usual big grin.

As I said earlier, it was a hectic time and this may well have impacted on Rita's behaviour because she hated noise and upset of any sort. As well as the to-do with Amy, later that same morning I received a letter from Amy's manager. The stated intention of this letter was to explain their funding policy, but there were statements made in this letter that I found extraordinary.

Firstly, *that Rita had been assessed as needing 24-hour care.* She does need this, but when was she assessed and by whom? And why did I not have a copy of this assessment? I had no knowledge whatever of Rita having been formally assessed by anyone. (In fact it later became apparent the letter was referring to the assessment that had, unknown to me, been made by the social worker in hospital. It appeared to be a critical document, though it was to be 7 July 2009, about ten months later, before I obtained a copy.)

Secondly, *that I had declined a residential placement for Rita.* I most certainly had not done so. The only mention of this subject had been in the first phone call with Amy when she had suggested that one option was to put Rita in a residential home. I had replied that I would prefer her to be at home if at all possible. That was not declining the residential option, merely expressing a preference and that was all that had been said on the matter.

Thirdly, *that Amy had explained to me that Social Services do not normally fund live-in carers "as my wife's needs can be met in a residential setting".* She most certainly had not explained that.

Fourthly, *that social care would only be funded up to a maximum of £400 per week.* This had not been said. If, when Amy offered me the grant on 7 July, she had said that the grant would be "up to" a figure, I would have immediately picked that up. A promise of £400 per week is a promise of £400. A promise of up to £400 is not a promise of anything, only a possibility. I had already told Amy that I couldn't afford £700 per week for a long-term carer and her promise of £400 was my justification for going ahead with Camelia's employment.

Fifthly, *what this letter did not mention was that fact that Amy had said to me that the £400 per week would be irrespective of the outcome of a financial assessment.* I have absolutely no doubt that she said this to me and this put an entirely different light on the matter.

During the rest of that Thursday morning, I replied to this letter to make the above points. I added a comment that it would be useful if Social Services had a leaflet that explained the rules governing the funding of services to patients. (Unknown to me then, they do, of course, have one entitled "Charging for Support Services" but I was not given a copy of this until 17 September 2009, 18 months after Rita had suffered her stroke! One might have thought this manager would have sent me a copy – but no.) I then wrote to *her* manager, two levels up from Amy, with a formal complaint concerning Amy's incompetent handling of my wife's affairs. With hindsight, it might have been better to make an appointment to discuss the whole situation with this manager before writing to complain. But I wrote first and that was one of several mistakes.

It was a great pity matters had come to this. Had I known then what I know now, writing this a year later, I would have queried the terms of the Social Services contribution to the live-in carer under their "direct payment" scheme. I had made the assumption that applied to my many years of working in the private sector, that more senior managers have greater authority over financial payments so that, although Amy did not have the authority to make a regular payment to a "service user", a more senior manager might have that authority. It also appeared that our local social services department had no idea how best to handle a situation when it went badly wrong. Had one of the more senior managers suggested a meeting with me, together with Amy, on the basis that there had been a very regrettable misunderstanding, but that we should discuss the matter fully, understand each others points of view, and try and work out a solution aimed at benefiting Rita, there would have been a fair chance of success. Why didn't I suggest this meeting? Well, I had in effect. At my request, two meetings had been set up with Amy, but she had cancelled both of them so that, during a period of eight weeks when she was nominally responsible for Rita's well-being (as I then understood the workings of the Social Services), she had never even met her, nor me. Contrary to possible appearances, I am a pretty cooperative sort of guy and I much prefer to get on with people rather than antagonise them. I *do* get on with most people, but I resist being railroaded and I do not tolerate errors of fact. That Thursday, I was not in the mood to suggest further meetings and this was a start of an escalating complaint that continued for more than a year.

At the end of a very eventful day, around 4 o'clock, an agency manager arrived with Camelia's temporary replacement. This lady was English and from Lincolnshire. We both knew the town of Boston so that was a conversational starting point. Camelia and her replacement spent an hour together in a "changeover" meeting to have Rita's general routines explained. I told the manager what had happened with Social Services and that I had to review whether I could continue to afford to employ a live-in carer. I gave her provisional verbal notice of termination of the contract, to be confirmed the following week. She then left with a rather grim-faced Camelia. The manager and Camelia also had a discussion/argument on whether Camelia was to be away for eight days (her preference) or seven days (the manager's preference). I kept out of that and left it to them to resolve this particular issue.

5

29 August to 18 September

On Our Own Again

Financial help from the Social Services was now unlikely, so I wrote to the agency to terminate the agreement for a live-in carer, with effect from the end of August. The cost of employing Camelia, including the additional cost of her keep, would run at approximately £40,000 per annum. This would soon severely deplete our savings and, once spent, what then? With savings behind us, we still had some freedom of action that I would be extremely reluctant to relinquish. Eighteen months later, our savings became very valuable in that they allowed us to take a course of action I thought best, without having to depend on getting agreement from any "authority".

Looking on the bright side, a live-in carer was not a perfect solution in any event. It was like having a lodger in the house, not of our choice and possibly from a different culture than our own. And I found myself doing the catering for three people instead of just two. Camelia was willing to take on a proportion of the household chores; certainly the ironing, some cleaning and, very occasionally, the cooking, but she never volunteered to cook.

There did appear to be help coming from other directions now. We had met volunteers from the charity, Success After Stroke (SAS). This would occupy Rita for probably one morning each week and might provide a little much-needed rehabilitation therapy. A day-care centre was also a possibility. Several friends had promised to continue coming in regularly to entertain Rita and, if I could get her into a rehabilitation clinic soon, I should be able to manage on my own. It was worth a try.

The next Saturday afternoon was warm and sunny so I took Rita to watch a local cricket festival. Her father had been manager of the Yorkshire youth team for many years so she was very familiar with spending long hours watching cricket. There were two games in progress and a large marquee with snacks and drinks available.

Anyway, she watched what was going on intently for an hour or so, then became quite stressed. I suddenly realised that, despite wearing a hat, she was overheating, so I took her home where it was much cooler in the house. But it was an hour before she recovered. This was the first time it really became clear to me that Rita never communicated her needs to anyone. It was up to me, or whoever her carer was at the time, to check that she was not too cold, hot, or stressed in any other way, and to do whatever was necessary to relieve the stress. We couldn't rely on her to tell us about any problems she had.

Margaret, our new social worker, arrived at 10.00 am on Monday morning. We spent 80 minutes discussing the various options she could offer. I exposed my continuing naivety concerning the treatment of disability by requiring an explanation of something that I had not fully appreciated earlier – that there was a clear distinction between the NHS and the Social Services. The NHS dealt with healthcare, which the Social Services didn't touch. Social Services were only interested in and responsible for care in the community. So, any rehabilitation for Rita was supplied by the NHS, whereas any residential care, for example, would come from the Social Services. That meant there were two large groups of people for me to deal with independently.

Margaret offered to arrange for Rita to have two days in a local day-care centre. This I was delighted to hear. There were two nearby and I should speak to both and choose which seemed more appropriate. The cost through the Social Services, including transport to and from the centre, would be £9.68 per day, which I thought to be very reasonable. None of this had been explained to me during the previous two months.

Margaret also suggested that I apply for a telephone carers' assessment as it was possible that could provide some extra funds for carers, not subject to financial assessment. She would also submit a case under their "exceptional needs" provision as that, too, might provide some funding. (It didn't.)

As the carer's assessment provisionally arranged with Amy in mid August had never materialised, I tried to make another appointment for one by telephone, but the first available was for the 1st October, more than a month ahead. I told Margaret and she said she thought she could arrange one through her own office. After the phone call, I walked into the kitchen. Rita was at the sink, washing faeces off herself and the sink, with no pants on. The soiled pad was in the vegetable recycling container. Camelia was outside, sitting in the sun and gazing into the distance, but came in quickly when I alerted her to what was going on.

Camelia did not seem the person we had been used to. Maybe it was because she only had another few days with us and so had uncertainty for the future again, or I suspected she had other family difficulties – though she never admitted to them. But she spent most of the time in her room. This was not the original arrangement, of course, which was that she would normally be Rita's companion. Even so, she stuck rigidly to her two hours freedom between 2 and 4 in the afternoon. I didn't make an issue of it because there were only a few days to go and I had better get used to looking after Rita myself again.

On Thursday we had a remarkable letter from the Social Services asking for Rita's signature allowing me to act on her behalf. This was about ten weeks after Rita left hospital. Rita could sign her name perfectly well, but certainly could not comprehend what the letter was about.

At the end of August, we had the follow-up consultation with the neurosurgeon who had "repaired" Rita's brain haemorrhage. This was short and not very productive. He was not sanguine about Rita's potential for recovery, but said he would organise an MRI scan to check on the state of the brain "repair" and arrange a visit to a neuropsychiatrist. Plus he would emphasise to our GP the importance of good treatment for the incontinence. If he ever did any of these things, there was no practical evidence of it to follow (apart from the MRI). Nor did his short report stimulate the stroke nurse at the hospital to put in place any practical help, as she had suggested might happen.

The first couple of weeks following Camelia's departure were difficult. Our daughter, Sue, came down from Birmingham with her two girls on the evening of Friday 5 September, arriving when we were both asleep in front of the TV.

Saturday started badly with a leaking pad and an accident in the toilet, so I immediately put on one load of washing and followed this with two more, despite a showery morning that changed to steady rain later. I could *not* persuade Rita to swallow her oxybutynin tablet, though she was no trouble with the smaller blood pressure ones. If I crushed the larger one, she detected the unpleasant flavour and spat the mouthful out. The girls became noisy and argumentative after lunch and this stressed Rita; she hated noise and crying children. She calmed later but did not go to bed until 10.00 pm, after which Sue and I discussed possible ways to organise Rita's and my lives to cope best with the situation. We thought of up to eight ideas, but none struck me as being in any way ideal, or even practical in the long term.

Rita seemed tired and without energy on Sunday morning. She didn't want to do the bed exercises, was slow moving about and it took me five minutes to persuade her to step out of the shower. There were another two loads of washing to be done.

Monday began with a dry bed though the pad was well soiled; the Tena Flex pads were proving to be much better than anything else we had tried.

For the third day running, Rita refused to swallow her oxybutynin tablet. I had hidden it inside one of the raspberries I had sprinkled on top of her bowl of muesli, but after finishing this, Rita spat out the tablet. Her breakfast took 75 minutes. She was worried about grubs in the raspberries (there were none) and insisted the tiny unformed seeds in her grapefruit slices should all be removed. I was relieved to have a friend come in to sit with Rita while I went to the surgery to collect another prescription.

Just before lunch, a manager from Headway, one of the charities that has been very helpful, phoned to ask for an update on Rita's condition. He seemed most concerned at the lack of progress with both the Social Services and NHS and said he would discuss it with his colleagues and see if they could suggest anything. I also phoned Margaret to ask her to arrange for Rita to attend the only local day-care centre willing to handle Rita's incontinence. The staff of the larger one were not willing to cope with it.

Rita was tired in the afternoon and sat on the sofa not wanting to do anything. She complained of chest pains on her right side, became more tired and wanted to go to bed at 8.30 pm. Sitting on the loo was difficult. She refused to bend at the waist and just lent over backwards, banging her back on the cistern as she went down. Then I thought we were not going to get her upstairs. She stopped halfway up when I was behind her.

Eventually, I decided to go in front and haul her up which was potentially unsafe but the only way, other than calling for help from someone. On Tuesday, she again stopped halfway up the stairs so subsequently I dressed her downstairs.

Rita got up and ate breakfast more quickly on Wednesday, but complained of bugs in the toast. We had an appointment with the GP at 9.50 am. After arranging a prescription with him for a liquid form of the oxybutynin to get over the problem of non-swallowing of the tablet form, I pressed him hard on trying to organise a professional assessment for Rita, to be followed by a rehabilitation programme prepared specifically for her particular problems. I pointed out that the haemorrhage she had suffered was bad enough, but by keeping her alive the very clever neurosurgeons had put us in an arguably worse situation than if she had died. Neither of us had any quality of life, we were just surviving. Her incontinence effectively gave us a sentence of house arrest. It wasn't an exaggeration to say that Rita had been abandoned by the NHS. She was receiving no rehabilitative treatment and I was getting no support or advice on how to look after her. We had seen a physiotherapist only twice in two-and-a-half months and no occupational therapists at all. The nurse consultant at the hospital, for all her pleasant manner, had provided no practical help whatever. The probability of Rita suffering a further injury from a fall due to my incompetence or tiredness was significant. I had been told by several people that the only way to obtain treatment from the NHS was directly from our GP, or by a referral from him to a consultant. He seemed to take this on board and said he would investigate what assessment or rehabilitation was available, its cost, and possible funding. But he came up with nothing.

That afternoon, we walked to the end of the garden to pick some crab apples to make a jelly and, as we returned, I carried the bucket and ladder with Rita walking beside. As we passed the large rosemary bush she stepped towards it and fell face down into it. It took a while to get her out and on her feet again, but no damage was done and she smelled very sweet for the next two hours.

Later I read to Rita, but was interrupted by a long phone call from the senior manager, Social Services, to whom I had sent the formal complaint. She wanted to make it clear that I had been misinformed on what funding was available, that it would be subject to a financial assessment and that the rules were inflexible. I said it would have been helpful to have been told that two months earlier. She said there was no mileage in the application to the Exceptional Cases Panel that Margaret had put in, but that she, the manager, wanted to separate what had happened from what might be arranged in the future. Of all that she said, this was the only point I readily agreed with. I explained my side: what Amy had told me and when; that I still had no information about the assessment that had apparently been made on Rita (referred to in Amy's manager's letter) and I would like to know more about this; that I was actively looking after Rita 14 hours a day, 7 days a week (not a way of life that could continue indefinitely); that she had had a fall today despite me being with her; and several other points.

The senior manager would get Margaret to come out again to discuss what other caring options might be available. That was the last I heard from that lady.

On Thursday, two of Rita's friends collected her for a visit to a nearby shopping mall where, at my request, they bought her a pair of sensible slippers, had lunch and brought her back at 2.00 pm. They seem to have managed better with her than I did. That afternoon, we visited the day-care centre I had chosen. Rita liked the place and we confirmed the booking for two days weekly, Mondays and Fridays, beginning the next Monday.

Things began to settle down a little. On Saturday, we were quite efficient getting up and dressed. Sunday – and it took just an hour to get showered and dressed, but then Rita took an hour and a half over breakfast, even though I helped with part of it. She wouldn't finish her porridge because it had "lumps". These then became "bugs".

Monday – and I drove Rita to the day-care centre. She would normally be collected but I thought I would take her the first week. She seemed to settle easily. Then at about 11.00 am I had an extraordinary call from the hospital appointments office to rearrange the next day's appointment at the Urology Department that I was informed I had cancelled. I informed them it was an important appointment for us and I most certainly had not cancelled it. After some time on the phone, the appointment was rearranged for 9.00 am the following day. This rather fraught meeting with a urologist is described in chapter 9.

On Wednesday 17 September, we had an appointment for Rita with the optician. We walked out to the garage and I left Rita standing by the door while I dropped a bag of rubbish into the bin. In that short time, she fell full length on the drive, luckily without anything worse than minor bumps.

Our daughter-in-law, Susan, arrived just after noon to join us for a light lunch and a chat. While she was with us, I had a call from the consultant neuropsychiatrist to the rehabilitation clinic that the stroke nurse considered unsuitable for Rita. We had visited it some three weeks before and were impressed by what they were doing. I outlined Rita's history and current condition. The consultant explained what they could do, the sort of treatment he would recommend, how it would be done and roughly how long he thought it would all take. What he told me seemed right for Rita. He sounded intelligent and knowledgeable. He made one point – that Rita was undoubtedly not getting the treatment she needed and deserved. Had she become aggressive as a result of the haemorrhage, as some patients do, and "hit a nurse over the head with a chair" as he put it, she would have been referred to his clinic immediately. Because she still had her (mostly) gentle disposition, nobody was taking any notice of her needs. He told me to be more assertive through the GP to get the referral from the Primary Care Trust. This I tried to do, but the PCT adamantly refused to refer Rita for that treatment.

At 2.30 pm the same day, the carers' assessment happened! Two ladies arrived from the local Social Services office and stayed about 90 minutes. I started by explaining Rita's current status and how our days were typically occupied. They expressed astonishment at the amount of caring I was doing and said it could not continue at that level. A sentiment with which I wholly agreed. They said they were there to help in any way possible. We talked round it for some time, then the senior one asked what did I think would be best for me, ignoring any constraints. I suggested that I looked after Rita for two months, followed by a month in residential care to give me respite, and continue on that three-monthly cycle. Oh, they couldn't do that! So what could they do? The most on offer that seemed to be of practical use was up to five hours of housework each week; cleaning, washing and suchlike. That really wouldn't touch what Rita and I needed.

Rather than wait another couple of chapters to record the outcome of this meeting, I will wind it all up now. The outcome was zero. In fact I heard nothing more from either lady, nor anyone else for several weeks. After those weeks, I telephoned the more senior lady, I think it was twice, to ask for their report on my "carer's assessment" that I understood was to be provided, with recommendations and statement of what they proposed.

"Oh, yes, I'll send you that," she said.

It arrived a few days later in the form of a summary of the information I had given them and nothing more. There were no conclusions, suggestions, summary of needs, recommendations, or any offer of help. As far as any benefit to me was concerned the carer's assessment was a complete waste of time.

6

21 August 2008 to November 2009

Further Negotiations with Social Services

My negotiations with Social Services extended for about 14 months, following my letter to the manager on 21 August (described in Chapter 4) and the written complaint to *her* manager. This was a long time, so here are just the "highlights".

Our new, and third, social worker (Margaret) visited us on 1 September. Usefully, she gave me a much better understanding of how Social Services works, what they are responsible for and how they interact with the NHS. We agreed that Rita should attend a local day-care centre for two days each week. Given the paperwork involved and that Rita needed to be assessed by the day-care manager, that her first day was 15 September was arranged pleasingly quickly.

Meanwhile, my written complaint had been passed to a senior operations manager who arranged to visit us on 22 October. She was very smartly dressed and drove a nice open-topped car. I gave another review of Rita's and my experiences over the previous four months or so. She made a lot of notes and told me she had around a dozen points to take up, back at the office.

Her reply, dated 7 November 2008, spelled our name incorrectly and was signed by her secretary. She included a detailed document describing the new Self Directed Support operating model, which had just been implemented. In her letter, she apologised for any miscommunication and misunderstanding between us and the County Council. Two things were conspicuously lacking from her letter – any comment on my specific complaints and any offer of future help in caring for Rita.

I didn't put together a reply until 29 December, partly because I was working 90 to 100 hours a week as a carer and lacked the energy; partly because I decided to wait to see if her visit produced any further help with Rita's care. It didn't. When I did reply, I pointed out that I was not complaining about a misunderstanding – which can happen at any time – but about several specific faults with the services provided (more accurately, services not provided) by her staff which she had ignored in her letter. An acknowledgement dated 14 January 2009 arrived wishing "… to reassure me that the points you have raised are being investigated and you will receive a considered response in due course". No sort of response ever arrived, despite a reminder I sent in mid March, two months later.

Intentionally or not, both the NHS and Social Services had appeared to follow a policy of slow response. Could it be that if things were left long enough, some will just go away or be forgotten. When re-reading my journal, I frequently saw "promises" that had been made to do things, or provide information, that were never met. It needed a fairly sophisticated system of forward planning (and a fairly cynical frame of mind to consider it necessary, which by then I had not developed) to make sure all these promises were followed up when nothing otherwise happened.

I felt I had been given the brush-off by this senior operations manager and telephoned her office several times from early April onwards. On 20 April, I spoke with the PCT Complaints Manager concerning Rita's assessment and he gave me the phone number of the Social Services Complaints & Representations Team. So I phoned them to say I had not had a reply to my letter of 29 December the previous year. A phone call an hour later assured me of a response. This was slow in coming, but eventually a meeting was arranged for 9 June, at our home, with an operational service manager (OSM).

This was a much better meeting. This lady had a straightforward approach, without flannel. She told me what should have happened when Rita was discharged from hospital and this sounded exactly right. But, as I pointed out, it *hadn't* happened. She made sensible comments on my list of specific complaints. In her letter to me following the meeting (four weeks later!) this OSM listed a number of changes she wanted to implement in the way their team managers dealt with potentially difficult situations. If these have in fact been implemented, they should help future "new" carers with their early experiences of the Social Services.

In particular, the OSM covered an aspect that had puzzled me for a long time – the assessment (prepared by the hospital social worker) on Rita that had apparently been carried out and was referred to in the letter from the team manager dated 19 August the previous year. I had asked for details of this assessment as it was unknown to me, but had received no reply and at least three subsequent requests by me for information on it were also ignored. With her letter, the OSM enclosed a copy of this 11-page assessment, written by the first social worker, dated 20 June 2008, while Rita was still in hospital. Every page of this was headed in red "Please bring this document with you if you need to attend hospital", so clearly I should have had a copy from the beginning, quite apart from the fact that I should have been involved in its completion. Page 8 was particularly illuminating. This summarised Rita's status, needs and the support that should be in place at home *prior* to discharge. As stated earlier, in answer to the heading "Outcome if needs are not met" it stated that "Mrs Guthrie will not be discharged from acute hospital setting without appropriate support". She had, of course, been discharged without it.

The appropriate support was defined as:

- A continence specialist nurse (who was only seen eight days after Rita's return home and just once during the first two months).
- Support from a GP (who admitted to me later that he had neither the training nor competence to supervise someone with Rita's specific and severe disabilities).
- Occupational therapists (who were not seen at all for about four months).
- Physiotherapists (who made two visits during August 2008, then only one more session until a year after Rita's discharge from hospital).

Had I seen this document when I should have had it, before Rita's discharge from hospital, my approach to that discharge would have been very different because I would have had a much better idea of what specific support should have been in place to help both Rita and me.

As previously noted, this assessment was dated 20 June 2008 (Rita's hospital discharge had been on 24 June) and was prepared by Social Services. It raised an interesting point. The appropriate support the hospital social worker defined included, mostly, support to be provided by the NHS, not Social Services. Did she have the authority to define the support to be provided by an organisation in which she did not work? Rita most certainly should have had a written rehabilitation programme prepared before leaving hospital (if the *National Stroke Strategy* document, discussed later, had been acted upon) and the Social Service assessment was the nearest thing to a plan – even though it was evidently ignored by everyone involved with Rita's treatment and I obtained a copy only a year later. The NHS and Social Services were supposed to cooperate in the interests of patients, but there seemed to be much scope for buck passing, and many bucks were passed, and obligations that were not met (moral if not statutory) at the time Rita was pushed out of the hospital.

Much later, on 2 September 2009, Rita returned home from 12 weeks at a rehabilitation clinic (see chapters 13 and 14). Rita's weight was then 64 kg, an increase of 4 kg during her time at the clinic. Social Services had arranged a six-week "re-enablement" course to follow immediately on Rita's return home, but could only offer an hour from 11.30 am to 12.30 pm, not the early morning one I wanted. An OT would come "as soon as possible" to prepare a rehabilitation programme for Rita. The carers arrived on time at 11.30 am each morning but, during the first four days, we had three different carers. This didn't help me at all as I had to explain much of what they should do (when I thought they should be telling me).

On Monday 7 September, five days after Rita had returned home, the agency OT arrived to write a carer's rehabilitation programme. She watched Rita make coffee and said she would have the programme ready by the next day, emphasising the importance of strict routines. She sent me an example programme that covered the whole day and clearly would have needed me to supervise it all. I had expected a programme specific to what the carers were doing. Much of it was far beyond Rita's capabilities and would have needed constant supervision from me – that alone made it impractical.

On 10 September, I took her shopping at the local supermarket before the carer arrived. This was not a success. Rita was rather like a small child, taking things at random from the shelves and putting them into the trolley. I got frustrated with her. Then, while at the checkout, she had a bowel movement. We rushed home but both her pants and trousers were soiled. We were both upset.

Things continued like this for about ten days, with carers coming in for an hour each morning and me looking after Rita for the remaining 23 hours of the day. The timing of the carers' visits made use of the day-care arrangements impractical. This was proving stressful for me; I had no respite. On 14 September, the manager and the OT came again to discuss how Rita was doing, plus the difficulties arising from not sending Rita to day care or SAS during this period. We decided it would be better if Rita returned to day care twice each week as before, and to SAS on Tuesdays; they would cancel the carers on those days. So the re-enablement course was reduced to two hours each week, meaning that nothing of any value could be achieved.

At the above meeting, the OT suggested she should see how Rita was progressing and got her out of the low chair without pulling her up as I would have done. It took two minutes but "nose over toes" eventually did it. The OT then suggested she should take Rita into the kitchen while the manager and I covered a few points. I don't know whether Rita was being perverse, but she insisted on going into the bathroom saying, "I know where my kitchen is. Oh, no. I was wrong, you're right". Then she walked into my office, with the OT trying to guide her towards the kitchen. I had only been speaking with the manager for a short time when we heard Rita shouting very angrily in the kitchen, "I know where my ..." and the OT appeared at the door looking worried saying, "Is she often like this?" Rita was now in the dining room and I took her arm, led her back to the kitchen and two minutes later she was happily peeling carrots. No more trouble. I was pleased to have the manager witness the occupational therapist lose control of the situation – it wasn't that easy to look after Rita, even for professionals. So much for rigid routines; they may not always go down well with the patient. Nonetheless, the OT said the carers should be advised to do the same thing with Rita each day: prepare soup, and coffee, dust, and walk up the garden. One day I found the carer preparing the soup herself, instead of Rita doing it under supervision, which rather defeated the object of the exercise.

Though it sometimes appeared so from the number of distractions, I had not lost sight of my prime objective: to establishing a rehabilitation programme for Rita. Letters and phone calls to and from various staff of the

PCT and Social Services led to a phone call from the Complaints Manager for the County Council at County Hall at 6.00 pm on 10 September. This call lasted around 45 minutes. As a summary, I confirmed why I wanted treatment for Rita. I gave examples of why, in my opinion, Social Services had not provided the support that should have been given. For example: Why had Rita's social worker not visited a severely disabled patient once during the eight weeks she was responsible for her well-being? Why did I not receive a reply to letters I wrote to Social Services? In particular, why had the assessment, defining the support to be given to Rita when discharged from hospital, not been activated? I could not be more specific on this because, at that time, I had still not seen a copy of the document, but I did know about it by then. The Complaints Manager said that a senior practitioner would be visiting us next week and should be able to help with the programme I wanted. This was how a fourth social worker became attached to and responsible for Rita, replacing Margaret.

On 17 September 2009, this senior practitioner arrived at the house. She explained what her responsibilities were and how she fitted into the organisation. I rehearsed a summary of our situation once again. She said she had not come to resolve my complaint, but to see how things could be sorted out for the future. That suited my aims. After considerable discussion, she offered to plan the costs for (1) a carer coming in for, say, two hours each morning, (2) possible sitting arrangements in the evening to allow me to go out now and again, (3) rolling respite time (two weeks every two months, possibly) and (4) emergency care should I fall ill. This seemed promising. She would return for another talk in early October. Just before leaving, she gave me a copy of the County Council pamphlet, *Charging for Support Services*. This was the first time I had seen this – or even heard of it – and it explains clearly the basis used for calculating whether or not caring services are self-funded. She commented I should have been given a copy before Rita left hospital 15 months earlier. This was obvious – and it would have avoided a lot of misunderstanding if I had seen it.

Incidentally, I never saw any planned costs for points (1) to (4) above.

The day following, a third continence nurse called in; from memory the fourth visit from them in 15 months. She was responding to my regular, if infrequent, complaints about the standard of pads they supplied for Rita. She was much more helpful than I had expected from previous experience. We were now using Euron "Micro" pads that were still proving not up to the job – they had insufficient capacity such that they were continually leaking. She offered to arrange, for the future, to provide the "Wings" version; these were similar in design to the Tena "Flex" pads that were so successful, but they cost less. We found they worked well – a solution at last! She said it was difficult to do any more for Rita beyond the medicines – desmopressin and oxybutynin – that Rita was already taking.

The next day Rita was very uncooperative while the morning carer was with us. She wouldn't do as either of us asked for the whole hour. I needed to stay with them throughout. After the carer had left, I read her daily report and noticed that she had not mentioned this uncooperativeness – just said, "Observed Rita doing ..." being the standard formula used by the carers in recording what they had done each visit.

When I queried this the next time we saw that carer, she said they didn't report difficulties because the patient might read them and become upset! But to me this raised an important question: *Were difficulties displayed by patients correctly reported?* If not, as had happened here, at a later date the fact that Rita could be difficult might be denied, as there was no record of it in her notes. This then posed the question as to the value of these notes if they are not completed accurately. Surely they should reflect what had actually happened? If widespread, this lack of factual reporting could be serious.

A follow-up to the phone conversation with the Complaints Manager on 10 September was a meeting with this lady and the OSM at County Hall on 12 October 2009. This must have been associated with a copy, sent anonymously, of Amy's file note concerning the phone call in July 2008 when she promised me £400 per week to help fund the live-in carer, Camelia. This file note arrived in the post on 7 July 2009 and included the statement '... Discussed with [my manager] who agreed we could fund £400 pw and Mrs(sic) Guthrie would then have to pay the extra funding himself to enable him to have 24-hour care at home. We could fund the £400 by direct payment to Mrs Guthrie'. There was no mention of the need for a financial assessment.

My reading of this note supported my record of the conversation, in my opinion. At the meeting, the Complaints Manager and the OSM acknowledged that the service we had received fell short of their expected standards in a number of respects, for which they apologised. They had amended their internal procedures relating to the interaction between their team managers and service users, particularly with respect to assessments on patients. They would reimburse me with the £400 per week I had spent over a period of eight weeks in the belief that I had been offered this. A cheque for £3,200 arrived soon after.

This ended my complaints with Social Services and represented a minor battle won. However, it took us no further forward in acquiring an active, in-community rehabilitation programme for Rita, and so represented a war lost.

7

The Charity "Success After Stroke"

Success After Stroke (SAS) is a small independent charity based about ten miles from us. It was set up, some years before, by a group of stroke patients as a self-help organisation specifically for sufferers from stroke. The intention was to provide a place where stroke survivors could meet socially each week and also receive a limited amount of speech therapy, physiotherapy and occupational therapy at the meetings, these therapies being given by qualified personnel.

At the time Rita joined SAS, it was well established with around 60 members meeting in two groups on Tuesdays and Fridays. (Only head injury victims could be members. Carers were very welcome to join meetings, but were not signed up as members.) SAS described itself as "… an active and motivated self-help group run by the members who are helped by dedicated volunteers and tutors in their efforts for rehabilitation, independence and confidence".

A typical Tuesday morning consisted of socialising, therapy classes, quizzes and discussion groups. About twice each month there would be a talk or slide show by an interesting lecturer. Other regular interest groups were arranged through the week, such as painting, swimming, pottery, an introduction to computing, and riding for the disabled. There were also regular coach outings to places of interest that were able to cope with 40 to 50 disabled visitors descending on them.

When Rita first joined, we were surprised to find some members travelling 30 miles or more to be there. Potential members were first assessed by the qualified staff. They checked that the new member would be able to make the most of the organisation and that they were willing to work towards their own recovery. Rita was given qualified membership only; her incontinence was a worry because there were not enough volunteer helpers at meetings to cope with her needs, so I had to find friends willing to take Rita each week and stay with her for the two-and-a-half hour meeting. Fortunately four of her friends were very happy to take turns and I went once a month too so that I could check on how well she was responding to this new experience.

Rita benefited hugely from being a member. She liked the friendly company and responded well to being with other people, especially when the atmosphere was relaxed and humorous, as it always was. Members were always pleased to see each other, delighted by any advances that anyone achieved and much fun and teasing went on. At last we had found somewhere that treated Rita as a friend, ignored her problems and were delighted with the small advances she made occasionally; the praise she received was completely OTT, but she was happy. She joined the swimming club on Thursdays and, at first, was reluctant to get into the water, needing a lot of persuading. Only two or three weeks later, she was going straight in and making tentative attempts to swim, with the help of armbands for support. Her left side was significantly weaker than her right so she tended to swim in circles, and even to corkscrew, but a few weeks later she was able to swim the length of the pool with support from one of the trainers. Other new members made similar rapid progress in the water.

Since that time, SAS has continued to evolve with new ideas being introduced. Rita's later success with Nordic Walking was much admired and, a little later, a regular Nordic Walking class was introduced for those members capable of and wishing to improve their mobility. SAS has won several awards for the success it has achieved in helping stroke survivors at all levels.

8

3 September and 2 October 2008

Review Meeting with the Neurosurgeon

For this follow-up assessment on 3 September, Rita and I drove down to the hospital that had saved her life. After our meeting, the surgeon wrote a one-page report on Rita's condition, dated 16 September, addressed to the nurse consultant at our local hospital, with copies to our GP and me. His comments were [with comments by me in brackets]:

- With regard to the memory loss; this is probably to be expected following a bad subarachnoid haemorrhage and she may never get the short-term memory back completely.
- He was pleased to see the incontinence was improving. [Was it?]
- Her disturbed gait could have been due to hydrocephalus, but the results of the scan taken shortly before the meeting suggested that Rita's slightly enlarged ventricles were not under pressure, which would tie in with gait improvement.
- He was sure she is receiving good care from the stroke services at our local hospital. [Rita had not, as already reported, received any help whatever from our local hospital, prior to this report, because the nurse consultant said she wanted to wait and see what the neurosurgeon recommended.]
- He recommended that Rita should see a neuropsychologist locally to help with her cognitive disabilities. [At the meeting he had suggested he would organise this himself.]

- He would also arrange an MRI scan at the six-month interval to ensure that the coiling remained satisfactory. [This referred to the platinum coils he had inserted in Rita's brain to seal the leaking blood vessel.]

The appointment for the MRI scan was 2 October. A few days later, I wrote to the neurosurgeon to query his suggested appointment with a neuropsychologist; to advise him that I could not contact the consultant nurse owing to what appeared to be a long period of absence; and that Rita was receiving no help at all from our local hospital on the grounds that they were not responsible for the care of a patient not residing in their PCT area. Also, that, at my request, our GP had now written to the PCT to apply for referral to a rehabilitation unit, and to ask if he (the neurosurgeon) would support this application should support be needed.

He replied by return to say that he would be very happy to support Rita's application for professional assessment and rehabilitation, either privately or through the NHS. Also, that the neuropsychologist he had in mind was about to take a six-month sabbatical so would not be available; he hoped the nurse consultant would be able to arrange this locally to us. Subsequently, I discovered that the neuropsychologist at our local hospital was currently away on long-term sick leave, so there was no one available from the NHS in this part of the country.

Some three weeks later we had heard nothing concerning the results of the MRI scan, so I phoned the neurosurgeon's secretary. She told me the he was away on leave, but that the records concerning Rita's MRI had appeared on her desk with "File" written on them, so she was sure everything was all right. I said I would much appreciate a word with him about it on his return, and could he please call me? We never received a call, or letter, so have no formal record of the results from that scan.

Referring back to the "six-week" review meeting with the nurse consultant on 12 August, she had used the, then, upcoming review with the surgeon, described above, as the reason not to organise any treatment or other support for Rita, because it was important to know what he proposed. In retrospect, that looks awfully like delaying tactics. Since receiving the surgeon's report, the nurse has not been in touch with us again about rehabilitation or anything else. The organisation of any treatment for Rita's recovery and rehabilitation, so far as these two hospitals were concerned, had just drifted into nothing.

9

May 2008 to December 2010

Incontinence, Urology and a Long Story

This chapter is about our interactions with the hospital Urology Unit, our doctor and the Continence Service regarding advice and treatment for Rita's urinary incontinence and its effect on our daily lives. There is no equivalent chapter relating to the bowel incontinence to which she was also subject because no doctor has once examined Rita or run any tests, or given us any sensible advice on how to treat this affliction. This is despite authoritative advice that patients having bowel incontinence should not be discharged from hospital until they had been assessed and a plan to treat this condition had been established with the family.

As Rita became more mobile in hospital she seemed to know, quite often, when she needed the toilet. The fact she never did find her way to it we treated as rather a joke, even though the door next to her bed displayed a large "Toilet" sign plus a picture of a loo. But it was a lot less funny once she was at home. I should have realised things were worse than they seemed from the number of wet and soiled clothes I took away for washing after almost every visit to the hospital.

When, at a multi-disciplinary meeting shortly before Rita's discharge home, I asked whether she was singly or doubly incontinent, the five or six staff present consulted their notes and agreed that she was only singly incontinent. This was untrue; she was very definitely doubly incontinent and remained so more than two years later. Either the staff kept inadequate notes and were unaware of the status of this patient, or they lied to me.

I have already described the problems during the first two months at home, trying to cope with the incontinence. I asked our GP to arrange an appointment with a urology consultant at the local hospital. This was fixed for Tuesday 16 September. The day before the meeting, I received a phone call from the hospital appointments office saying she wanted to rearrange the appointment set for tomorrow that I had cancelled.

"I most certainly did not cancel it," I told the secretary. "Please find out what has happened."

She phoned back a little later to say she had found the member of staff who had cancelled the appointment – on the grounds that he/she did not think it was the appropriate clinic for Rita – but had omitted to tell me what had been done. On reflection, the secretary now said, they thought Rita should attend after all; the next appointment she could offer was 28 October, around six weeks later.

"That is not good enough. The matter is urgent and another six weeks is too long," I said. After a short silence, she said, "There is a cancellation for 27 September."

"That is still not acceptable," I said. "Someone at the hospital has cancelled our important appointment without even telling us what they have done. How can they do that?"

"It's not very good, is it," said the secretary. "I'll see what I can do and call you."

By 12.45 pm there was still no call so I rang them. "We've just got an appointment for you at 9.00 am tomorrow morning. Can you make that?" said the secretary.

"Yes, we will, thank you," I replied.

We had to get up at 6.30 am to get Rita showered, dressed, fed and drive 15 miles through the rush-hour traffic to get to the urology department by nine o'clock. We made it with five minutes to spare and had the first appointment. We sat outside the door of the consulting room. Nine o'clock came and went. Several other people arrived. At 9.45 am, the consultant arrived. He may have had a good reason for being late, but we received neither explanation nor apology. It also seemed a rather hurried meeting, with one metaphorical eye being kept on the line of irritated people sitting outside his door. Rita was given no examination, though a urine sample was taken to check for infection. We would need to come back again for tests, so were told to make an appointment on the way out. Oh yes, this consultant only dealt with bladders, not bowels. The fact that Rita was doubly incontinent meant that we needed to see a different consultant for bowels. He commented that what I was doing to help Rita was exactly right (disappointingly, I would rather have learnt some new procedure that would take things forward) and the medicines prescribed by our GP were just what he would have suggested too.

On the way out we made an appointment for 7 October for a bladder test, but not for bowels – we didn't have the necessary referral from our GP. The consultant we had just seen had said he would have a word with a colleague about this, but we heard nothing more.

On 4 November, we had the follow-up appointment with a colleague of the first consultant. He wanted to carry out a bladder inspection and biopsy but said it was still too soon after the haemorrhage to carry out these procedures, so he would set a date in late March 2009. His view was that control of bowel movements by a combination of constipation and enemas, as suggested in the report by the first neuropsychologist, Dr Peter (chapter 12), is not usually satisfactory. He increased the daily dose of oxybutynin and gave a trial prescription of an evening pill (I think that was the start of desmopressin) to reduce the overnight production of urine. This combination did improve matters somewhat.

During the period between September 2008 and February 2009, my diary has frequent complaints of the difficulty in caring for Rita, her slowness at doing things, her uncooperativeness when being dressed or taken to the loo. I was finding things more than difficult. It is one thing caring for someone 24/7 when they are appreciative and helpful; when they are uncooperative it is several stages worse. An example occurred when the OT called in on 29 January to see if a powered "pillow lifter" would be any help in getting Rita out of and back into bed. It took us ten minutes to fit it to the bed and during that time Rita went to the back door, pulled her pants down and peed on the floor. This gave the OT an opportunity to see for herself what could happen when Rita was left to herself for just a short period. And the "pillow lifter" proved to be of no help.

Our next visit to the urology department on 30 March 2009 was for the aforementioned bladder inspection and biopsy, I was told. I should have realised a biopsy would have needed admission to hospital, not just an out-patient appointment. The consultant voiced the opinion that Rita would never recover fully from her incontinence (actually she did, much later, in South Africa), but suggested a renal scan and bladder inspection. That appeared to be the end of the consultation. I suggested that, in view of Rita's repeated urinary infections, would it be an idea if she went on a prophylactic course of antibiotics? The consultant agreed and prescribed an ongoing two-week course on 100 mg daily of trimethoprim, alternating with two weeks of nitrofurantoin, also 100 mg daily.

A month later, on 29 April, we were back at the hospital for ultrasound scans and X-rays of Rita's bladder and kidneys. They would be in touch with us about the results.

Following these scans, I telephoned our doctor, and the hospital, on a few occasions to ask whether the results were available. Eventually, we were sent a date for a meeting with the consultant on 21 July. I phoned the hospital to say that Rita was now at a rehabilitation clinic, so was not available. However, as it was only to discuss the results of the scans, I was told her presence was not needed. So I arrived alone to see one of the urinary consultants. Had I brought a letter written by Rita to say I could have the results on her behalf? No, but I held Power of Attorney over her affairs. Had I brought a copy of the PoA? No.

"Sorry, he couldn't discuss the results with me." However, the consultant did release the information that there was nothing to worry about, that he would write to our GP, copy to Rita, so I would be able to read that letter, and he recommended continuing with the prophylactic antibiotics.

The letter said there appeared to be no abnormalities with either bladder or kidneys. Also, that his colleague had previously recommended that Rita have a flexible cystoscopy examination and he would check she was on the waiting list for this. He added the note that "during the process of rehabilitation she, I presume, will also have bladder-training skills taught to her". This comment shows that this consultant suffered from two misconceptions – that there was an active programme for rehabilitation and that Rita was being taught bladder-training skills. Neither was true. This sort of comment showed the importance of a case manager, or equivalent, to tie things together and make sure they happened, or that there is a good reason why they did not. It was similar to the "assumptions" made in the neurosurgeon's letter nine months earlier concerning treatment that he thought Rita would be receiving at our local hospital, but was not.

By early October 2009 (this was after Rita's 12 weeks in the rehabilitation clinic, chapter 13), her incontinence remained bad. I told our GP (on 9

October) that Rita had wet 11 pairs of trousers during a period of three weeks, plus a major soiling of her bed, despite me taking her to the toilet, on average, eight times each day. I also recorded this on a written note to the doctor that evening and included my view that the NHS was not in any way providing Rita with the treatment recommended in the *National Clinical Guideline for Stroke*. The doctor phoned on 13 October to say he had arranged an appointment with the stroke consultant the following Monday, 19 October. Also, that he was prescribing a stronger antibiotic for Rita as her last urine sample was "inconclusive". She went onto Keflex (cephalexin) for eight days, with immediate effect.

The summary I gave the consultant was to the effect that Rita's incontinence had received no real treatment during 18 months, other than the prescription of pills. She had undergone a small number of urology tests, but these had not led to any corrective treatment and there had been no attempt to either examine or treat her bowel incontinence. The situation had worsened during the last month and I showed him my detailed recorded history. It had reached the stage where I couldn't keep the house hygienic and I was close to failing to cope with the situation.

The consultant then ran some more tests on Rita. He thought she seemed a lot brighter than on the earlier visit and that, physically, she was in pretty good shape, so most of the problem was probably in the "messaging" from the brain. The bowel could be controlled by a daily dose of codeine, followed by an enema twice a week – a far from attractive-sounding course of action. The action he suggested was to double the daily dose of desmopressin since, at only 0.1 mg a day, the present dose was low. After a week, a third 0.1 mg daily would be added. I should monitor the results and arrange to see our GP for a check-up. At the same time I was to give 30 mg of codeine at 6.00 pm daily if the bowels continue to open; but not if they didn't. We were to come back to see him once more in six weeks. I increased the desmopressin to 0.2 mg, but never raised the dose to 0.3 mg per day.

It was about this time that the Social Services re-enablement programme was ending. The manager of the domiciliary care agency, which was providing the carers, told me that she had sent a thorough report on Rita's condition to Social Services, emphasising how much care Rita needed and that Social Services should, in her opinion, be providing this. It was kind of her to do this, but we heard nothing from Social Services concerning this recommendation.

Two days later, on 21 October, a good friend (a retired theatre nurse) looked after Rita for a couple of hours and commented on how tired she seemed. She was also very tired in the evening and weepy when she went to bed. The carer, on her last visit, was concerned at how badly Rita was moving. She tried walking with her in the garden, but soon returned being afraid Rita would fall.

Rita continued to be tired and listless. On Thursday 29 October, we set out for the swimming session with her SAS friends, but halfway there Rita was suddenly sick in the car. I took her home, cleaned up, and she then sat in an old soft chair looking sorry for herself. The next day I emailed the stroke consultant and our GP to say that, in view of Rita's general listlessness and the sickness the day before, I was stopping the codeine forthwith, until or unless I heard from them. I did not hear from the consultant so presumably he agreed with my action.

The GP phoned on 3 November to suggest using Imodium (loperamide), when necessary, in place of the codeine to control Rita's bowel movements. The continence nurse also called. She gave Rita a scan and said she did not think Rita was retaining urine. She would again try to get permission for Rita to use the Euron "Wing" pads exclusively. I was delighted because this time her efforts were successful. We were soon using the "Wing" pads all the time. This gave more protection against wetting her clothing and, probably, against picking up infections. It had taken nearly 18 months to reach that stage.

It seemed that deleting the daily codeine from Rita's list of pills, plus the use of better pads, produced a distinct improvement in Rita's condition. She was brighter, seemed less tired and was more cooperative, which was a big bonus for me, but she still walked badly. It was not all good news as we had a fright by way of an emergency admission to hospital for a transient ischaemic attack (TIA) in mid November (chapter 15).

Rita acquired another urinary tract infection in mid January. She was given a stronger antibiotic, taken twice daily for ten days, but I didn't record its name.

At a meeting with the manager from the Patient Experience Team of the PCT, on 20 January 2010, as an example of the difficulties I was having with getting adequate treatment for Rita's incontinence, I pointed out that Rita had been down to have a cystoscopy examination six months ago, but still no date had been set for this. She picked this up immediately and said she would make sure a date was fixed. I said we were going to South Africa shortly for six weeks and, in view of this, a date during the first half of April would be best. This was agreed.

A few days later an appointment letter came for us to see the first consultant in the hospital urology department on 2 February. Not quite as agreed, but it showed some action and we were able to attend then. Regrettably, I had to cancel the day before because Rita had another emergency admission to hospital with a nosebleed and was kept in overnight. I asked the appointments secretary to re-arrange for the first half of April, which she agreed to do. On our return from South Africa at the end of March, I found among the mail *another* appointment with the urinary consultant, for 22 February this time, and dated the day we left for South Africa. Maybe this is what was referred to when, at a "health professionals" meeting 17 months later, I was accused of not keeping appointments. When I am 6000 miles away and don't even know the appointment has been made, I am not likely to keep it.

We had a follow-up meeting with the stroke consultant on 25 January 2010. After a review of recent events, he recommended increasing the daily dose of desmopressin again, from 0.2 mg per day to 0.2 mg both morning and evening for a week, then to the same dose three times each day to see how it improved urine control. This would be 0.6 mg a day in three doses. He told us this would be perfectly safe as 0.2 mg was a very low dose. Also, I should increase the use of loperamide to control bowel movement; this also was a safe medicine.

He emphasised how important it was to stimulate Rita's brain in order to develop new neurons, as the damaged ones were lost and could never be recovered. But he didn't suggest the best way to achieve this stimulation. I asked his opinion on going to South Africa. He thought it was a good idea and she would benefit from the better climate.

During January 2010, Rita had three nosebleeds, the first and third needing hospital treatment, the second a fairly mild one was while at day-care one morning. Following the last one, Rita was first taken to the local hospital, then transferred to another hospital 20 miles further away because, despite it being Sunday, there was an ENT consultant on duty. He wanted to know about the medication she was on, especially as tests had shown her blood sodium level to be significantly too low. He told me it was probable the increased dose of desmopressin that was the cause of the low blood sodium. (By then I had increased it to 0.4 mg per day, but not gone up to the suggested 0.6 mg daily dose.) The ENT consultant told me to revert to 0.2 mg per day immediately and never to go above that level. Also, that Rita should not drink too much, never more than 1.5 litres of water per day. This was contrary to the advice 18 months earlier from the continence nurse. Rita was kept in hospital overnight and this time her nose was cauterised.

I brought Rita home on 1 February and saw the GP yet again, the next day, to re-jig her medicines for the next weeks. Both he and the ENT consultant agreed there was no reason not to fly to South Africa on 8 February, provided there were no more incidents, which there were not.

After a successful six weeks in South Africa (chapter 19), our next urology appointment was on 20 May at a small hospital about 40 miles away. Apparently, Rita's bladder was fine. There were no problems with it, but it was a bit on the small side and "active". The consultant apologised for dragging us so far from home and said he would set up future clinics for her locally. So the story still seemed to be that Rita's urinary system was physically sound, it was brain messaging failure that caused the lack of control of the bladder. At that time, she was using two to three continence pads each 24 hours, on average. The "accident" rate (which I defined as a leakage causing bed or clothes wetting) was now quite low at around one to two each month. This was partly due to the much better quality pads and partly due to the fact that her incontinence was improving slowly with time.

Much later in 2010, from 23 September onwards, we spent about ten weeks in South Africa (chapter 28), so the next appointment in the urology department was not until 29 December. A very clever machine measured the rate and volume of Rita's peeing – luckily she was able to "perform" in such strange surroundings. The nurse then ran a scan and told us that she had retained about 250 ml in her bladder. I would have thought that merited some suggestions for treatment, but the nurse merely filed the information for a consultant to review at some later date. There was no feedback to us of any sort following that test.

And that is the summary of Rita's urinary and bowel treatment for double incontinence over a period of 32 months following her stroke – apart from a last visit from a continence nurse in December 2010, shortly after our return from those ten weeks in Cape Town. She declared herself, rather inelegantly, as "gobsmacked" at Rita's improvement. As the treatment in South Africa seemed to be helping significantly, and some time later Rita's incontinence was 100% cured, I saw no need to further trouble the urology services of the UK.

10

October 2008 to February 2009

Full-time Caring – The Experience

This period was spent trying to get some action in place to support Rita's rehabilitation towards recovery, plus simultaneously dealing with her difficulties, especially irrationality, cognitive dysfunction, poor balance, incontinence – *and* – being responsible for her 24 hours a day, which generally meant a total of 14 hours actively caring for her in every 24. Friends and family were trying hard to be helpful, but their efforts were not pulled together or controlled by anyone knowledgeable. It was going to be some time before I understood properly the distinction between "care" and "rehabilitation". Many people can help positively with the care aspect using just experience and common sense, but it needs professional therapists to provide effective rehabilitation treatment. It had become evident to me that it *is* possible to make a good recovery from severe stroke. Celebrities have demonstrated this possibility well enough. Several well-known people have made remarkable recoveries from a bad stroke, but how did they achieve this success? Were they able to access more professional treatment than the average patient and did this make the difference?

I was finding things a little easier because Rita settled quickly at the day-care centre. She was collected and returned at (approximately) regular times and seemed always happy to go. The manager kept in contact and would always call me if she had any concern about her welfare.

Rita also enjoyed the weekly Success After Stroke meetings on Tuesday mornings. The physiotherapist there spoke to me several times concerning Rita's condition, suggesting that I should be firmer with the GP about getting some regular rehabilitation therapy in place. She would write to her contacts to try to organise a neuropsychologist to see Rita. For me, the time off from looking after Rita was hugely valuable, even though I might still be doing housework, shopping or whatever, at least I could do it at my own speed and without interruption.

Rita's brain haemorrhage had been unexpected, to say the least. It was probably the combination of her previous excellent health and the expertise of the neurosurgeons that pulled her through the trauma. Had either one of those been missing, I am sure she would not have survived. As it was, and as I have described already, she came out of hospital with major physical and cognitive difficulties. From being a highly motivated woman, always busy and helping people, she gave the appearance of having lost all motivation and was quite content to sit in a chair, lick her lips and pick at her fingernails for hour after hour. She had no interest in the television, newspapers or books for most of these months – just simple crosswords that she could not complete without help. She could not undertake the simplest household chore without close supervision and regular prompting. She had no consideration for other people's needs and frequently behaved irrationally. She was lost in both time and space – having no idea of what day it was, nor the date – and no ability to find her way around places she had known for years, such as the local town. Although her balance and mobility were poor, she *was* mobile and so could not be left alone for more than minutes at a time because her actions were unpredictable. Nor could she be given instructions or requests to do, or not to do, something because she forgot them immediately.

Suddenly I had to take on several more areas of responsibility. These included all Rita's household jobs that she had managed so competently and for so long. Shopping, cleaning and cooking I could cope with without too much bother, though not to anywhere near the standard that Rita worked to. In addition, I had Rita to look after. I found this very, very difficult. She was no longer the person I had lived with for so long, now needing so much help. Her irrational behaviour was terribly difficult to understand when I had known her as an intelligent and very rational companion. I needed to be with her, or nearby, throughout the day and we were physically in closer contact than at any previous time during our marriage. The only breaks were when someone else would stay with her or she attended day care, and this day care seemed to be far more valuable to me than to Rita!

On an average day, Rita needed attention by 7.00 am, slept little during the day, and didn't go to bed till around 8.30 or 9.00 pm. This meant I was nominally in charge 14 hours a day, seven days a week. This, I suggest, is unsustainable over a long period without the danger of accidents or the carer themselves falling ill. Additionally, I had frequent meetings with Social Services staff, the GP and other surgery staff, plus other professional people I thought might be able to provide some help with Rita's ongoing treatment; all these taking up time.

Quite frequently it was suggested I should do more research into treatment for stroke. "There is lots of information available online," I was told. That was true, but I had neither the time nor energy left after all essential work had been done. That is why the suggestion in the *National Stroke Strategy* – that carers of severely disabled stroke survivors should be allocated a "named person" to help and to advise – is such a good idea. I know this diatribe sounds like a big whinge or a string of complaints. It is, rather, intended as a factual statement of how I felt and what I had to do as a result of Rita's sudden illness. From many discussions I have had with other carers, my experience is commonplace. Others commented on situations worse than mine. Despair and depression were mentioned and, more often than not, the carers had given up trying to change things, deciding merely to live with the situation they were in. I was determined to push things as far as I possibly could and make a nuisance of myself until something positive was achieved, but just doing that required much effort.

I arranged for a private physiotherapist to come in to check Rita. She was concerned about Rita's posture. She gave us a list of exercises to be done daily. These went the usual way of exercises that I was supposed to persuade Rita to do – she refused to be persuaded. And I was past making an issue of it. The physio didn't seem interested in developing a longer-term programme that would have a good likelihood of success in helping Rita.

Then an occupational therapist (the first one we had seen since Rita left hospital) called to see us on 17 October 2008. She was a charming young girl, keen to help, and she made several suggestions for getting

Rita to move better and more safely around the house. With help from a hospital OT, she set up a six-week therapy programme for Rita that ended shortly before Christmas, coming in two or three times each week. This helped Rita with household tasks such as making drinks, dusting, preparing vegetables and so on, though six weeks was too short a period to produce a major advance. As, by Christmas 2008, it seemed likely that a rehabilitation programme might be authorised by the PCT (this hope turned out to be too optimistic), I agreed with the OT that her programme would not be continued into the New Year. What progress Rita had made was lost again over the next one to two months.

Rita was using fewer continence pads during the day, but still having quite regular accidents. Generally, she just appeared to have no knowledge of when she wanted to go to the toilet. Despite being mobile, she remained unsteady on her feet and was liable to tip over without warning, usually forwards, but her legs sometimes just gave way and she collapsed like a sack of potatoes. It became a fine line between keeping close by her to prevent a fall, and looking after her so closely that she became too dependent on me. I had been warned by the hospital physiotherapists that I should be wary of allowing her to become over-dependent; that it was better to make her do things for herself, even if it took longer and she objected to being ignored. But this dependency became steadily more marked. Just as an example, Rita became unable to get onto her feet from the sofa if I was in the room. But if I was not in the room and the doorbell or the telephone rang, she was on her feet quite quickly.

Later on, I found time to read a few books on the subject of caring for severe disability and several comments seemed particularly relevant to our situation when lined up together:

- Sufferers of a traumatic brain injury, such as a stroke, usually have potential for some recovery; not necessarily complete recovery, but often substantial.

- This recovery is likely to be more successful and quicker if treatment is begun as soon as the patient is physically stable. It must be given by professionals, or at least be supervised by them. It is likely to be needed over extended periods of time when severe injuries are involved.

- For several reasons, spouses are the wrong people to provide rehabilitation and, although they can help considerably if given simple training and are supervised fairly closely to begin with, attempting the job on their own will almost certainly lead to failure. *Very true, in my experience!*

- Families, especially those individuals who are to become the main carers, need training, advice and support to deal with the unfamiliar problems that will arise, especially during the early weeks and when disabilities are severe.

These books talked about rehabilitation teams, community teams, rehabilitation programmes that involve the family, case managers, training for carers, access to further treatment when necessary – as if all this support was commonplace and automatically available. It sounded great, but none of this had been accessible to Rita and me. The books were silent on what action could, or should, be taken when the above help was *not* accessible. However, some ideas on the therapy Rita should be having were falling into place.

In the autumn of 2008, our GP wrote, at my request, to the, then, PCT asking for Rita to be referred for a rehabilitation programme. She was quickly assessed by a neuropsychologist, commissioned by the PCT, who recommended treatment. So things were beginning to look quite promising, but by the end of March 2009, no decision had been made. Would she or wouldn't she be given formal rehabilitation, and time was passing. All recommendations were that therapy should be given as soon as possible after a stroke and it was then nearly a year since Rita suffered hers. Nothing was done without a battle, it seemed to me and, more often than not, nothing happened anyway. By the end of negotiations with the UK health authorities, I had approximately seven full A4 files of letters and documents to and from hospitals, the Social Services and the PCT.

As well as taking up a huge amount of time that I didn't have, this fight for treatment had another insidious effect. I began to feel that everyone was against me. No one was on our side trying to help Rita overcome her problems. No one was even interested once they had got her out of hospital and back home. It was all very demoralising. Time was passing and Rita had not received the early treatment that she should, apparently, have had to allow the best probability for recovery. Much later, in a letter dated 24 June 2010, a senior manager of the PCT Patient Experience Team wrote to me to say, "… the information I have received from all the professionals involved in Rita's care is that any rehabilitation potential will not be sustained, due to Rita's cognitive impairment". This claim could hardly have been more wrong, as is described later in Part 2.

As winter progressed, Rita was able to go outside the house less and less often, which she objected to strongly, being an outdoors person. But she was too immobile to keep herself warm and the weather was too often wet, windy or cold – or all three. So we were cooped up in the house most of the time, which got on both our nerves after several weeks. Due to Rita's immobility, she also needed the house warmed to a higher temperature than I found comfortable. So, when Duncan, our younger son, suggested we should join them for a holiday on the Mediterranean island of Gozo in February, we accepted immediately (chapter 11).

11

14 February to early April 2009

Holiday on Gozo and the Three Weeks Following

Our son Duncan and his wife Susan owned a holiday home on Gozo, the small island to the north-west of Malta and separated by a 25-minute ferry crossing. They were spending the spring school half-term there so suggested we should join them, and then stay for another three weeks before returning home. This might give us both a decent break from the English winter. It didn't take long to agree. A couple of weeks beforehand we did what we had resisted for a long time and purchased a wheelchair for Rita. We had increasingly felt the need for one and, on Gozo, our activities would have been severely curtailed had we been limited to the distances that Rita could walk. We bought a lightweight folding chair that fitted comfortably in the boot of our car and would cause no difficulty with airlines in taking it abroad.

The taxi taking us to Gatwick picked us up at 5.30 am one morning. Rita was not walking well and at Arrivals I had her in the wheelchair plus a trolley of luggage to manoeuvre but, lacking porters, some helpful passengers gave me a hand as far as the check-in desk. It was a long flight because it landed at Catalina on the way. A people-carrier met all of us in Malta for the 45-minute bumpy, swinging-too-fast-round-tight-corners drive across the island to the Gozo ferry. We reached the house at about 9.00 pm local time, all very tired. We had a pasta meal and I put Rita to bed at around 11.00 pm, very weary but she had done really well on the journey.

It can be cold, wet and windy on the Med in winter. The first night *was* cold (the coldest for five years, it was claimed locally) and it took a while to warm up in the morning despite the wood-burning stove that acted as a space heater in the centre of the living room. Rita and I later sat in a sheltered spot in the sun to read and both of us were quickly asleep. We were wakened near midday to drive over to Xlendi on the leeward side of the island where we found a restaurant open.

The week with the family was very pleasant; warm when the sun shone, as it did a fair amount, but cold at night when there tended to be a fresh wind.

We visited favourite spots on the island and explored others we had not seen before, but Rita's poor mobility was a big constraint on at least one of the party; despite having someone close by, she succeeded in falling three or four times during the week. The limitations of the wheelchair became apparent. It had many good features, but travelling over rough ground was definitely not one of them. It was brought to an abrupt halt by any ridge or hole in a pavement of 8 mm or more higher/deeper, of which there were many, with the danger of unloading the passenger face down onto the ground. Gozo is a fascinating ancient island, a great holiday destination, but is not wheelchair-friendly. There are too few pavements, too many steps or ridges in the pavements that do exist, and kerbs that are high enough to make pushing a loaded wheelchair around quite a challenge.

The family left for home on the next Saturday, leaving Rita and me on our own for another three weeks. Later, reading my notes of the next ten or twelve days, I wonder how I coped with the situation. Rita had deteriorated over the months. She was now less independently mobile than when she left hospital and had a fall, on average, every two days. These did not cause her injury. I managed to be close enough to catch her when I saw it happening and, although I could not stop her going down to the ground, I could slow the process such that she went down reasonably gently, without hurting herself.

Her incontinence had hardly improved at all. She had little idea of when she needed to "go" to the toilet. There was a bowel movement during the night pretty well three nights out of four. On 1 March, it had been a major one and in the morning, faeces were all over the bed and her clothing, then smeared around the bathroom before I got control of the situation. Rita would not stand independently but clung to me, making it very difficult to clean her and the surroundings.

Her walking was poor. She wanted to hang on to me if the ground was at all uneven, which it usually was. Her legs had developed the "jitters", especially the left one which wouldn't move forward ahead of her hips – just jitter. I tried giving her support by letting her stand holding the handles of the wheelchair and pushing it forward, using it like a mobile frame. But she made no more than 50 yards before giving up. Her cognitive function was poor; she would only drink with regular promptings not to forget her coffee/tea/juice, etc, and breakfast took her upwards of an hour to eat. I was looking after her closely for around 14 hours each day and really missing the breaks that the day care back in the UK had given me.

The third of March was our forty-seventh wedding anniversary. After a prolonged breakfast, we climbed together up the wide stone stairs, talking about which restaurant we should go to for a celebratory meal. I was not concentrating as I should and Rita suddenly pulled her hand out of mine and went over backwards, banging her head on the stairs and knocking herself unconscious. I quickly checked for a pulse, put a pillow under her head and ran next door to ask our neighbour, Jane, to phone for an ambulance. It arrived within ten minutes. The two paramedics eased Rita onto a stretcher – she was now just coming round and vomited – wrapped her in a blanket and headed off to the hospital. Jane insisted on driving me there (I had no idea where it was in Victoria), but being a small island, it took little more than ten minutes to reach it.

When we arrived at A&E, there were no other patients, so Rita was receiving immediate attention. She was sick again and, when cleaned up, the doctors gave her a range of tests including an X-ray of her head, which didn't show anything amiss. Meanwhile, I had given a summary of Rita's condition and brief history to the senior doctor on duty. In view of Rita's history, they decided to transfer her straight to the much larger – and brand new – hospital on Malta for a CT scan. The Gozo hospital also took a photocopy of Rita's European Health Insurance Card; this would cover the cost of the treatment. There was no interest taken in the travel insurance policy that I produced for their use!

The ambulance crew took me with them. Rita was on a stretcher, I was sitting rather uncomfortably on a side-facing seat by her, with no view outside the vehicle. So another uncomfortable bouncy ride followed, across Malta to the large and spanking new Mater Dei hospital, somewhere in the vicinity of Valetta. I never did find out just where it was; it was too newly built and none of the maps we owned showed its location.

The CT scan was done immediately. The doctors said it showed no internal bleeding or other damage. But Rita remained very drowsy and unresponsive, though the ECG and her blood pressure were OK. The ambulance crew had asked how I intended to return to Gozo after the tests had been run. I said I didn't know. "We'll wait for you then," they said, and delivered me back home in Gozo sometime later!

I phoned our three children and had something to eat. Just before I went to bed, the Mater Dei hospital phoned to ask some more questions; they were concerned at Rita's unresponsiveness.

Not surprisingly, I had a poor night. After some breakfast, I drove over to the Arcadia shop in Victoria at 8.30 am to buy a week's supply of food that would have been difficult with Rita in attendance. I had forgotten how easy it is just to look after oneself. Soon after my return, I had a call from the Gozo hospital.

"We have a problem," they said. My heart sank. "Yes?" I asked.

"Yes, we have lost the photocopy of your wife's Health Insurance Card. Could you bring it in again as soon as possible please, for us to take another copy!"

At 10.00 am, as instructed, I rang the hospital on Malta. The nurse was not very communicative, but said Rita was "fine, more responsive than yesterday". Later in the morning they rang to say Rita would be kept in Malta for a further night. After lunch, Jane very kindly drove me over to the Mater Dei hospital again; she knew where it was in Valetta. It was just as well I didn't try because, being so newly opened (though that doesn't seem a good reason) there wasn't a single road sign to the hospital that I saw.

There were few directional signs in the hospital building either and we got into entirely the wrong part of it, wandering along endless empty corridors till at last we found our way to Reception and were directed to ward Yellow 1. Rita was sleeping and didn't want to wake. When eventually she did respond, what she said was lucid and clearly spoken, but brief. She just wanted to sleep, not talk. We had a few brief words with a junior doctor who suggested we try to get back there the next day by 8.00 am when the consultants do their rounds.

On a different subject, our daughter Sue rang that evening to say she had phoned the PCT for me, regarding the ongoing application (begun by our GP the previous October) for authority to provide Rita with rehabilitative treatment in a clinic. Apparently they had sent two emails addressed to me, but had my surname wrong, so they never arrived. They were now writing again. Not that it seemed to matter much because it had already been decided to defer a decision on Rita's residential rehabilitation programme yet again, now to the April meeting of the panel. Will this never come to a conclusion? There was a storm that night that blew part of the roof off the neighbouring house, just missing Jane's car.

We were off at 5.15 am next morning with Jane (how kind of her to drive again), heading for the Valetta hospital once more. I was expecting Rita to be as she had been yesterday. To my surprise she was *much* brighter, cheerful and talkative. She was sick again after being given her morning medication, but the consultant said he was sure that there was no new damage. These symptoms were the after-effects of concussion that were now clearing. He would arrange to have her sitting up to see how she managed. Later he would decide whether she could be transferred back to Gozo today, but it might be tomorrow.

We were back in Gozo around midday. Our old friends of many years, Ian and Mary, had already planned to join us on Gozo for the last week of our holiday. Mary had left a phone message to say she had brought forward her flight to Malta and was coming over today to help. By the time I read the message, she was close to landing in Malta. I left a text message on her mobile on how to reach the Gozo ferry, and met her at the Mgarr terminal at the Gozitan end. It was great to have both company and expert help; Mary had been a hospital occupational therapist before retiring.

Friday, 6 March was windy and unsettled again. I called the Gozo hospital. Rita was now there and Mary and I drove over at around 9.00 am to find her being walked up and down by a physiotherapist. She was doing quite well. We stayed about 40 minutes and then were chased out. I took Mary into Victoria for a walk around the Citadel and old town, then over to Xlendi for lunch. The sea was rough, waves pouring over the small jetty and lapping at the door of Ta' Karolina restaurant where I had intended to have lunch, so we braved the spray from breaking waves and got into the nearby hotel.

That night was rough with strong wind and heavy rain. I was up in time to be at the hospital at 8.00 am to meet the doctor on his rounds. From near the hospital, I could see big waves breaking on the Maltese coast several miles away. Rita was being washed when I arrived. The doctor said they would keep her in until Monday for observation, but everything looked OK otherwise.

I took Mary to see Dwejra Bay, the location of the Inland Sea. Spectacular waves were crashing through the cave joining the Sea to the Med and were actually filling it to the roof. It was hard to imagine taking a boat through that cave as we had on a calmer day during a previous visit to Gozo. We spent two hours with Rita during the afternoon. She was very bright for the first hour then, over five minutes, switched to being unresponsive and had trouble eating her meal. We were a distraction so we left her to it as she had plenty of support from the nurses.

On Sunday, Rita was bright and smiling and really enjoyed the fruit salad we took to supplement the rather limited hospital diet. At the end of visiting time, Mary and I drove to Marsalforn for a walk around the seafront and lunch at the Latini Restaurant, before returning to the hospital in the afternoon. Rita was bright for the first hour, then went quiet again.

The next morning, Monday, I saw the doctor at 8.00 am again. He said it would be fine to collect Rita before lunch, which we did at 11.30. I asked about taking her on a plane on Saturday. "Too early," he said. Rita seemed quite bright but moved very slowly. It took a long time for her to get out of the car and into the house, then over an hour to eat a ham sandwich and a tangerine, and she fell asleep at the table. Later I read to her, 20 pages from a book set in the Scilly Isles and described places that we were familiar with; she enjoyed that. When Rita was in bed, Mary and I talked over the hassle of changing flight times back to the UK. As the doctor had written nothing on Rita's discharge papers from the hospital relevant to flying (or not), we made the executive decision not to change anything and to return home on Saturday as planned.

Rita seemed to have a good night and we managed with the loo and showering, though it needed both Mary and me to get her down the stairs safely. We drove gently around the island in the sun, with a short walk and a stop for coffee. Rita continued to walk and eat very slowly. Ian flew into Malta during the afternoon and I met him at the ferry while Mary cooked the evening meal. Again it took both Mary and me to help Rita upstairs to bed at about 9.00 pm.

The next morning, Wednesday, I thought Rita had picked up another urinary tract infection and I rang round for a doctor. I managed to locate one who arrived at the door 45 minutes after I had called him. He checked Rita's pulse, heart and blood pressure and gave me a course of Zinnat (cefuroxime) to take over seven days.

Over the next two days, Rita seemed better, but continued to eat very slowly, and neither Mary nor I could get her to take the Zinnat tablets. She chewed them, then complained about the horrible taste. After she had gone to bed, the three of us had a long discussion on the situation of Rita's long-term treatment: what might be done; who should be doing it; but we resolved nothing.

On Saturday, Rita took two hours to eat her breakfast with either Ian or Mary sitting with her constantly. In the early afternoon we set off for the airport. The flight home was straightforward, with the taxi there to meet us at the UK end. The only difficulty was that Rita was sick in the back of the taxi twice on the way home. It was dark, there was no light in the back and the driver didn't have a torch, so it was a messy job trying to clean up by smell and feel! The driver was relaxed about it, anyway. Once home, I threw all the smelly clothes in the washing machine, started it running and we went to bed at 1.00 am.

The next morning, Sunday, I spent five minutes trying to persuade Rita to take a Zinnat tablet, but when I left the room she just spat it out. She then took more than an hour to eat half a bowl of Rice Krispies, half a glass of cranberry juice, a quarter round of toast and marmalade (with hidden Zinnat that she found) and a sip of coffee. Monday was just the same, more than an hour to eat very little breakfast. It was a relief to send her to the day-care centre at 9.00 am, but when she returned at 2.45 pm, her pants and shirt were wet, so there had obviously been a problem. I spent most of the evening drafting a letter to our, then, Member of Parliament, the Rt. Hon. Sir Alan Haselhurst, to ask for his assistance in obtaining rehabilitation treatment for Rita. (Sir Alan remained our Member of Parliament until May 2010 when boundary changes were implemented at the General Election and we "lost" his substantial help.)

On Tuesday morning, Mo, a very good friend who gave us so much help, kindly took Rita to SAS. I went to see our GP and listed to him all our problems; he had nothing to offer by way of help. When I got home, I wrote to him listing again the points I had talked about. I did not receive a reply to the letter. On her return from SAS, Mo told me that Rita was drinking far too little and it must be much more. I measured her fluid intake on the 18 and 24 March. It was 625 ml and 760 ml, respectively. No one suggested how, actually, you persuade someone to drink when they are not willing to do so. Rita had a drink by her most of the time during those days, but ignored it. When I reminded her she took a sip, no more, and forgot it again until the next reminder. Eventually she became angry with me for pestering her.

Meals inevitably took an hour or more and I needed to change to soft foods only. Toast was chewed and chewed and, often, spat out because Rita claimed to be unable to swallow it. This period was really difficult.

On Tuesday 24 March, following an intervention by Sir Alan Haselhurst, I received a call from the PCT Commissioning Manager to say that the (newly appointed) stroke consultant at the local hospital would see Rita on 6 April for an assessment. She added that there *may* be a route other than the Exceptional Cases Panel for residential rehabilitation. The neuropsychologist who had seen Rita last autumn also phoned the same day and suggested, in view of Rita's current symptoms and not drinking enough, she should have a full blood test for renal function, etc.

Wednesdays were days when our GP was not at the surgery, so I made an appointment with another of the doctors (trained outside the UK) who tested a urine sample I had taken and believed there was no urinary infection present. She did agree that Rita should have a full blood test and the next time a blood sample could be taken was the following Monday. She added two comments: that she didn't understand the PCTs in this country; anywhere else Rita would have had automatic rehabilitation; also, rehabilitation would be more difficult now than when she came out of hospital as new pathways would have been built into her brain that would be difficult to retrain.

I did try some more private physiotherapy and took Rita to a local clinic on 21 and 26 March. The physio we saw was appalled at Rita's lack of treatment and said he would write to our GP (which he later did) and speak to someone he knew at the PCT. Nothing came of his efforts, so far as I know. Also, I asked a self-employed lady physio to come in on the 25th too. She got Rita moving surprisingly well. Both physios gave me lists of exercises to give Rita, but I became discouraged as she positively refused to do any of them for me; I was just too tired and had too many others things to think about to make an issue of it.

A friend, who knew Sir Alan Haselhurst, phoned on 26 March to say he had spoken to Sir Alan who had already written to the Commissioning Manager at the PCT expressing his concern. Sir Alan would be seeing the head of the PCT next week and would raise Rita's case with her.

The next days continued in much the same difficult vein until Saturday when Rita was sick twice, each time in the middle of eating a meal, which was worrying. Oddly, the day after she seemed brighter, began to chat again and walked up the garden more quickly than at any time since before we went to Gozo.

On Monday I took Rita to the surgery to have samples of blood taken. The nurse could only get one sample, couldn't find the vein again and we had to return four days later, on Friday, for the second sample. The improvement in Rita's attitude continued through the week and we went out for short walks, though she had another sickness spell and also fell while walking. Her fluid intake on 1 April was 855 ml, better, but still far from sufficient. The lady physiotherapist called in to give Rita another session, but had a hard time getting her to do anything at all. The sickness continued intermittently, but seemed not to upset Rita.

On Monday 6 April we met the consultant at the hospital Stroke Unit (see chapter 12). On the 8th I had a call from the Complaints Manager of the PCT, who had been sent a copy of my first letter to Sir Alan Haselhurst. The manager's comments seemed sensible and positive and I was a little encouraged. He also said he would contact the district nurses to try and arrange some help for me while other things were sorted out. I was past being surprised that nothing came of that "promise". The day following, we had another session at the clinic, when the physiotherapist said he would now write to the PCT stressing the importance of organising a rehabilitation programme for Rita.

So, at last, I began to feel happier – based on little evidence really. Maybe something positive would be done for Rita in the not too distant future?

12

October 2008 to March 2009

Negotiating Rehabilitation

Ignorance was such a problem that first year. I wanted Rita to have a rehabilitation programme, but did not really understand what that was, nor the difference between caring and rehabilitation. If I had known then what I learned two years later when Rita was given an effective therapy programme in South Africa, I would have gone about things differently. I had a lot to learn.

This chapter is a summary of what I tried to do after discovering there was not "lots of help" available when Rita was discharged from hospital. During the three months following her return home, she had been given two physiotherapy sessions and none of occupational therapy. Nor had I received any training – nor been given any practical advice – on how to look after someone with severe disabilities.

I spoke to our GP about the first stage: to get a professional assessment of Rita's condition. This seemed to me to be a sensible first step. He phoned me on 22 September to say he wasn't achieving much progress on finding someone to do this. But then, on 10 October, a physiotherapist arrived, apparently to give Rita another assessment. She seemed to concentrate on different aspects from those that interested the first physio we had seen in August. This time the concern was more with Rita's posture. At the end she gave me a list of exercises for Rita and suggested going to a gym two or three times a week. I did not recognise this as a general assessment that might lead towards a rehabilitation programme.

Shortly after this, through the daughter of a friend, we received a generous offer. A consultant neuropsychologist from a north London clinic was willing to visit us to see Rita and suggested 1 November, a Saturday. I was delighted.

The consultant, whom I will call Dr Peter, arrived after lunch accompanied by a clinical manager and they stayed for two hours. He asked a lot of questions and, at the end, we watched Rita attempt to make a cup of tea – she failed dismally. Dr Peter's subsequent report was not optimistic. To summarise: he concluded that Rita had been left with severe cognitive and some physical problems. The cognitive difficulties would continue for the foreseeable future, though small improvements may be possible with rehabilitation. The best way to progress would be with rehabilitation in a familiar environment (home). A residential course would be his second choice. It was important to have control of the incontinence first, but his suggestions clearly required input from consultants locally. It was also important that I organised regular respite for myself. Ideally, Rita should be under the care of an "elderly care physician" who would supervise her care in the community. I should speak to our GP on how to achieve this.

Two weeks earlier I had discussed with our GP the apparent lack within the NHS of neuropsychologists locally, which made an in-community programme difficult to set up and manage. So we agreed it was an argument for funding rehabilitation at a private clinic and the GP would push for this. He immediately wrote what I thought was a good letter to the, then, Primary Care Trust (PCT) covering our region saying that, in his opinion, Rita required input from a multidisciplinary team which could provide intensive therapy and that, to date, she had been badly let down by the rehabilitation services.

This seemed to achieve the right result as a letter came back from the PCT in early November saying that they would arrange for a neuropsychologist at a clinic near the hospital to assess Rita and recommend a treatment plan for the PCT's consideration.

In addition, the six-week OT programme described in chapter 10 began and ran until Christmas. This was helpful, but not long enough to cause a significant difference to Rita's disabilities and was a one-off, limited programme of therapy, not part of a planned programme. I was told there would be a final report following this, but nothing arrived. I did not press for anything more because I thought a residential programme for Rita was quite imminent.

This second neuropsychologist saw Rita on 12 November. He commented that her executive skills were very poor and that her further care should be in a specialised brain injury unit. He was rather surprised the PCT had not considered her for such a provision in the past.

Five days later, the Exceptional Cases Manager wrote to say the neuropsychologist's proposals would be considered at the next meeting of the Exceptional Cases Panel (ECP) on 21 January 2009. (Why Rita was being considered as an exceptional case was never explained.)

The outcome of this meeting was that advice was to be requested from the Consultant in Stroke Medicine who had treated Rita in May/June, nine months earlier, in our local hospital. Well, *I* knew that this consultant had retired something like three months previously, so they were unlikely to get the required information from him. I made some phone calls and learned that the replacement consultant had been appointed, but that he was away from the hospital and would not be back before the next ECP panel meeting in February. Consequently, a decision on Rita's case was deferred again.

Rita and I were away on Gozo between 14 February and 14 March. On our return, I learned that the ECP meeting was again deferred, to April. The PCT Commissioning Manager had made this decision because, after our return from Gozo, there was not sufficient time for the new stroke consultant to assess Rita and write a report before the March meeting of the Panel. It then transpired that the consultant had not intended to see Rita anyway. He was going to base his advice on what "his team" told him of her history when she was in the Stroke Unit ten months earlier, a few weeks after her stroke. Thus there had been, in principle, no need for the postponement.

This was the point at which I decided to involve our Member of Parliament, Sir Alan Haselhurst, and wrote to him, as first mentioned in chapter 11, summarising the difficulty I was having in getting treatment for Rita. Soon after that things began to happen. The stroke consultant *was* going to assess Rita after all and an appointment was made for 6 April. The Commissioning Manager phoned to say there might be a route around the ECP requirement before rehabilitation was authorised. I had a phone call from the Complaints Manager of the PCT that sounded positive and that action was being taken.

The meeting with the consultant was at 4.00 pm on 6 April. He spent around an hour on the assessment. Rita thought the year was 1980, but did quite well on several of the other tests. At the end of the hour, the consultant told me he would write to the PCT, copy to me, recommending that Rita be put on a rehabilitation course (I think he was referring to a residential one). The copy letter didn't arrive, but I spoke to the PCT on 17 April and they confirmed they had received the consultant's report.

Going back to the end of March, I had decided I should be more proactive about investigating a residential clinic myself. After a little research, I got in contact with one about 30 miles from home with a view to investigating whether it would be worthwhile setting up a private rehabilitation programme. The neuropsychologist, Dr Peter, who had assessed Rita the previous autumn (described at the start of this chapter) was also the consultant to this clinic. During a phone discussion, he recommended it as a suitable place for Rita to have treatment. Following my enquiry, the clinic's Therapy and Admissions Manager replied to suggest that a 4–6 week assessment period would be a good starting point – hopefully leading to an informed decision on the best way forward. This would cost me in the region of £1400 to £1500 per week and would include a therapy package.

This seemed worth exploring further and our daughter-in-law, Susan, joined us in a visit on 30 March. We were shown round by the Admissions Manager. On the basis of this brief visit, it looked well organised. The manager was strongly of the opinion that a six-week stay at her clinic, where they had all the expertise, would be best and would allow time for a thorough assessment of Rita's condition, leading to recommendations on the optimum rehabilitation programme to follow. I would be involved in all the planning. Following that there would be support for Rita as an outpatient. This all sounded good.

I told the Admissions Manager that I would like to go ahead. She wisely suggested I should wait until the current negotiations with the PCT ended, since there was a possibility they might still fund the programme. Soon after this, I had two calls from the PCT Complaints Manager, the second on 20 April to say that the ECP was definitely meeting on the 22nd and that they now had all the necessary information. This followed, presumably, the letter from the stroke consultant and also Sir Alan Haselhurst's intervention.

By the end of April, Rita's condition was deteriorating once more, especially her mobility. She had less stamina for walking and the wheelchair was in almost constant use. At that time, a private physiotherapist was coming in about once each week and was able to get Rita moving fairly well, but the improvement didn't last. On Sunday 19 April, she had been particularly unsteady and fell in the garden. Later in the evening, she twice wet the furniture on which she was sitting without saying anything, which made me pretty depressed.

The next day, Monday, the PCT Complaints Manager phoned to say that all the information for Rita's "case" was now available and it would be considered on Wednesday.

On 21 April, the District Nursing Manager arrived, rather unexpectedly, to assess Rita. He decided there was no need for a registered nurse to look after her as I was capable of doing everything necessary, but that I badly needed a break. I agreed with both these sentiments! Also, he concluded that a rehabilitation programme for Rita was essential – it should have already happened – before any decision on long-term care was made. I felt this comment backed up my decision to ensure Rita was given a full rehabilitation programme before definitely consigning her to a care home.

(The next day I measured Rita's fluid intake and found it was deteriorating once again, only 760 ml throughout the day.)

On the afternoon of Thursday 23 April, our doctor, again unexpectedly, arrived at the door. He had received a faxed letter from the PCT to say that the Panel had authorised a six-week residential course, probably at the clinic I had already been to see. They were talking to the consultant psychologist to the clinic for his opinion. This, of course, was Dr Peter who already knew Rita well. During the discussion with the GP, I said that my view was that six weeks was too short to really prove anything and I would like to follow up with an out-patient period from home, together with training for me. He agreed and said he would support this.

The following day I spoke first to the clinic's Admissions Manager, then to Dr Peter. The former said that getting approval of the residential period was the big step; once in the system it was usually possible to arrange an extension, given justification. Dr Peter told me that the Commissioning Manager had said to him, "initially 4–6 weeks, up to three months maximum, if justified". This sounded better. We now only had to wait for a bed to be available.

While this was going on, Sir Alan Haselhurst was keeping in touch through correspondence with the PCT Complaints Manager. He wrote to me asking whether I was in accord with the action being taking by him, which had included contacting the Complaints Team for Adult Care and also requesting an assessment by the local District Nursing Team for free nursing needs. This explained the visit from the District Nursing Manager mentioned above. I thought Sir Alan had worked wonders and wrote to say how grateful I was for his efforts to help my wife.

The Commissioning Manager phoned me on 28 April to tell me the stroke consultant had recommended the chosen clinic because the local hospital did not have the necessary facilities and the other two possibilities were too "intense" in their treatment. The PCT would fund six weeks there, followed by a further six weeks, if Dr Peter gave a positive assessment after five weeks. I said I was very happy with this arrangement. At the end, I would like Rita home on an outpatient basis, plus advice for me on her continuing care from then on. The Commissioning Manager seemed to agree with this and said I should apply for a Continuing Care Package at the end of the courses, through her initially. Regrettably, by the time Rita finished at the clinic some four months later, I had forgotten this verbal suggestion and never applied for the continuing care, which was very stupid of me.

Rita's status was poor around the beginning of May. She needed the wheelchair to go up the garden, refusing to walk. On 4 May, a phone call from the day-care centre told me she had wet through all her clothes for the first time. When she arrived home, her replacement trousers were wet again, despite the continence pads. It happened again the week following. Maybe it was me getting overwrought. Mo told me that Rita did well when she took her out, but Mo was always optimistic.

The next days were really about killing time. By 13 May, there was still no vacancy at the clinic. That afternoon, Rita started to walk through a door, changed her mind, turned round and fell across a coffee table, bruising her ribs. Her irrationality was worsening. Even sitting down on a chair became problematic. I could persuade her to get nearly into position with the chair behind her, but never quite right and she finished up sitting sideways on, or onto the chair arm. It was very frustrating.

She did enjoy an outing to Hoveton Hall in Norfolk, organised by SAS. Two SAS volunteers managed to get her to walk about 200 yards, one each side, through the walled garden, but for the rest of the outing I pushed her in the wheelchair, around the beautiful gardens full of colour. Back at the bus park near home, I left her in a small group of volunteers and members while I fetched the wheelchair from the bus. Without warning, she tipped over and fell flat on the asphalt to everyone's consternation, scraping her cheek. She was quite shaken, but it could have been much worse.

On 26 May I had a call from the residential clinic. There would be a bed for Rita there from 10 June, certain. So that was good news. Another call on 5 June to say the bed *was* available on the 10th, did we still want it? What a question! So, on 9 June I packed Rita's things for a long stay and the next day we set out for the start of 12 weeks of residential rehabilitation (chapter 13).

13

June to September 2009

The Residential Rehabilitation Clinic

We drove to the residential clinic in the early afternoon on 10 June. It was raining heavily. We met ten to twelve of the staff. They all seemed very pleasant and friendly though the number of new faces rather overwhelmed Rita. The General Manager took us on a short tour, after which I spent time with the Assistant Clinical Manager and answered a lot of questions concerning Rita's needs. Rita had her own room, of course. I left her, sadly, at around 5.00 pm looking rather forlorn and woebegone.

The next day I phoned and was told Rita had settled well. On Friday afternoon, I drove over to see for myself. Rita was involved in an exercise group that I watched for 45 minutes, after which we sat in the garden. I put some flowers in her room, completed a form that was required and sorted out a few of her clothes to take home again, ones I had omitted to label with a name tag. I returned on Saturday, this time with Sue and the two grandchildren. We sat in the garden while the girls played games on the lawn and with two rabbits that were in a hutch. We brought home several bags of wet clothes to wash, including three pairs of urine-soaked trousers from just 24 hours. I rarely had that many before in a day, and decided I must find out what they were doing.

The next day, Sue drove home the long way round, via the clinic. I spoke to her in the evening. She said she found her mother in a group downstairs and thought that she was soiled. This turned out to be the case and Sue called a care assistant to clean Rita. This assistant said Rita should use the call button when she needed to use a toilet. This button was to be found under the bed. But, as I had told the Clinical Manager during the admission meeting, Rita never has and is unlikely ever to use a call button. There would need to be a considerable improvement in her condition before she began to do so.

After five days of clinic life Rita seemed perfectly happy when I found her, but was walking badly and was again soiled. Nurses told me that Rita spent a lot of time walking slowly round the corridors and was continually getting lost. They had gone to the trouble of putting about 20 A4-sized signs on the walls saying "Rita's room" with an arrow pointing in the appropriate direction but, as at home, she only noticed these signs when they were pointed out to her. I arranged for the clinic to take over the laundry now that all her clothes were labelled and also arranged for the "family meeting" on the following Friday, 19 June.

I drove to the clinic three or four times a week, with Rita's friends filling in some of the intervening days. On the 18th I found her cheerful and sitting with some of the other ladies. We walked to her room, but slowly as her left foot would not go forward properly. We again did a little quiz and mental arithmetic. Her multiplication and division remain far better than simple addition that, strangely, she was unable to cope with. If 11 is to 121, 13 is to … what? Her answer, 169, came within a second.

The following day, Susan drove with me and sat with Rita while I joined a meeting with Rita's "key workers", the Admissions Manager, Therapy Manager/Physiotherapist, and Clinical Manager. We discussed what needed to be done and set a programme of work, starting immediately, that I thought looked promising. When I visited Rita again the following day she was walking better than for some weeks, not holding onto things and not needing her hand held so much.

On 30 June, I spoke to the Admissions Manager. She was very pleased with the way Rita had settled, thought she was making good progress and that it was very likely the PCT would agree to extend the programme to 12 weeks. I found Rita finishing lunch. She was bright, but her walking had relapsed and was as bad as it had been several weeks before – hanging onto anything nearby to keep herself upright. I had a meeting with the speech therapist (one session each week), the OT (two longer sessions a week), and the physiotherapist (30 minutes each day). The OT said Rita was doing well and could now get in and out of bed on her own; she would take Rita out for a meal in a café. The physio was disappointed at the relapse in walking and didn't know the reason; otherwise was reasonably happy with progress. They all agreed how important it would be to give me guidance and a programme for rehabilitation on Rita's return home. The OT wanted to contact Social Services and arrange a care package. I also saw the Clinical Manager and asked about the incontinence. They seemed only to be managing the condition rather than attempting corrective treatment.

On 2 July, Mo came with me to see Rita and chat with her while I had the meeting with the neuropsychologist, Dr Peter. He was delayed by other problems and I had just 30 minutes with him and the senior therapy manager at 5.50 pm. His views were that our targets were reasonable, that we should emphasise activities of daily living and independence, but only safe ones, none involving hot water or ironing. Rita had not enough cognitive processing facility to decide what she wanted to do. It was important for me to understand her lack of decision was *not* a case of lack of motivation even though that was what it seemed. It was also important to concentrate on personal care and concrete activities. At the end of the time at the clinic, they would help to establish continuing rehab at home. The OT could come out to advise me. On the way home Mo, who had recently been on holiday in Botswana and South Africa with her husband, told me they had a friend who had been to South Africa for rehabilitation where it had cost £500 per week instead of around £1500 in the UK. I asked her if she had any suggestions for where I could take Rita the next winter. "Cape Town," she said. "A lovely climate and caring society; it would do Rita good."

Rita improved quite steadily over the next two weeks, a little up and down, but generally brighter and walking better again. Several friends commented along similar lines. A few times while I was there, she took herself to the toilet and managed fairly well apart from being unable to do up her trouser buttons. On 24 July, the OT brought Rita home for a few hours to see how she managed. They became a little lost on the way as the OT relied on Rita's directions near to home. Rita could be both very definite about the right way to go and totally wrong! Rita made a coffee with some supervision and prompting, later on making the sandwiches for lunch – pâté and salad. That took a lot of patient supervision and prompting from the OT, but they were finished eventually.

On 23 July, I had received two copy letters from the PCT Commissioning Manager, the first addressed to the clinic confirming that Rita could stay there a further six weeks. The second was to the Clinical Manager for Unscheduled Therapy, asking her to assess Rita at the clinic, presumably to set up any necessary treatment when she returned home.

During my visit early the next week, we tried a walk along a road outside the clinic, a round trip of about 400 yards. Rita managed it, but was dragging her left foot again and seemed less bright in her conversation. I wouldn't have assessed her conditions as very different from a month before and she also had a very wet pad while I was there. This was a somewhat disappointing visit. Later, I telephoned the physiotherapist to ask whether I could pay for more physiotherapy while Rita was at the clinic – a pity to miss the opportunity while she was there. But she said Rita was already getting daily physiotherapy and more would probably be too much for her; she didn't recommend it. My opinion was that Rita had more stamina than she was being given credit for and, while she was resident at the clinic, it would be a pity not to take advantage and have as much physiotherapy as possible.

There was more evidence of the up-and-down nature of Rita's condition. Four days later, 1 August, she was walking better, eating more quickly (with less food on the floor, I noted!) and she remembered a visit from friends the day before. Two days after that the physio told me Rita was maintaining progress towards the set targets and that, provided Rita had a rest on her bed after lunch, she would give her a little more therapy during the afternoons. Rita wasn't keen on the idea of resting in bed, but condescended to give it a go "for a trial period".

The next day I took advantage of Rita being looked after and flew to Cape Town, partly as a holiday but mainly to spend eight days seeing whether I thought South Africa was a suitable place to take Rita during the 2009/10 UK winter (chapter 17).

I returned home by the usual overnight flight from Cape Town and was on the road from Heathrow by 7.30 am. I drove straight to the clinic. Rita was still finishing her breakfast – on her own, the last one at the tables. She was bright and cheerful, said she needed the loo and, in the room, we found she had a soiled pad. I stayed to chat for about 40 minutes, then drove on home to recover from the 12-hour flight.

The next day, Saturday, I called to see her again. She was just finishing lunch this time, sitting on a wet pad so I got one of the nurses to change her. We went into the garden and I told her all about my impressions of

Cape Town, showing her pictures and maps of the city and Cape Peninsula, and suggested that we might have a holiday there. She was excited at the thought of that. I asked her why the park in the centre of Cape Town should be called the "Company Gardens" and she immediately said, "Because of the East India Company!" I wouldn't have known that. Her long-term memory remained impressively good. We then had four games of dominos. She didn't play nearly as well as two weeks before, seemingly unable to put a domino in the right place, but laughed about it all the time.

On Monday it was arranged that the OT, plus assistant, would bring Rita home for a discussion on arrangements for her return there, this to include the local OT and social worker. They became lost again and didn't arrive till 11.45 am. The local OT came, as arranged, at 11.00 and we had a chat. She had little optimism that Rita would progress much further and said it would be necessary for me to come to terms with the idea that long-term care in a home might be the best option. She went back to the office for a while, returning at noon. When the others arrived, Rita seemed very bright, walked round the house well, up the garden as quickly as I have seen her, and got on and off the bed without help, offering several witty asides. All three therapists thought there should be a second banister rail, a better grab handle in the downstairs shower and possibly a better door alarm. The local OT would organise these.

Rita's social worker joined the party at 1.00 pm to discuss the rehab programme that would follow Rita's imminent return home. The therapists agreed with the social worker that it would be best to arrange six weeks of re-enablement followed by four weeks "unscheduled therapy", which would be the OT's responsibility under the Unscheduled Therapy Manager. Timing was tight for getting Social Service's approval for all this, apparently. The clinic's OT would get reports sent by Friday – four days' time – and emphasise how important it was to avoid a gap in treatment.

All this sounded promising. Rita should receive good continuing therapy on her return home for at least a reasonable period. It tied in with the discussion I had had with the Senior Operations Manager on 9 June when she had said there would be a constructive meeting relating to her further care, with the social worker as the first point of contact.

Unfortunately, when the time came, it didn't work out at all well.

On 24 August, nine days before the end of Rita's time at the clinic, the OT brought her for another home visit. With quite a lot of prompting and done rather slowly, she dusted the living room and staircase, got on and off the bed and made sandwiches for lunch. The OT made a number of suggestions on how best to organise friends to help and said I could locate physiotherapists and occupational therapists, for private treatment, by consulting the appropriate colleges on the Internet. The clinic staff seemed to be making a good effort to ensure Rita had the necessary continuing care when back home.

Rita was still up and down from day to day. On 26 August she was very dreamy and couldn't be bothered with an afternoon quiz run for the residents. She just sat and examined her fingernails, nor would she make any effort at a crossword. Yet three days later, Sue and the girls came over with me and we found Rita back to her brighter self, though attempts to play UNO with the girls failed dismally. Sue visited again the following day on her way home and got involved in trying to find some of Rita's trousers that fitted. She said that buttons are coming off and zips failing – she was sure Mum had put on a lot of weight. When Rita returned home on 2 September, I found she had added about 4 kg to her tummy.

Despite the efforts of the clinic's staff, the plans for continuing rehabilitation fell apart very quickly. The details of the final report from the clinic's therapists are listed in chapter 14, with the further therapy in chapter 15, but, briefly, the re-enablement team would only come for an hour each day from 11.30 in the morning. That eliminated any possibility of Rita attending day care during the week as usual. That regime didn't work for long and the re-enablement team was soon cancelled on the day-care days. The staff that came were, as before, carers, with no training in rehabilitation and, as before, their efforts were largely a waste of time. It became obvious that Rita needed support from trained therapists.

After this had continued for about six weeks, on 15 October the OT brought a local community physiotherapist to "assess" Rita. I say assess, but they used none of the tests employed at the clinic, as described in chapter 14. The two of them watched Rita get on and off the bed and concluded that physically she was good, but her mental processing was very slow. The carer arrived at 11.30 am and we all watched Rita dust two rooms. While Rita heated coffee and soup under the carer's supervision, the three of us talked over the options. Incontinence was my top priority (that morning there had been faeces spread over the Kylie sheet again) but the community physiotherapist thought the prospects for much progress in Rita's cognitive dysfunction were limited.

I should have commented that a poor cognitive function was not a valid reason for not providing physiotherapy and OT, but I knew much less about the interrelation of things then. It was in South Africa, a year later, that the physiotherapist, Adele, explained that Rita's inability to remember things was totally irrelevant to her need for good treatment. And her poor memory became irrelevant to the way Adele provided the physiotherapy. The other thing I forgot to point out was that a programme of continuing therapy, after the re-enablement had ended, had already been agreed for four weeks. "Unscheduled therapy" they had called it. Also, the PCT Commissioning Manager had told me, over the phone a few months earlier, that I could apply for a Continuing Care Package. I had forgotten this too. That was a combination of me rarely thinking quickly enough "on my feet" and my age. At 73, my memory was definitely worsening and I had to rely a great deal on writing things down – and then of course remembering that I *had* written them down somewhere! It is worth noting that all the NHS staff involved with Rita operated entirely passively. It was always up to me to take things forward, to remember what had been agreed. None of them ever behaved proactively and came to Rita and me to suggest a course of action, or what useful help might be provided.

The conclusion to the discussion was that the two ladies said there should be counselling available (with whom?) for me to talk through all the possibilities for continuing treatment; the GP should organise that, apparently (one buck going to our GP), but the OT would speak to Rita's senior practitioner (a second buck being passed to Social Services – ignoring the fact that it is not Social Services' remit to provide rehabilitation).

In retrospect, it looked to me that the community physio and our local OT had decided on the outcome of their visit before they even saw Rita. They viewed Rita's cognitive dysfunction as a severe disability – which it was – and that there was effectively no chance of significant improvement in her overall condition – which was not true, as later events would prove. They ignored the facts that Rita had received no rehabilitation treatment during the first year following discharge from hospital and that she had improved significantly when it was provided for a relatively short time at the clinic. They ignored the facts that severely disabled patients need trained therapists in order to make progress, and that it is usual for little or no progress to result from the untrained attempts by social service carers – or from the best efforts of untrained, inexperienced family or friends;

but this did *not* prove that progress was not possible. They shelved the difficult question, "Why spend tens of thousands of £s 'saving' the lives of very ill people – who would then be severely disabled – if nothing is then provided to effect the recovery that is known to be at least partially possible for the majority of stroke patients?" In omitting this essential therapy, the lives of several others in addition to the stroke survivors – these being the untrained, "volunteer" carers such as me – were thrown into disarray.

Avoiding the provision of after-treatment for stroke patients is a negative approach and, one suspects, an approach controlled by limited budgets, lack of resources and short-term thinking.

The end result was that, despite all the "promises" that continuing help would be given to Rita on returning home after 12 weeks of residential treatment, she received a small number of visits from an OT, but not one full session of either physiotherapy or occupational therapy from NHS staff from early September 2009 onwards.

14

Rehabilitation Clinic – Final Report

There was, of course, a final report written by the various therapists and nurses who had treated Rita for 12 weeks in the residential clinic. I assumed this was addressed to the PCT as they were the commissioning agents; I received a faxed copy. How much better was Rita, after this course of treatment? This is a brief summary of the main points of the report. Any recommendations from the clinic are in italics [my comments are shown in bold type in square brackets].

Functional abilities: Her Rivermead mobility index had improved to 13/15 from 10/15 on admission. She was now able to change direction and walk through narrow spaces without losing coordination or balance. Her walking was smoother and with significantly less shuffling.

Her Berg Balance score had improved from 37/56 to 45/56.

She was now able to stand and sit in a neutral posture, and reported less dizziness. A Cawthorne-Cooksey assessment showed that Rita's score had improved from 10/27 to 5/27. She was now able to: get up from beds and chairs of varying heights; actively participate in her self-care routine; make snacks and hot drinks; participate in household chores – but not on her own. A qualification with all these statements was that supervision and verbal prompts were required.

This attempt to put a quantitative measure on Rita's progress is admirable, but the numbers meant nothing to me, of course, without a much better understanding of the tests being used.

Physiotherapy: Rita had a full range of movement, 5/5 in all four limbs (Oxford Scale) though with a slight weakness in her left side and a better performance during the morning compared with the afternoon. Current physiotherapy treatments were directed at stamina, pace, balance work (household chores), stair mobility, negotiating obstacles, changing direction and decreasing dizziness. Recommendations: *It is vital that these skills are carried over to the home environment. Ideally Rita should be seen by rehabilitation professionals.*

Occupational Therapy: Rita had worked well with the OT staff, participating in one or two sessions weekly. They had undertaken many functional tasks that Rita enjoyed. They concluded that provided the tasks were presented with a minimum of steps, a minimum number of items involved and were not too lengthy, Rita was very able to complete them to a good quality, with verbal prompting. In other words, progress made, but still some way to go. The recommendations were that, in order to support Rita's maintenance of current functional level, *it is imperative that skilled rehabilitation support is provided at home.*

Speech and Language Therapy. On admission, Rita's receptive and expressive skills were intact. It was the cognitive difficulties Rita presented with that impacted on her ability to participate in communication. Therapy targeted compensatory strategies. The recommendations on discharge were that speech and language therapy should be provided at home and also that a therapist should review Rita's management of her swallowing. **[My unprofessional opinion of Rita's capabilities was that her speech was near normal (ignoring cognitive difficulties) and she rarely had any problem with swallowing food.]**

Continuing Rehabilitation. Rita's social worker had been asked to organise a further six-week course from the Social Services Re-enablement Team (chapters 13 and 15), which she did. A number of minor modifications to the house were recommended and fitted, except for a door alarm system that was demonstrated and did not work. It was suggested that I consider privately purchased rehabilitation services and access the websites of the Chartered Society of Physiotherapists – with particular need to locate a neurophysiotherapist – and the College of Occupational Therapists. The OT had liaised with the Continence Team who would re-assess Rita on

18 September. It was also hoped that the OT and physiotherapist local to our home could provide some support within the home after the first six weeks. The nurse's opinion on 18 September was that it was difficult to do anything to improve Rita's incontinence beyond what was already being done. She did suggest some ways in which incontinence problems on long flights might be mitigated, as the possibility of travelling to Cape Town was now being considered.

15

September 2009 to January 2010

Life at Home Following the Residential Rehabilitation

Following Rita's return from the rehabilitation clinic, the Re-enablement Team was willing to come for an hour daily *only* at 11.30 am, which was far from ideal because, being in the late morning, it prevented Rita from attending the day-care centre or SAS. Predictably, this programme didn't work at all well, as described at the end of chapter 13, and was soon reduced by cancelling three days of "therapy" each week so that Rita could attend day care, as before. It was also my view that, however good at caring the members of the Re-enablement Team were, they were not trained OTs and certainly not physiotherapists. They were not maintaining the standard of therapy that the clinic had provided, and Rita's worsening performance when back at home demonstrated this.

As recommended, I searched for a neurophysiotherapist local to us. The nearest I could find was 17 miles away, across country. Rita and I arranged an assessment session with this therapist, at which we were told much the same concerning Rita's status as we had heard from others. This physio did not suggest a course of therapy that might lead to an improvement in Rita's condition and gave the impression that she was not confident that Rita could ever make much progress. When even the therapists were not confident of success and lacked a positive outlook, I saw little value in using their services, so I did not pursue this possible line of treatment.

As I recounted in chapter 13, the local OT and physio came to see Rita on 15 October and spent a little over an hour with us. The three of us talked over the options available, the former two with a noted lack of optimism. I mentioned that incontinence was my top priority for treatment, but the physio thought the prospects of much progress in Rita's cognitive dysfunction were limited, which meant little optimism for an improvement in her incontinence. It was suggested that counselling should be available for me to discuss all possibilities – the GP should organise this – but the OT would talk to Social Services. My impression was that neither the OT nor the physio thought Rita would improve from here, other than very slowly at best. They left with no way forward being agreed, other than the above rather vague suggestions. Two months later, the counselling did happen (chapter 18), but this followed a rather different tack from the one these therapists suggested, and it was of little value to Rita.

So, the situation was that Rita had received three months of expensive residential rehabilitation and had made significant progress, but was regressing now that there was no continuing professional follow-up treatment. The impression I received from Social Services was that their preferred solution was for Rita to be placed permanently in a residential care home. My view was that the rehabilitation had shown Rita had the potential for recovery (to an undetermined level), but that considerably more than three months was needed. It remained essential to test Rita's recovery potential more thoroughly before consigning her to a care home.

A good question was: Why did I not set up my own, private, rehabilitation programme? My view was that, if there is a technical job to be done, whoever does it should be appropriately trained and competent to do it. I may be competent to do a number of different things, but organising an effective rehabilitation programme for a stroke survivor was not one of them. Anything I did in this respect would be shooting in the dark. I *might* organise something that did Rita a lot of good, but it would more likely be inadequate in several details. I did employ local physiotherapists from time to time and they helped Rita, but they never set up, nor suggested setting up, anything that could be called a rehabilitation programme. Some eight months later I did seriously investigate using a professional brain injury team (chapter 26), but that was surprisingly difficult to activate. This line of attack was quickly overtaken by events in South Africa. From what I know now, six years later, I was right not to attempt setting up my own rehabilitation programme. It could not have worked because I did not have the necessary training or expertise.

During October 2009 to January 2010, Rita's general health slowly became worse once again. Her incontinence, cognition and mobility showed no signs of improving. In November she suffered the TIA mentioned earlier. Then, during January, she had two major nosebleeds that I could not stop and I had to call an ambulance each time. Nevertheless, I took the risk of flying her to Cape Town on 8 February 2010 for a six-week holiday, described in chapter 19.

16

What is a Stroke?

After more than a year of struggling to understand and deal with Rita's multiple disabilities – especially the difficulties of trying to organise rehabilitation treatment for her – and the frustrations resulting from the fact that the provision of rehabilitation therapy was very far from automatic, it is time to take a rest from a long tale of boring tribulation and talk about what led to all this trouble.

What *is* a stroke? Why do they cause so many problems? Why is it that recovering from a stroke is apparently so difficult for so many people, yet others make an almost complete recovery from major strokes? What is needed for recovery? How much depends on the treatment and how much on stroke survivors themselves? Is it essential to go to South Africa to get the right treatment? ('No' should *most definitely* be the answer to the last question!)

During the summer of 2009, 15 months after Rita's stroke, I still could not answer many of these questions satisfactorily. Writing this chapter in the summer of 2015, I believe I can. I now regard myself as something of an expert in the successful rehabilitation from at least one example of a serious stroke – having, rather fortuitously, discovered a way by which Rita made a dramatic recovery, despite an earlier prognosis that such a recovery was not possible.

But the above claim, concerning my expertise, needs qualification. I am trained as a scientist, but have no formal medical training. My expertise in stroke comes from caring full-time for Rita, a seriously disabled stroke survivor, first for two-and-a-half years, when effectively no progress was made, then two-and-a-half years when Rita made what has been described as an "amazing" recovery. Before this recovery happened, I was told by several health professionals that it would not be possible. This represented a totally negative prognosis for Rita. So when success did happen, it was described as "amazing", but only because it was so unexpected. It wasn't a miracle and it didn't depend on magic. As explained in Parts 2 and 3, I am confident I know how and why Rita was able to recover from all her disabilities (except for the poor memory).

My knowledge of stroke comes from seven years of caring for Rita; from meeting many other stroke survivors who didn't make the progress she showed but might have done had they received similar treatment; from trying pretty well everything to find a solution, and from reading many books and other documents. As a result, I have built up my own picture of what a stroke is and how the various disabilities it may display might be treated. It is important to remember that in this account, for two reasons, I am talking about severe strokes causing major disabilities. The first reason is simply that this is the type of stroke of which I have had most experience. The second reason is that, if the disabilities from a severe stroke can be successfully treated, those from a milder stroke should be easier to cope with.

So, to summarise the important facts as I see them:

Stroke is an injury, not a disease. It is similar in many respects to other acquired brain injuries (ABIs) that are caused, for example, by road traffic accidents, sporting accidents or just falling from a ladder. The category of "stroke" differs from the other examples given above in that it is an ABI caused by an internal failure within the body, rather than an external injury, such as being hit by a bus. But as a generalisation, all ABIs need similar treatment, whatever their cause. The human body is good at recovering from injury, given appropriate treatment – so the question then is – why don't more stroke survivors make a better recovery? This point is covered in more detail in chapter 40.

Strokes – like road traffic accidents – are usually unexpected. They happen without warning. Not only may the patient have suffered a life-changing injury (at least in the short term), but close family and friends find their lives are suddenly changed too, and almost inevitably for the worse.

Strokes are of two types. In one, there is a blockage of a blood vessel in the brain which then starves a section of brain of essential oxygen. In the other, a blood vessel bursts spontaneously and floods a section of brain with blood. This also seriously damages the brain. About 15% of the total are of this second haemorrhagic type, as was Rita's. Without fast treatment within a few hours of the stroke, in both events the affected parts of the brain die. A complication in treatment is that the stroke doctor must identify the type of stroke he is dealing with. A clot-busting drug given to a patient with a bleed is very likely to kill them. The stroke Rita had is technically known as a sub-arachnoid haemorrhage.

Strokes may cause both cognitive and physical disabilities that can display very different symptoms between one survivor and another. The *type* of disability suffered by the survivor depends on where in the brain the stroke occurred. The *seriousness* of the disability depends on the extent of the injury, a mild or a serious stroke caused, for example, by a minor blockage or a major one. In this regard, stroke is unlike most illnesses that cause recognisable and specific symptoms. There is a wide range of possible disabilities that can be displayed by stroke survivors. This presents a major problem for the main carer, who is often a spouse "volunteered" for the job. This untrained, often inexperienced carer struggles to understand what has happened to their loved one – and what exactly their needs are – when lacking professional advice which is too often not provided (in our region of the country anyway). Cognitive problems are especially tricky because personalities may change. Irrational behaviour is unpredictable and can cause situations that a lay person has difficulty in understanding.

A Stroke, it is worth emphasising despite it being obvious, happens in the brain. During a short period, which may extend for a few weeks following a stroke, only the brain is directly damaged, despite much apparent evidence to the contrary. From the neck down, the survivor's body is physically undamaged even though several physical disabilities may be very evident, such as paralysis, poor mobility, poor manual dexterity, incontinence and more. But none of these represent actual damage to the body which, in itself, remains essentially unaffected. Initially, all the damage is within the brain. In a healthy person, this controls the body, but it has ceased to do so in some respects following the stroke (see also chapter 39).

If the **Stroke** victim receives rapid treatment, it may be possible to "save" the potentially damaged parts of the brain and they survive. As a result, the patient recovers quickly from the disabilities, which is a wonderful outcome. If the treatment is too late, or is unable to save the damaged brain, recovery is far more difficult and prolonged. Rita's brain operation was delayed by 10 to 11 hours after the stroke occurred. This was too late to save the damaged areas of her brain which were behind her right eye in the frontal lobe – the decision-making areas. But that cannot be the end of the story! If it was, no one would recover from that situation – but they do. It is well known that survivors of serious stroke do sometimes get better, given time and effort. How can this happen?

It is now known that the brain is "plastic". By that is meant that it changes (reacts) to external inputs. Brains change throughout life, all the time. In the same way that bodies should be exercised to stay in good health, so should brains. "Use it or lose it" applies as much to one's brain as one's body. The result of this plasticity is that the loss of parts of the brain to a stroke need not be disastrous. It is possible, sometimes at least, to train other parts of the brain to "take over" the jobs of the lost parts. Perhaps surprisingly, this is not a highly technical thing to do, but it does need effort and determination, especially by the survivor under the guidance or direction of trained therapists – and a lot of time is needed when disabilities are major.

I was told by a number of health professionals that, after a period of time, it would be impossible for Rita to recover from her disabilities – they would have become permanent and she would then just have to learn to live with them. The period was variously said to be 6 months, 12 months or 24 months, depending on who was talking to me. It was never longer than 24 months. This story is a myth (in my view) that is widely believed. I don't believe it because Rita's highly successful recovery programme only began 30 months after her stroke occurred. One good reason why this myth is so widespread is that it is seen to be what happens. The number of occasions when badly disabled stroke survivors suddenly make a dramatic recovery two years or more after their stroke is tiny, at best. So why should this claim *not* be believed? I suggest it is better viewed as a self-fulfilling prophesy. Though it does remain true that the sooner rehabilitation begins, the better the chances are for success, the reasons I disbelieve the claim that there is a two-year limit on the ability to recover are explained in Part 3, chapter 41.

To summarise; **a stroke** is an injury that occurs within the brain. The body itself is not directly affected in the short term, despite all the apparent evidence there may be to the contrary. Because the range of disability caused by stroke is so wide, there is no guarantee that recovery is possible for all individuals, but I believe far more stroke survivors should recover to at least a reasonable extent than does commonly happen. (This suggestion needs to be proved. I'll come to that in Part 3, Appendix E.) Recovery is easier and more likely to be successful if treatment is begun early, but it *may* start at any time after the stroke and still be successful. One reason why the success rate is poor is that, for the best results, more time and effort from professional therapists is necessary than is often available from health authorities, in my experience. The right *treatment* for recovery is well documented within the UK. It is described clearly in documents such as the *National Stroke Strategy*, published by the Department of Health in 2007, the *National Clinical Guideline for Stroke*, fifth edition published by the Royal College of Physicians in 2016, and *Stroke Rehabilitation in Adults, Clinical Guideline [CG162]*, published by NICE in June 2013 (see the Reference section for details).

In my experience, it was difficult to activate, or access, this therapy. In addition, a successful recovery is very dependent upon the attitude of the patient and main carer, *and* on their ability, willingness and determination to make every attempt to achieve recovery. A positive approach by everyone involved is so important.

17

August and November 2009

Assessment of Cape Town for a Holiday

Our time in Malta during February and March 2009 had hardly been a success. It was in the summer following our return that, while chatting to Mo, I asked if she could suggest a warm place I could take Rita the next winter. She immediately suggested South Africa – specifically Cape Town in the Western Cape that she knew quite well. The truth was Mo would rather we went to Botswana where she had lived for several years. She loved the country and its people, but conceded that Cape Town would be easier to organise and more appropriate to Rita's condition. The climate would be perfect and the cost of living lower than in the UK, she said.

Thinking about it, there were obvious pluses. Midwinter in England was midsummer in South Africa. English was widely spoken, an important factor given Rita's condition. Medical services, should they be needed, were reputed to be good. There was no possibility of jet lag – and they even drove on the left. Mo had mentioned the housing was cheap too, compared with the UK. I might even look at the possibility of a holiday home – but this was getting much too far ahead of myself.

So, when Rita was established on the residential rehabilitation programme, I booked a flight and a small hotel in the centre of Cape Town for a week. It was too far and too big a risk to take Rita there "cold", but a week should give me a good idea whether it was safe, or even sensible, for us to go for an extended holiday.

It worked out that I had eight full days there, from 4 August 2009. The "Hollow on the Square" hotel was just off Adderley Street and a five-minute walk from the main railway station. The overnight flight gave me an afternoon to wander round and get my bearings in the city. The first full day was mainly taken up with a city bus tour to add to my lamentably poor school-boy knowledge of the geography of that part of the world. In a new place I feel completely lost until I have got hold of a local map and found my bearings.

The remaining tours I had booked in advance were slotted into the next seven days and included a drive down the west coast of the Peninsula to Cape Point and the Cape of Good Hope, then back up the False Bay coast with visits to the penguin colony at Boulders and the Kirstenbosch National Botanical Garden. I also spent a day driving east to Hermanus where the small group of us watched southern right whales from the low cliffs above deep water. It was a spectacular sight to see these huge creatures so close to the shore. Lastly, I had a day touring the wine district around Franschhoek and Stellenbosch. Being midwinter, the vines were no more than leafless stumps, but it was a beautiful day and wonderfully pretty country. Being without a partner, for three of the tours I got the front passenger seat next to the guide. He had two jobs, to drive and to talk, and it proved an excellent way of learning about life in South Africa as well as having a great view of the countryside. I quickly became enraptured by Cape Town, the surrounding countryside, the sunny climate – even in winter – and many miles of spectacular coastline. What I couldn't do was ascend Table Mountain by cable car. It was closed every year for maintenance between mid July and mid August!

I was advised never to go out alone at night and if I did, I *must* use a taxi. I must not wander alone off the main streets and must keep money, credit cards and valuables well hidden, preferably leaving as much as possible in the hotel. One goes with the flow, it's silly not to, and luckily the hotel had a very nice restaurant where I ate most evenings. I observed these recommendations except for carrying around an SLR camera that was too big to hide. Reviewing this chapter, more than six years later in 2016, I can say that Rita and I spent a total of 30 months in and around Cape Town and the Cape Peninsula with no trouble whatever.

Mo had a friend, Marion, who lived in Fish Hoek, a small seaside town on False Bay, halfway down the Cape Peninsula south of Cape Town, and she asked if I could call in and pass on some papers. I arranged to see

Marion after about four days and travelled down to Fish Hoek, an hour's journey and about 25 stops on the rattletrap Metrorail train with a first-class return ticket costing about £1.50. Marion had been rather dubious of this means of travelling, but conceded it should be safe during the day, provided I went first class. The biggest problem I had was identifying which was the first-class seating!

Marion met me at the station. She was a lady with many commitments and we spent the first 30 minutes at the large Fish Hoek library while she finished some voluntary work, then went to her home for coffee. While chatting, she asked why I was travelling alone. I briefly told her about Rita and mentioned it was possible I might look for a small house to bring Rita to during the UK winters. "I can help," she said and promptly phoned an estate agent friend, Ron, who promised to be round that afternoon to discuss my needs. I was beginning to feel a little rushed! Pending his arrival, we had lunch at Bertha's Restaurant on the edge of Simon's Town harbour. Ron turned up at 2.00 pm with details of two houses for me to view that afternoon. If I could return to Fish Hoek the next morning, he said he would have another three to inspect. I was beginning to feel even more rushed and said very quickly there was no possibility of me making a decision to buy on this trip. No matter – he was glad to help.

Of the five properties, two were very acceptable indeed. One was too big with four bedrooms. It was beautifully built with tiled floors throughout, three bathrooms, a large tiled patio-style garden and a big swimming pool. At the then Rand:£ exchange rate, the asking price was close to £130,000. But what about medical care, laws on money transfer, laws on property ownership by foreigners and maintenance and security when absent? How long would we be permitted to stay in South Africa each year, etc, etc? I said thank you, and made a commitment to myself to make a thorough investigation of the possibility of bringing Rita to the Western Cape during winter months.

So I returned home knowing that I liked Cape Town, thought we could afford to buy a small holiday home there in the Fish Hoek region – supposing all the outstanding questions could be satisfactorily resolved – and that the climate would do Rita a world of good. But there *were* a fair number of questions to resolve. On discussing it with our children, the reaction was a mixture of surprise, plus a view I would be taking on too much, what with everything else I had to do and look after.

A few days later, Ron, the estate agent, emailed me to say the Fish Hoek Home Nursing Services Trust was a highly competent organisation that provided carers and nurses when needed – to look after elderly people throughout the Fish Hoek area. If I decided to bring Rita, I should certainly contact them for help. He had asked them to email me details of what they could offer.

Before taking Rita to Cape Town, I needed to return again to find suitable accommodation, set up caring arrangements and resolve as many of the other unknowns as possible. As soon as I announced this plan to the family, our daughter-in-law Susan said, "I'll come too!" So that was agreed. I have a great respect for her organisational abilities and how she can get things done. Our youngest grandchild, then 11 months, would tag along. We booked flights for a week's stay from 27 November and began compiling a list of everything we needed to find out and organise.

Everything was "Go" until two weeks beforehand. On Saturday 14 November 2009, the carer arrived at the dot of 7.30 am to shower and dress Rita. She sat her at the table, with some difficulty, to have the cereals and juice I had got ready. Shortly before eight, I realised that Rita was not eating and she shook her head at the grapefruit and cereal. I realised she could not speak, just mumble, no intelligible words at all. I gave it five minutes – no change – so rang 999 for an ambulance. The telephonist ran through the FAST sequence with me that pretty well confirmed a stroke and, almost before I had put the phone down, the paramedics were at the door. They transferred Rita to a wheelchair and were off to hospital. I followed shortly after. When I arrived at the hospital, Rita was in A&E with a doctor and was seen by several staff quickly, including the consultant. They all asked a lot of questions, of course. Rita was given a CT scan and an X-ray, then transferred to the Emergency Assessment ward and, later, to the Stroke Unit.

I stayed with her till about 4.00 pm. By then she could not move her arms or legs when asked to, but did move them involuntarily from time to time. She would reply "Yes, thank you," and "No, thank you," to all questions, but said nothing else. She couldn't give my name, or the children's, or her date of birth, or where she lived. Obviously, she was kept in overnight.

Visiting on Sunday was not permitted till 3.00 pm and I was told not to phone before 10.00 am. I began phoning the Stroke Unit at 10.45 and eventually got through at about midday. The nurse said they could not assess Rita properly because she would not respond, only saying "Thank you" to every question. The CT scan showed no further bleed and an MRI scan had not been done. They were giving her some food and drink. Daughter Sue drove down from Birmingham. I contacted the carer to ask exactly what had happened when she was showering and dressing Rita. Apparently Rita had chatted as she usually did; the first difficulty noticed was when seating her at the table for breakfast.

Rita was asleep when we arrived at the Stroke Unit, but seemed quite bright when she awoke. She recognised us, smiled, talked, waved her arms around and was altogether much better than the day before. There was no doctor there on Sunday and we didn't know how well she could stand and walk, but I was pleasantly surprised at the improvement.

By Monday afternoon, Rita had been moved from a private room into a ward with six beds. She looked slightly stressed with a poorer colour and her speech was not as good as on Sunday. There was still no doctor available but I had a long chat with a hospital OT who would assess Rita's mobility on Tuesday.

While all this was going on, I visited a solicitor who was advising me on whether Rita was entitled to nursing care. I then negotiated with the council over a blocked road drain that had got too close for comfort to causing our kitchen to flood a few days before and I bought a new fax/telephone to replace our old one that had just died.

The council responded quickly to the drain problem. On Thursday, a team arrived with a "jetter" and spent an hour cleaning out the road drains nearby. They expressed surprise at how many they found and the strange underground set-up. The boss of the gang had been doubtful that our storm drain ran into the road ones, but (at my risk, he said) they kindly jetted out our drain from the house end, removed an obstruction, proved that it did indeed run into the road drain and discovered an ancient manhole cover buried under about a foot of earth next to the road that would definitely have to be replaced. Luckily this would be the council's responsibility.

On Wednesday and Thursday, Rita was out of bed and dressed by the time I arrived at the Stroke Unit. She started bright and chatty but quickly tired and became withdrawn. There was a doctor checking her when I arrived the next day. He said they were definitely treating her for a minor stroke, as if there had never been any doubt about it, but that was the first time that was said categorically to me. It was no surprise. Before I left, the nurse consultant wanted me to see an assessment on Rita that she and the nurse had just completed. This I read and agreed. It concluded that Rita was not able to do much at all on her own.

Our son Gary flew over from France and I met him at Stansted Airport in the early evening. Rita was quite emotional when she saw him the next day. On Monday, Rita's senior practitioner (social worker) phoned to ask what was happening with Rita. I didn't know, of course. We were both at the multidisciplinary meeting on Tuesday, chaired by the consultant. All the staff attending the meeting said Rita was now medically stable and was fit to go to the care home on Wednesday, as had been previously organised for my respite time. So Susan and I would be going to South Africa on Thursday after all!

The stroke consultant commented to me that it was unlikely, following this latest stroke, that Rita would recover to the level she had achieved previously. He added that there was no way to cure her incontinence; it was effectively untreatable. I was still not convinced about this, if only because no one had seriously tried to cure it.

On Wednesday morning I arrived at the Stroke Unit at 11.30 am as instructed and a member of staff, very nervously (it was her first day on the Unit) went through the details of the Unit's assessment of Rita and gave me a copy. This was for "care" only, not nursing care, and was a series of pages very different from the ones I had been shown the previous Thursday. The nurse, from Botswana, sorted through all the medicines listed on the "which and when" card to be sure I understood. Rita seemed fine but certainly couldn't walk out to the car so I borrowed one of the Unit's wheelchairs. Once home, she needed the loo immediately and spent the next 35 minutes painfully producing a very hard stool. She seemed really bunged up.

After lunch, I repacked Rita's clothes and drove her over to the care home of which Rita's day-care set-up was a part. Rita already knew and liked several of the care home staff. The next morning I visited her for an hour. She seemed quite reasonably cheerful, but could only manage 30 yards along the corridor before needing to sit down. In mid afternoon, Susan arrived with baby Maya and a huge quantity of luggage that we packed into my car, together with my own bag, and we set out for Heathrow.

The flight to Cape Town was fine. Susan had organised our seats in front of a bulkhead to provide support for the baby's bassinette during the night and, next to this – surprise, surprise – was a disabled toilet. That would make a real difference in coping with Rita on the long, 11-to-12-hour flight in two months' time. The toilet easily accommodated two people and was, apparently, standard on that model of the Airbus. I saw that as a big bonus.

By 10.00 am, we had disembarked at Cape Town International Airport and had located the Toyota Yaris I had booked. Our apartment was found easily at the south end of Fish Hoek Main Road (High Street). From our balcony on the second floor, we could look north-east down another road to the seafront, beach and aquamarine sea 200 metres away. The house had been built a few years ago. The owners lived on the top floor. There were two apartments on the second floor and below that an office and washing facilities for the staff. The ground floor had garages and secure parking behind three electrically controlled gates, but probably not room for much more as the house was built into a steep hillside and the floor accommodation increased steadily towards the upper levels. We had two double bedrooms, both en suite, a large living/dining room and limited but adequate kitchen facilities. We also had use of the large covered balcony facing the sun to the north, being in the southern hemisphere. Susan had done well to find that for us.

We enjoyed a really good week. Two days were spent in the Cape Point National Park exploring the small roads leading to spectacular bays on both the east and west coasts, some of which are inaccessible to tourist buses, with short walks along pristine beaches. We watched baboons (from a distance), various antelope, ostriches and tortoises roaming wild. We toured round the old town of Simon's Town, good shopping, Susan informed me. We spent a day at the Kirstenbosch National Botanical Garden (claimed to be the finest in Africa), visited the beautiful Constantia Valley with its vineyards dating back to around 1685 and, of course, went up Table Mountain.

But the main purpose of the visit was to find answers to a long list of questions, so I had several meetings organised. Susan's baby helped with these – babies are very popular in South Africa and, at 11 months old, she was an attractive child (even though I say it as her grandparent) with her red hair, big smile and good behaviour. She got every meeting off to a good start. I had emailed Ron, the estate agent, who said he had moved to another office but Glenn would look after us. Glenn was very helpful, not only in showing us several more houses but in answering a lot of questions on the buying and selling of houses in the Western Cape, plus security issues, maintenance of holiday homes and such like. As I told Glenn, I was not planning actually to purchase anything that trip but that didn't stop him putting in time for us.

Glenn also recommended an attorney (solicitor) who was happy to answer all my legal and financial questions. Unless I was being naive or missing something, the system for UK residents to buy property in Cape Town was all sorted out. The purchase of houses by foreign nationals appeared to be welcomed in that it brings money and work into the country. I could find no worrying constraints and came away with a booklet that seemed to cover every aspect about which I had concerns and more. My list of potential problems melted away and left me with just the one – "What am I missing here?" If there was a hidden problem, I had not found it.

Then we had a meeting with the nurses running the Fish Hoek Home Nursing Services (that I usually refer to as FHHN). They were hugely helpful. There would be no difficulty in providing carers to look after Rita. Starting at 7.30 am was no problem. Changing the hours at short notice, should we need to, was all part of the service. Rita would need carers, as opposed to nurses, but there would always be nursing back-up, available 24 hours a day, should there be an emergency. One nurse pointed out that Rita and I would need some help when we arrived at our accommodation from the airport, so they would arrange to have a carer waiting for us who would be ready to take charge of Rita for a few hours while I got things unpacked and settled in. The attitude of all the people we met during that week was that they viewed their responsibility as being there to help. Susan remarked that everyone seemed to have a "can do" approach to things. It was all very refreshing.

Then there was the question of finding accommodation for Rita and me for six to eight weeks. Where we were was very nice, but too expensive for that length of time and, in any event, Rita could not have managed the two flights of stairs to the second-floor apartment. However, as noted earlier, the house was built into the base of a steep hill and I had seen a small funicular running up the outside of the house. I asked the owner about it, who said he had designed the house for his old age and put the funicular in should he need help years into the future. Yes, it was available to use now. We already had access to it – that explained the extra external door in our kitchen that seemed to lead nowhere. So I asked for a quote for a one-bedroom flat for six weeks and was given a price less than 40% of the normal weekly charge for two bedrooms. That settled where we would stay as the housekeeper kept the rooms very clean and it was so convenient for both shops and the beach. I was sure that I had to bring Rita to Fish Hoek after Christmas to see how she liked it.

Our drive to the airport for the return flight produced a small but interesting event. The recommended route via the M4, M3 and N2 roads seemed a long way round. (Don't think of motorway when you see an "M" road in South Africa, the M4, which ran through Fish Hoek, we would call the High Street.) From the road map, I saw a shorter route was to go north to Muizenberg, turn east and follow the road for several miles alongside the beautiful Muizenberg beach towards Sunset beach, then turn north on the M22 that heads almost directly to the airport through a district called Mitchell's Plain. What I didn't know, and probably should have done, was that Mitchell's Plain is a huge township. The M22 is a dual carriageway road cutting directly through it, but with robots (traffic lights) every "block" of 200 m or so. After ten or more minutes of this, I commented to Susan that I hadn't seen a white person in a car since we joined the M22. We were not threatened in any way and nobody seemed to be watching us, but I still felt a little uneasy just from the reputation –justified or not – that South African townships have in the UK. After a few more miles we knew we had to turn right, but it came on us unexpectedly and I was stuck at a red light on the wrong, inside, lane.

"You should be in the outside lane," Susan said helpfully.

"You're the navigator with the map," I retorted, then noticed the passenger in the pick-up truck alongside. This vehicle had been following us for five minutes and I had seen the two black men in it. He was waving to me and indicating that we should turn right. They must have seen our luggage stacked in the back with Maya, and we were obviously going to the airport. I waved back and nodded, mouthing, "I know". He then made big sweeping movements with his arm, clearly indicating that they would wait, at the green light, while we turned right in front of them. This they did, most helpfully, and deserved a big wave of thanks. This was an encouraging end to my second visit to the Western Cape.

18

December 2009 to July 2010

Psychological Support: How I Acquired a Community Psychological Nurse (CPN) of My Very Own

Early in October 2009, our GP had mentioned his practice could now refer patients to a counsellor and asked if I would be interested in speaking to someone about my difficulties. On the basis of trying anything that might help, I said I would. Presumably as a result of this referral by the GP, on 9 December I received a letter from someone who called himself a Psychological Well Being Practitioner. He wrote to say that, "We aim to help people as quickly as possible and … we would like to arrange an initial screening appointment via telephone". Then, in bold type, **"I will call your number … on Monday 14 December 2009 at 11 AM".** I prepared what I wanted to say to this gentleman and stayed in all morning. No call. At midday, I phoned the number on the letterhead. The office telephone was not answered, there was no facility for leaving a message and there was no call from him during the rest of the day. Not the greatest of starts.

The next day I phoned again at 10.45 am to ask about Monday's non-phone conversation and this time got through to the office staff. Apparently the author of the letter had rung in sick; they had tried to telephone his clients (but not me, obviously. How many appointments does he have in one day?). They explained that he would be back in the office on Thursday and would ring before 11.00. "Very sorry about yesterday." There was no call on Thursday either. I left the ball in their court.

The next Tuesday, 22 December, did produce a phone call from the "Psychological Practitioner". He asked a series of, in my opinion, largely irrelevant questions, then sighed and asked what the problem was. I told him. He didn't seem to know what to say and, after a pause, rang off after telling me he must speak to his superior. Within a short time I had a phone call from our GP saying he had had a call stating that I was very low at the moment. "No," I told him. "I was rather better than I had been recently; but I had just given a psychological practitioner a summary of the events of the past 18 months." Soon after came another call from a nurse asking if she could visit me that afternoon. She was a senior nurse from the Community Mental Health Team for Older Adults, and she stayed for three-quarters of an hour. At last, someone with some common sense and a sense of humour. We got on well. She told me her job was to help carers and – now knowing an outline of our situation -- suggested that Rita should attend the day-care centre for, say, four days a week instead of two. She would organise that with Rita's social worker and would also arrange for one of her team to see me after Christmas. I said that what Rita most needed was a rehabilitation programme including physiotherapy and occupational therapy (OT). Regrettably, that wasn't something that she had authority to organise. I would have to work on that myself.

Unsurprisingly, nothing further happened following that meeting until after the Christmas and New Year period. On the morning of 3 January 2010, I heard Rabbi Lionel Blue say on Radio 4's Thought for the Day "That no one can live a day without hope". Really? That's a statement that has fairly serious implications when hope is in short supply.

Later in the day a nurse – I will call her Rachel – from the hospital Mental Health Team called at the house after Rita had gone to day care, and we chatted for 90 minutes. She listened sympathetically to another relaying of our history and had a few ideas. After she left I brought our planned holiday to Cape Town a little nearer by e-mailing the Fish Hoek Home Nursing Services (FHHN) to organise daily care for Rita while we were in South Africa.

The Monday after that, Rita's senior practitioner called round in the late afternoon following the promised referral from the mental health nurse. I have a note in my journal to the effect that she, not I, was responsible for Rita. I don't now understand this because I cannot remember the context. If that were true, she should be around a bit more often. I don't believe I can have taken that down correctly. Anyway, she would arrange an additional day of care, each week, for Rita. To do this would take a few weeks. I could also get in touch with a different care centre close to the High Street. They might take her for an extra day, too. A lack of enthusiasm came across.

The social worker would also investigate an assessment for Rita by the Brain Injury Rehabilitation Trust (BIRT), but would need to do this through a senior operations manager in the Social Services. Nothing had come of this suggestion by the end of April, four months later. She also said it might be possible to organise a sitter in the evenings, through the Social Services, to give me a night out occasionally, with the carer coming in at 8.30 pm to put Rita to bed. I heard nothing more of this either.

On 13 January, Rachel, the community psychological nurse (CPN), came during the afternoon for another chat. She was very pleasant to talk to but I was not sure we achieved much beyond the pleasant chat. She returned on the 27th for a further talk, to no great conclusion. She suggested I should take antidepressants. I pointed out that this suggestion was treating the symptoms of the problem, not the cause. I *was* depressed, but not suffering from clinical depression. If Rita had been getting the treatment she should have had and I could see she was making some, if only slow, progress, I would not feel depressed. So I declined the pills. It is too easy to be diverted from the basic cause of the difficulties we have, just to make someone feel they have done something useful by prescribing pills. Pills often seem to be a universal panacea for every ailment. What Rita needed, in my view, was a rehabilitation programme and she wasn't getting it – and I did not need pills, nor was I going to let Rachel feel she had done something useful by prescribing them.

This suggestion from the CPN reminded me that, during the initial six months or so when Rita was first home, we had had several visits from local authority employees and others who "helped" by handing out what was, eventually, a large collection of leaflets – nearly two inches deep by the end – telling me what stroke is, how it is treated, what care might be available, who to go to for more information, and so on. One memorable one listed 99 organisations (I counted them) any of which "might" be able to help us. But it was up to me to sort out which might be useful to us for our situation. Unfortunately, these visitors claimed they were not allowed to advise on which could be the best for Rita's set of disabilities – in effect, they were not allowed to provide advice which is, of course, exactly what a new and inexperienced carer needs. So they went away thinking they had given us help by passing on the leaflets, whereas what was truly needed was practical assistance. I didn't have the time to read all that stuff and couldn't interpret it sensibly anyway because I still knew too little about what stroke is and exactly what Rita's collection of disabilities were. The Stroke Association is a past master at producing information leaflets. If you would like beautifully designed pamphlets in full colour, packed with lots of useful and accurate statistics and information, go to the Stroke Association. If you want practical therapy, try elsewhere. Latterly, I made a suggestion to these leaflet producers that there was a subject, not touched by any previous document so far as I knew, which would be a *really useful* subject for a leaflet! When carers discovered that the rehabilitation programmes, treatments, therapists, etc, that had been "promised" never materialised, this leaflet would tell them exactly what to do next, and who to go to, to ensure this practical help really did happen as it should have done. That would be really, really useful.

At the time of writing, an answer to this good idea has not yet appeared in print.

Sorry! Ignore the last long paragraph. That is just my newly developed cynical attitude getting the better of me again.

Rachel and I had regular talks every two or three weeks for the next few months (except when Rita and I flew to Cape Town). She was always pleasant, sympathetic and tried to find ideas that might provide guidance, but had no authority to actually offer practical help, it seemed, other than prescribe those antidepressants. She was one of the "professionals" invited to the meeting on 18 June 2010, described in chapter 24, but I think I only saw her once more after that, other than when she, the GP and senior practitioner visited me soon after that meeting.

Rather than chatting to me, if she could have given practical help to Rita by way of therapy, her time would have been better spent.

19

8 February to 25 March 2010

Six Weeks in South Africa

The 11- to 12-hour flight overnight was, unsurprisingly, not a comfortable ride. Rita found it difficult to sleep and seemed to be awake whenever I looked at her. She needed three visits to the loo. These all went well, having the room to deal with things in the surprisingly spacious disabled toilet of the Airbus. There were none of the wet clothes that I feared might happen and we did doze for a few hours during the early morning, waking with the inevitable numb-bum syndrome of economy class seats. We landed on time at 10.30 am and were taken off the plane by a lift-bus with about a dozen other disabled travellers.

We passed quickly through passport control and the baggage was waiting for us on the carousel. A porter was immediately in attendance and took us to the car rental desk with just three groups in front of us and two ladies behind the desk. That didn't prevent a 30-minute delay. Both groups at the desk spent 10 or 15 minutes on their mobile phones (known as cell phones in South Africa), presumably trying to talk their credit card banks into authorising the payment. The charge on my card, with a six-week rental ahead of us and the substantial deposit required, amounted to around £1500 equivalent in Rands.

"Have you told your bank you are in South Africa?"

"Yes."

"Well, I'll keep my fingers crossed over this one," she said as she took my card. Her colleague looked up. "You'll need to cross more than that," she commented. But a few minutes later she gave a big African smile.

"You've got your car," she said. It turned out to be a larger one than ordered, of a well-known make but a totally unknown model to me. It was either under-powered or badly out of tune as it needed a low gear at any hint of a hill, but we were never in a hurry, nor going far, so we got used to it.

I knew the route from the airport to Fish Hoek from my earlier visit with Susan, my daughter-in-law. While we were still a few kilometres away, I switched a Vodacom SIM card into my cell phone and rang ahead to warn the nurses of our estimated arrival time.

A nurse arrived at the apartment the same time as we did, with a carer by her side. While I unpacked, the carer gave Rita a shower and change of clothes, then made a welcome cup of tea. A break from unpacking gave me a chance to go into town to pick up enough food for our immediate needs and, soon after 4.30 pm, all the unpacking was done, Rita was rested and the carer left us. Rita was falling asleep as soon as we had eaten and it was an early night for us both.

The next morning, I was up by 7.30 am to look out for the carer and open the security gate. As forecast, it was raining steadily. Dawn (the carer, not the day!) arrived on time and got Rita showered and dressed efficiently while I put things together for a light breakfast for the three of us. Rita was still tired and slow, and picked at her food. I walked the 200 metres into town and called at the Fish Hoek Home Nursing to pay our initial account of R3000. I had a short conversation with the managing nurse who was most pleasant and had a competent and confident air about her. On the way back, I called in at the local laundry to check how it worked (needless to say, as one would expect).

Later, I spoke to the secretary/administrator at the apartments. The laptop I had taken would not connect with the Internet using the Wi-Fi in the apartment, owing to claimed "connectivity problems" and never could be persuaded to do so. No problem. The secretary was happy to give me a key to the office and, for the rest of the time there, I used her computer whenever I needed to email the UK, this being most days to keep in touch with a slightly worried family.

We were, of course, in the apartment where Susan and I had stayed two months previously. This had been reduced to one bedroom by the locking of two doors. It was just what we needed. As expected, Rita could not manage the two long flights of stairs, but the funicular allowed easy access, being capable of taking two adults and the wheelchair comfortably. The first day was the only one during the six weeks that it rained all day. After that there were occasional short showers, then the sun came out and everything was dry within 30 minutes. The carers were able to take Rita outside, into the town or on the seafront, for at least two hours every day.

During the six weeks we were there, Rita was looked after by three carers taking turns, seven days a week. Two Muslim ladies, Fouziah and Fatima, and Doreen, whose family was from Swaziland. She did tell me her native name, but this was, for me, unpronounceable. All were very caring and Rita enjoyed their company. Because they were with us for four hours each day, there was no rush and everything happened in a relaxed fashion, which suited Rita well. They arrived on the dot at 7.30 am (except Fouziah, usually rushing in a few minutes late) in their spotless uniforms and they were never in a hurry to leave if something needed to be done. I enjoyed our breakfasts together. We learnt a lot about what might be called "native" life in South Africa.

Fatima told us she normally did overnight caring, but there was none available just at that time. She had a quite diffident personality and needed to be encouraged to take Rita along the seafront, for example, and buy drinks in a café. However, once she started doing so she managed perfectly well. Doreen was the most open, just a thoroughly nice person and would do anything she could to help Rita. Fouziah was the "bolshie" one – she won't mind me describing her as that. She seemed to have regular disagreements with her employers and continually talked about getting another job, but she never did during the time we knew her. She twice misread her rota and forgot to turn up in the morning, much to the distress of the nurses who issued profound apologies that were quite unnecessary. On the other hand, Fouziah was the one who produced the best results with Rita. She "pushed" Rita all the time, encouraging her to do more than the previous day which, given Rita's lack of motivation, is just what she needed. It was Fouziah who volunteered to take Rita on the bus into Simon's Town, including a ride in a "rikki" (local taxi), a visit to the rather good Simon's Town museum and organising her lunch in a café there. I was impressed and grateful.

After five days we had developed a routine. The climate was equable; around 25 °C during the day with a lot of sun and usually a strong breeze, sometimes building up to half a gale. That was not a drawback as Rita and I both enjoyed windy conditions. The carers would take Rita out in the morning, into town to do a little shopping or along the seafront, finishing at an outside café, away from the wind, to watch the world go by. I did my own thing during those hours, often shopping and sometimes driving a few miles to explore the surroundings to find suitable places to take Rita during the afternoons. Usually a light lunch was followed by a siesta for Rita, especially during the first week while she was getting used to the new surroundings. I was becoming more interested in the idea of finding a small place to buy so that we could spend much longer in the Western Cape during future winters. It was already evident that Rita was responding well to the new environment and I loved the place.

I made contact once more with Glenn, the estate agent, who was expecting me to call and had found two or three places in Fish Hoek to look at. In asking him to find something convenient for the shops and the beach I had made a mistake. These criteria were only met by older houses, near the town centre, built 50 to 70 years ago. The ones available at the time we were there were all "projects" in that the kitchens and/or bathrooms were badly in need of bringing up to modern standards – not something I wanted to get involved with.

Estate agents in the Western Cape seemed to operate in a different manner from those in the UK. Glenn proceeded to contact the other dozen or so agents in Fish Hoek, sending them my outline specification, and he showed me several houses ostensibly allocated to other agents under "sole mandate" agreements. If he showed me a house on another agent's books and I subsequently bought it, there was no difficulty; they had a system for splitting the commission between them under some private arrangement. This seemed very sensible and I didn't see any need to enquire further about the details. It did mean that when, a week later, he told me we had exhausted all the houses for sale in which I might be interested in central Fish Hoek, things were starting to look more difficult.

I had checked the windows of several other agents in passing. Glenn appeared to be right. But I did see two or three houses in one of the windows whose prices were within our range and looked quite good from the photos and outline accommodation. "Where are Sunnydale, Milkwood Park and Capri?" I asked Glenn the next day.

"You didn't tell me you wanted to go there," he said. "They are few miles west of Fish Hoek about half way to Kommetjie, which is on the Atlantic coast."

"Well, as there is nothing in Fish Hoek, I'm willing to look somewhere else if the house is good enough," I replied. Glenn managed to look willing and said he would check what was available around these locations.

Less than a week after our arrival, Rita had obviously settled well. She was enjoying the seaside atmosphere and being able to spend much of every day outside. The carers took her out after breakfast in the wheelchair, first pushing her, then letting Rita walk while holding the chair in front of her for support. When she tired, it was back in the chair until she had recovered, then another spell of walking. I spent one morning in Simon's Town doing a little food shopping, including some local wine (not available in Fish Hoek where there is a local by-law prohibiting the sale of alcohol), and looking round an art exhibition at the library, just resisting buying a beautiful wood carving by a local artist. We had nowhere to keep it and it was too fragile to risk taking on an aeroplane. Rita and I spent some of the afternoon watching the surfers from Jager's Walk, skirting the south side of Fish Hoek Bay. Then Rita surprised me by pushing her wheelchair all the way home, a distance of close to half a mile. This was a major advance in her mobility.

Being the 14th of the month, it was Valentine's Day, so I booked a table for dinner at the restaurant overlooking the beach, 200 metres from the apartment. We had excellent butternut soup followed by fish, prawns and calamari with fries and rice (not sure about fries *with* rice) and then Cherry Julien. Very good, very filling and we couldn't manage coffee.

During the second week Rita was walking further each day, with help from the carers, and was starting to leave the wheelchair in the apartment, having sufficient confidence to be able to make it back if she felt tired. From what Fouziah told me, she was probably walking close to a mile in several short stages. The less than satisfactory aspect of her behaviour was that her incontinence was worsening. She seemed not to be aware when she needed the toilet. It was necessary to put small Kylie sheets (that I had taken with us) on the furniture as I found her regularly sitting on the sofa in very wet clothes, without apparently realising it. I could not forecast when she was likely to need the loo. I could not understand her not knowing when she needed to go, let alone when she was actually peeing and I got quite uptight about that aspect of her behaviour.

I enjoyed several morning drives and walks along the spectacular coast, over the hills (mountains?) to the Atlantic coast, into the very pretty

Constantia valley, and onto the long beach at Muizenberg. We took an interesting tour of the Groot Constantia vineyard, set in very beautiful rolling country looking south-east over False Bay. They claimed to have nine different soils on the estate and so could make a wide variety of wines, though none in great quantity. This was followed by a visit to the much smaller Klein Constantia vineyard a few miles away. Their speciality was a sweet dessert wine, Vin de Constance, which I was told was a reconstruction of the wine favoured by Napoleon.

The South Africans are keen on their sport. At 6.15 am on Sunday 25 February, there was much clapping and talking going on outside the apartment, so eventually I dragged myself out of bed and peered out. The road was closed to traffic and hundreds of runners streamed along from the Simon's Town direction towards Kommetjie. This continued for nearly an hour. Two weeks later, the annual Cape Town Cycle Tour was held, as usual, on the second Sunday in March. It was advertised as the world's biggest in terms of number of entrants and was limited(!) to 35,000 participants. It was a 110 km ride from Cape Town down one coast of the Peninsula and up the other, back to the city. This involved closing most of the main roads on the Peninsula for the greater part of the day. The route went right past our apartment. It took a long time for 35,000 cyclists to pass by.

Then there was canoeing most summer evenings on Fish Hoek beach when the sea was not excessively rough, weekend races for children on the beach, surfing with boogie boards, and the more adventurous kite-surfing along a defined length of beach. Kommetjie had the nearest beach for professional surfing, about ten kilometres west of us on the Atlantic coast. The underwater reefs must have been just right because, for a short length of Kommetjie Long Beach, gigantic rollers, from across the Atlantic, rose high in the air and collapsed in spume and spray for 200 to 300 metres. Yet half a mile away, the sea could be almost calm in comparison. Rita and I spent several hours watching from an elevated platform. Typically 12 to 20 surfers in wet suits took turns to "claim" waves and race along them.

Glenn phoned to say he had checked out two more houses. One he ruled out because it was decorated internally in purple and maroon, but the other, just on the market, he thought we might like. He had arranged for us to see it on the afternoon of 24 February. This bungalow was more what I had in mind. Three bedrooms and two bathrooms, both fully tiled. The main bedroom was very roomy with a large en suite having a "wet room" shower at one end, perfect for a carer to help Rita. A good kitchen, with a wood-burning stove in the living area. There was also a large covered stoep (veranda), facing north. Beyond this was a swimming pool, roughly 4 by 8 metres, with a nice brick surround. This was heated by a basic but effective system of solar panels covering at least half the north-facing roof. (We later found this would hold the water temperature to 30 °C for several months during the summer.) The garden was a little bigger than I had in mind, but there was a large double garage and security fence. I had rather set my heart on being near the sea and this was three miles away. On the other hand, it was close to a large shopping mall. It was tempting.

Another meeting with Glenn followed the next day, Friday. He answered all my queries about how maintenance could operate when we were not there and the security of the purchasing system in South Africa. Should we make an offer? Yes! Glenn guided us through filling in the Offer to Purchase, a formal document that is signed and witnessed. The Offer would be delivered to the sellers by hand. If they accepted our offer we would be committed to purchasing the property.

Glenn phoned me around 10.00 am the next day. Our offer had been accepted! In the South African system of house purchase there is only one attorney (solicitor) involved, acting for both parties. The seller has the right to choose the attorney, but at Glenn's suggestion they chose the attorney whom Susan and I had met the previous December, so I was happy with that. We were in no hurry to complete the purchase. We agreed with the sellers to aim for the end of May.

Rita and I visited the house twice more before returning to the UK, to find out how things worked – the security alarms; pool maintenance; electricity meter; borehole pump and garden watering system. The neighbours to the west, Dickie and Monika, offered to look after the house for us when we were in the UK and it was empty. I was a little dubious of this generous offer. Shouldn't we use a professional company? However, the attorney was entirely happy with the suggestion. He thought it was much the best idea to use someone "on the doorstep" who would know immediately if anything went wrong. So we agreed what they should do for us between the purchase and our next return to Cape Town and I gave them some cash to cover likely expenses. Once we were in residence there, they quickly became our very good friends.

The temperature rose during the days in early March, up to 35 °C in Cape Town, according to the local papers. It was not too humid though and, as we were not being very active, was quite acceptable. Our carers amused me. They were continually mopping their brows and wishing it would cool down – they really couldn't get on with this heat – over 30 °C was much too hot. It *was* Africa for goodness sake! What did they expect? The Capetonians were great complainers. If it was not the heat, then it was too windy. They didn't know how well off they were in the beautiful Western Cape!

The 3 March was Rita's and my forty-eighth wedding anniversary. We had a better day than the year before and Rita didn't finish up in hospital this year. When Fouziah left after her four hours, we drove through Simon's Town to the Seaforth Restaurant at Boulders for an early choice of tables on the terrace. We got one overlooking the beautiful view across False Bay. Rita enjoyed her hake and strawberry coupe. I chose kingklip, a fish unknown to me before coming to Cape Town, followed by the sweet Malva Pudding.

A week after we had arrived, I decided Rita should see the Kirstenbosch Gardens, a half-hour drive north of Fish Hoek. We arranged for Fouziah to stay with us for the full day, so she could come on the outing to help with the walking and toileting. The Gardens are located on the lower south-eastern slopes of Table Mountain and were established a century before, so were not altogether wheelchair friendly – in fact that was overstating it. The two of us took turns to push Rita up quite steep paths, and manhandle her and the chair up rough granite steps. But it was all worth it. The flowers and plants were magnificent with many totally unknown to Rita and me. I particularly wanted to see the collection of cycad trees that predated the arrival of dinosaurs on earth. The attraction was increased by several sunbirds that were after nectar and performed acrobatic tricks to get at it, being much more interested in a meal than the closeness of visitors with cameras. After two hours of walking round, having lunch on the restaurant terrace and another hour looking at flowering shrubs, Rita was well tired and ready for home.

Towards the end of the six weeks, I wanted Rita to see the Cape of Good Hope National Park before we left and thought she could cope with the walking involved. This time we took Doreen for the day. Although, in many ways, South Africa caters well for disabled people, there are a few points it misses. There are concessionary rates but for South Africans only, not aged foreigners like us. Kirstenbosch allows those over 65 free entry on Tuesdays, but only for local residents and those who can prove their age! I knew what the rules were, but I still tried my luck at the entrance to the Park, a few kilometres south of Simon's Town.

"We are both over 70. Do we get the concessionary rate?"

"No, sorry."

"One of us is disabled. Does that help?"

"No."

"One of our party is here as a carer. Is there a reduced rate for her?"

"No."

It was still a worthwhile payment to see the spectacular Cape Peninsula.

Although Doreen had lived most of her life in the Fish Hoek area, she had never been to Cape Point nor even into the Cape National Park, despite having two daughters working in the restaurant at Cape Point. We spent a short time walking along Buffels Bay, then to the Two Oceans Restaurant for coffee, where we booked a table for lunch. Doreen's two daughters spotted her and rushed out for quick introductions, then rushed back to continue their work. We drove down to Platboom Beach, then to the car park at the Cape of Good Hope, where Doreen and Rita had another short walk on the flat while I scrambled around a bit, but without time to follow the path up the cliff to the top.

By the time we returned to the restaurant, all the tourist coaches and minibuses had arrived on day trips from Cape Town. We were being directed to park half a mile from where we wanted to be. But I waved Rita's UK blue disabled badge. We were immediately signalled through and parked in a disabled space adjoining the restaurant. There had been a private function on that morning so, as an aperitif, we were each offered a free glass of leftover champagne. Halfway through the meal, around five of the waitresses suddenly formed a group in the centre of the floor and began singing. All the other waitresses looked up, stopped what they were doing and hurried over to join in. They delight in their singing; it was a joy to watch and listen. They gave everyone in the restaurant a couple of songs before returning to work.

The afternoon was spent again exploring the little side roads that Susan and I had followed three months previously. The types of flowering plants had changed quite dramatically with the different season. We had a superb day out.

Our six weeks in South Africa were clearly a success. Rita's mobility made better progress than in any similar period since her brain haemorrhage.

After our return home, whenever anyone mentioned South Africa, she brightened immediately, said how much she liked it and really seemed to remember something about her time there. I have tried to put my finger on what, particularly, made such a difference to her. It is difficult to be sure, and I may be wrong, but three possible reasons stand out.

The first was obviously the climate that was very equable. As we were close to the sea in three directions out of four, the temperature was rarely too high or too low. It could be very windy, but that did not worry Rita who tends to like a good breeze. It rarely rained for long and, during the six weeks we were there, Rita was able to go out every day except the first for at least a couple of hours, usually much longer. And my experience of eight days the previous August, being their midwinter, was very pleasant; in just shirtsleeves when the sun was shining.

Secondly, we employed carers for Rita for four hours every day for much the same cost as we paid for one hour in the UK. This made everything more relaxed. There was no rush and Rita responded better to guidance from others than from me. Rita and I generally spent our mornings independently which meant that we enjoyed our time together more in the afternoons.

Lastly, and least easily measured, was the attitude of pretty well everyone we met. They all seemed to have the attitude that they were there to help, to provide a service. For me, the estate agent and the attorney could not have been more helpful. They provided a service the like of which I had not received in the UK during any of our previous four house moves. At our last meeting, the estate agent promised to drive past our new, and empty, house from time to time and let me know if he saw anything untoward. Rita had the benefit of the carers. Compared with wage rates in the UK they were paid very little (the cost of living was, of course, lower, but not by that much), but this did not affect their attitude to the job. The three we had, Fouziah, Fatima and Doreen, all, in their different ways, gave Rita the best possible care and seemed to enjoy helping her. When we left, they were really proud of the progress she had made with their help.

A story of our return to the UK underlines the last point. On Wednesday afternoon, 24 March, we drove back to the airport for the flight home. I left in plenty of time because, in December, I had got lost in the road system around Cape Town International Airport, not helped by it being unfinished because of major improvements in hand for the 2010 World Cup. This time I found the rental car return site without difficulty, but it was more than half a kilometre from the terminal. After the inspection of the car for scrapes (fortunately none), I asked the attendant if anyone could help me get Rita, the wheelchair and the luggage over to the airport.

"No problem," he said. "Get back in the car. I'll drive you over." This he did, having locked his little office. He also found us a porter. There was no suggestion of a charge for his services. The large, genial porter guided us into the terminal.

"Which airline do you want?" he asked. I told him. "A bit early aren't you?" he said. "The check-in desk isn't open yet." I realised I had misinterpreted the 24-hour clock for the time of departure and we were *an extra* two hours earlier than I had planned. Better to be much too early than much too late. I suppose.

"Is there somewhere where we can get a meal and also keep an eye on all our stuff?" I asked the porter. On the first floor, he told us, and guided us up in a lift, whistled up the manager of a café and saw us seated at a table with the wheelchair and trolley of bags in a space nearby. "Just stay there," he told us. "I'll keep an eye on the check-in desk and when it opens, I'll come for you." This he did, about an hour-and-a-half later. With a big smile, took us down to the check-in floor and stayed with us, quite unnecessarily at this stage, till we were actually at the desk. There was no suggestion that he wanted payment for his services. Obviously, he received a tip.

The next morning we arrived, a few minutes early, at Heathrow Terminal 3. Together with about a dozen other people in wheelchairs, we were last off the plane. By the time I had toileted Rita again and wheeled her to the baggage-claim hall, almost everyone else had been and gone; there were just our bags and four or five others circling the carousel. Rita sat in her wheelchair while I loaded our baggage onto a trolley and looked round for some help. Three or four porters were sitting and chatting a little distance away. I walked over.

"Can one of you help us please?" I asked.

"Sure," said the nearest. "It'll cost you eight pounds." "Eight pounds!" I repeated in some amazement. He turned to a companion for support.

"Yes," said the second. "Company rules. If you need help with baggage or whatever, we have to charge you eight pounds." "But it's only 150 yards to the arrivals hall, through customs, from here," I pointed out.

"You're in the UK now, mate," I was told. Too right!

20

Rehabilitation – My Explanation of Best Practice

I am sticking my neck out here in suggesting I am an expert in rehabilitation from the disabilities caused by a stroke, since I knew nothing about the subject on 19 April 2008, the day after Rita suffered hers. But I have learnt an awful lot since then and, on that basis, I'll make a claim to begin this chapter:

"The treatments needed to achieve successful rehabilitation from stroke or other acquired brain injuries are well known within the UK. Recovery may not always be possible, but when it is, the patient could – maybe should – recover to a reasonable, even a substantial, extent. If the patient is capable of recovery, then the degree of recovery will be dependent on two factors: the quality of the rehabilitation therapy and the determination of the patient to work hard at rehabilitation over what might be a long period."

Two pieces of evidence to support this claim are, firstly, that there are well publicised instances when celebrities suffered serious strokes or head injuries that resulted in severe disability, yet, after a period of time, they recovered well enough to take up their former careers once again. Examples are the actress Patricia Neal, who was able to return to acting after three strokes in quick succession; Richard Hammond, Top Gear presenter, who suffered life-threatening head injuries in a car crash, but returned to presenting TV programmes; and Andrew Marr who, in 2015, presented his own TV programme once again, following a major stroke. Maybe it helps to be a celebrity, but it does show that recovery is possible – an encouraging thought to keep in mind.

Secondly, and as importantly, how to recover from a stroke is well documented! Regrettably, this documentation rarely appears to be brought to the attention of the average carer or stroke survivor, in our region of the country anyway. It was between nine months and more than a year before I discovered most of this documentation – and learned enough about what the best treatment was for me to make a significant contribution to Rita's rehabilitation. By this time, it was really too late to change course. As I have commented elsewhere, if I had known in 2008 what I know now about stroke rehabilitation, I would have approached Rita's recovery in an entirely different manner. This is one reason why it is so important to give early advice and support to carers.

I was told that once Rita was discharged from hospital, help would be provided. I still held the naive belief that whatever treatment was advisable for Rita would be put in place when she came home. I did not query sufficiently closely the actions that were proposed. This was, of course, partly because I had no idea then what was the best practice; nor the extent to which Rita – and I – would need help. Nor, really, just how serious Rita's disabilities were. I was not given, nor even told about, the available government documentation on the subject of rehabilitation that *does* describe the treatment recommended for brain injury patients when they are sent back home to the tender, but usually untrained, mercies of family carers. Much of what I learned during that first year came from one or other of the four charities with which I built close contacts.

Six months after Rita came home, I joined a Headway course for carers that began in January 2009 (six half days at fortnightly intervals). Those attending were each given a book, *Head Injury, a Practical Guide*, by Trevor Powell. This 220-page book is full of information and good advice. A few quotes from it concerning assessment and rehabilitation follow *(quotations by kind permission of the author, Trevor Powell, and publishers, Speechmark Ltd)*.

Page 46: "During all stages of rehabilitation, and throughout the process of care, accurate assessment is vital." Page 47: "Formal assessments will be carried out by occupational therapists, a speech therapist, a clinical psychologist, physiotherapists and nurses." Then to paraphrase, I hope reasonably accurately, the comments that expanded these statements: "A common feature of head injury patients is that they are all different. No patient is quite like any other. The assessment helps the family to understand what is wrong, why behaviour may be otherwise inexplicable, and establishes the very important basis for writing a rehabilitation programme specific to each victim of stroke."

Then, on the subject of rehabilitation, page 38: "The process of rehabilitation starts almost immediately after injury... This process of formal rehabilitation, applied by professional clinicians, is likely to be limited by time constraints, but the informal rehabilitation, as applied by family members and carers, can go on for a very long time. .... There is evidence that, once people are discharged from a formal rehabilitation environment (hospital) and return to the home environment, their performance falls away unless the family have been integrated into the rehabilitation programme." This, of course, describes exactly what happened to Rita. She was never given a programme for rehabilitation following discharge from hospital and there was no carer training at all.

In March 2009, our friend Ian sent me an e-mail with a document attached that he had found during a "trawl" of the Internet – the *National Clinical Guideline for Stroke* published by the College of Physicians. This 180-page guideline was aimed at medical staff and detailed the best procedures to be adopted for different types of head injury and treatment of their symptoms. It covered both the early (emergency) treatment in hospital as well as the process of recovery. The following is a small selection of quotes from it, relevant to Rita's condition on discharge from hospital, when a formal rehabilitation programme, designed specifically for Rita, should have started.

Page 96: "All patients with loss of control of the bladder at two weeks should ... only be discharged home with continuing incontinence after the carer (family member) or patient has been fully trained and adequate arrangements for continuing supply of continence aids and services are confirmed and in place." "All patients with loss of control over their bowels at two weeks should ... have a documented, active plan of management [and] be referred for specialist treatments."

Page 101: Personal activities of daily living. "Specific treatments that should be offered include ... training of family and carers in helping the patient."

Page 110: Carers (informal, unpaid). "The carer(s) of every patient with a stroke should be involved with the management process from the outset, specifically ... during the rehabilitation phase, carers should be encouraged to participate in an educational programme that ... teaches them how to provide care and support.

At the time of transfer to the home setting, the carer should be offered an assessment of their own support needs … be offered the support identified … be given clear guidance on how to seek help if problems develop. After the patient has returned to the home setting, the carer should … be given clear guidance on a regular but not necessarily frequent basis of how they may seek help if problems develop."

Page 113: "Transfers of care – discharge from hospital. Hospital services should have a protocol … to ensure that before discharge occurs: patients and families are fully prepared [… and that] … all patients should have access to specialist stroke services after leaving hospital, and should know how to make contact."

All the above comments sound wonderfully comprehensive and explicit. Of all these recommendations, the only one activated for Rita and me was the "carer's assessment of needs". As described elsewhere, this did not help me as none of the identified needs were addressed.

A second valuable document, which I first heard about from a manager of the Stroke Association who visited SAS in May 2009 to present an award recognising the work the charity was doing, was the *National Stroke Strategy* (NSS). In many respects this was similar to the *National Clinical Guideline for Stroke* (NCGS). The NSS listed, and then explained in detail, what it called Quality Markers covering the whole of the stroke pathway. The one most relevant to Rita's needs was QM10:

"QM10: High-quality specialist rehabilitation. People who have had strokes access high-quality rehabilitation and, with their carer, receive support from stroke-skilled services as soon as possible after they have had a stroke, available in hospital, *immediately after transfer from hospital and for as long as they need it*" [my italics].

The NSS expands substantially on this briefly summarised recommendation.

All the above statements sound eminently sensible and helpful. Any prospective carer reading them would be given a lot of confidence concerning the help and training they could expect (and have something specific to argue about if the treatment did not materialise). Under these regimes, the patient will benefit from a programme of rehabilitation specific to his or her needs, carried out or at least supervised by health professionals. The main family carers benefit from advice, training and support on how best to deal with the new responsibilities that have fallen to them. Maybe it does happen this way in some parts of the UK. It did not happen for us and, so far as I could judge, it did not happen for the many other carers and their patients who I met during 2008 to 2010.

Following on later was the National Institute for Health and Care Excellence (NICE), *Stroke Rehabilitation in Adults, Clinical Guideline 162*, published in June 2013 (previously *Stroke Rehabilitation: long term rehabilitation after stroke*). This is a thorough analysis of best treatment, but was too late to be of help to Rita or me. This document can be downloaded from the Internet.

I found all this vital information a year or more too late and, of course, wish I had had it much earlier (though how I could possibly have found it by myself with everything else to be dealt with and my level of ignorance at that time, I really don't know). The great majority of these recommendations were not implemented for Rita's care. I can remember only two that were. As already mentioned, I was offered and did receive a carer's assessment by Social Services staff, some four months after Rita left hospital. This resulted in no benefit to me whatever. As described earlier, Rita had a review meeting with the nurse consultant six weeks following discharge from hospital. Although it was clear from needs identified at the meeting that help was required, nothing was offered – other than implausible excuses why help could not be provided. Nor was Rita offered the six-month and first-year reviews. The next was a two-year review held on 20 May 2010, with the nurse consultant.

During this last meeting, we talked for 75 minutes about the lack of NHS support compared with the *National Stroke Strategy* recommendations and the difficulty of dealing with "our" PCT – the dreadfully prolonged timescales, for example. The nurse consultant did point out that the Quality Markers in the *National Stroke Strategy* were targets that must be reported on – not aspirations, as I had been led to believe by the assistant director of "our" PCT. The nurse apologised several times for not being able to help in the past, and not seeing how she could in the future. This was down to lack of resources and the fact that we lived outside the area covered by her hospital PCT. She intended to write a letter in my support (I never saw a copy of this) and promised to help at any time if I thought she could. This seemed a rather empty promise as she had already explained why help was impossible.

I did ask whether her hospital, that had treated Rita, was now implementing the *National Stroke Strategy* Quality Markers. "Oh, yes, certainly," was the reply. They had made very good progress with the early stages of treatment, including the FAST system, and were getting stroke sufferers into hospital and treated much more quickly – so saving lives. A lot of people were less badly affected than they would otherwise have been. Good, but what she didn't point out was that they would, also, almost certainly be saving the lives of people who would otherwise have died under the old slower system – possibly even increasing the number of badly disabled survivors. Thinking about it afterwards, I came to the conclusion they had got this all back to front. Wouldn't it have been better to ensure that the lives saved had adequate treatment ready for them, rather than piling up disabled people with no proper long-term care aimed at treating the inevitable disabilities from which they suffered, and to help the amateur carers looking after them? That should have been the first target to achieve, I thought. I did have one rather cynical idea. The neurosurgeons who had saved Rita's life were highly skilled and committed to their work, but once Rita was stable, that was the end of their responsibility for her and she was passed – in a highly disabled state – to a system of inadequate treatment. Were the surgeons even aware of this? Did they realise they might be seen as running an expensive production line of living disasters?

So I asked the nurse, "Had they done anything to organise better rehabilitation treatment at the hospital during the past two years, in line with the NSS?" They hadn't started on that side of it yet, said the nurse. The "front end" of the stroke pathway had been seen as more important.

At a subsequent carers' meeting organised by the Headway charity, I asked whether the Headway staff thought the number of disabled stroke patients in the community was increasing, steady, or decreasing. In their opinion, there was a steady increase in the number of disabled people.

Yet another document Ian had found was entitled *Cerebrovascular Event Rehabilitation* which was really a five-page summary of the College of Physicians' report already discussed, but expressed differently and, in some respects, even more strongly. It begins by defining rehabilitation. "Rehabilitation is a complex set of processes usually involving several professional disciplines and aimed at improving the quality of life for people facing daily living conditions caused by chronic disease. Rehabilitation starts in hospital, but continues after the individual has returned to the community. It is extremely important in terms of making the patient as independent as possible with enormous implications for the physical and psychological well-being of the person and cost to the community."

It goes on to summarise the key recommendations around rehabilitation, the ones relevant to Rita being:

- Patients should have as much therapy as they are willing and able to cope with and should have 45 minutes a day of each appropriate therapy in the early stages.
- All patients discharged home directly after acute treatment, but with residual problems, should be followed up by specialist stroke rehabilitation services.
- Hospital services should ensure that patients, families and primary care teams are fully prepared for the patient's discharge.
- Service commissioners should ensure that they commission services for the full stroke pathway, … on to … later rehabilitation in the community and long-term support.

Towards the end, the report refers to rehabilitation in the community and adds, rather ominously: "The time of transfer from hospital to home, residential or nursing home care is important. There is some research-based evidence that this is often poorly managed."

So there are four relevant documents that describe clearly and precisely how seriously disabled stroke (and other acquired brain injury (ABI)) patients should be treated. They show that the best treatment for badly disabled stroke survivors is well known in the UK, and was well known in 2008 when Rita suffered her stroke. The NICE publication (2013) was too late to be of use to Rita in 2008 and the one entitled *Cerebrovascular Event Rehabilitation* was perhaps directed more towards trained therapists and doctors, rather than for widespread use among untrained carers. However, the *National Stroke Strategy* and the *National Clinical Guideline for Stroke* were highly relevant. The treatment and advice actually offered to Rita and me bore absolutely no relation to the recommendations and the "best practice" described in those four documents. Was it surprising we had difficulties, as do many other stroke survivors and their carers?

What puzzles me greatly is why none of the health professionals employed by the NHS, local authority and Social Services, who were in contact with us in one way or another, and there were many of them during 2008 to 2010 (I can name in the region of 70), gave us a copy of one of these useful documents, or even mentioned their existence. That information would have helped me enormously during the months when it first became my responsibility to care for Rita and would probably have avoided many arguments and misunderstandings I had with these professionals, quite apart from saving a lot of expensive time. I regard it as negligent not to provide stroke survivors and their main carers with this extremely valuable information.

As a little light relief, the book *The Selfish Pig's Guide to Caring* by Hugh Marriott is well worth reading. The author writes well and the text is very amusing. He raises – and answers – such thoughts as many carers may have had like, "Why not push them down the stairs?" But, in his book, Mr Marriott appeared to have resigned himself to the fact that help from authorities will not be forthcoming (as we also found). I have not done that, nor have I accepted that what professional people say is necessarily correct, because I have proved it is not – and that quite often. Hidden agendas may raise their ugly heads here. Finding, ultimately, all this valuable documentation certainly helped me in my search for a way to activate Rita's recovery. Many factors were involved, as described in Parts 2 and 3. And I am delighted to say my wife is now back with me in more than just a physical presence; she is in excellent health.

Lastly, because this chapter asks the question "What is best practice for stroke rehabilitation?", I should say what I believe it to be. Combining all the above-mentioned documents together and summarising them very briefly, my conclusion is that best programmes for stroke rehabilitation will contain these six features:

1. A careful and detailed assessment of all the disabilities suffered by the stroke survivor.

2. Appointment of a Case Manager who will be the "point of contact" between the main family carer and the health and care authorities – someone the carer can go to when they have problems that need answers.

3. A written rehabilitation programme based on Point 1 and addressing all the problems found.

4. A named team of therapists. Continuity of treatment is important; therapists need to know and understand the patient's difficulties. The best way to achieve this is to name the therapists selected.

5. Initial training for the main family carer on how best to deal with the disabilities shown by their patient.

6. That the programme of therapy will continue "for as long as it is needed". This is rather a vague statement. I interpret it to mean that the programme will last for a minimum of 12 weeks, then continue for as long as significant progress towards recovery is seen to be made.

There is a qualification to be made to Point 6. Rehabilitation can be hard work for both the stroke survivor and carer, in that the survivor should always be attempting to do things that are just too difficult for them (pushing the boundaries!). This needs determination. When the exercises are not difficult, they are likely to be boringly repetitive. This needs perseverance. If the survivor and/or carer decide they do not want to continue with the programme, their views should be respected and the programme terminated.

I have taken the title of "Case Manager" from the *National Stroke Strategy*. Our GP once confided to me that he did not know where to go to find one of those. I think the title "manager" is wrong. In South Africa, Sister Jenny, the nurse with years of experience in helping elderly people, performed this task admirably well for me – probably without actually realising she was doing so.

So far as Rita was concerned, she was assessed on several occasions (Point 1). Apart from the time spent at the residential clinic, I could not place a tick by any of the remaining points 2 to 6.

21

April 2009 to June 2010

The "Complaint" Against "Our" PCT Leads to a Prolonged Investigation

This might have been a very long chapter – and probably still seems so.

The fact was that I never made a formal complaint directly to the PCT. However, because it was taking so long for a decision to be made concerning a rehabilitation programme for Rita, on 14 March 2009 I wrote to our, then, Member of Parliament, Sir Alan Haselhurst, to ask for his help. He quickly wrote to the CEO of the PCT and it was his letter(s) that, I believe, ultimately resulted in the approval of a 12-week period of residential rehabilitation. The fact that I wrote to Sir Alan appeared to have been taken by the PCT as a complaint against them.

Certainly, this interpretation explained why the PCT Complaints Manager telephoned me on several occasions. On 20 April, he called to say that the Exceptional Cases Panel (ECP) was meeting in two days and they had all the information needed to make a decision on Rita's period of residential rehabilitation. This followed months of my trying to get a decision. The Panel consisted of seven members plus a lay member and an observer, none of whom would have seen Rita. He was taking my "complaint" seriously and would write to me shortly.

This letter arrived about a week later. He told me that he proposed to carry out two reviews: one of Rita's history to see if there were any learning points for the ECP, and, secondly, an internal review of the Stroke Care

Pathway. Both reviews would be completed in about five weeks, by the end of May. If they were not, he would write to explain why. A further letter arrived on 19 May to confirm that he would be reviewing the former by the end of the month and that the Commissioning Manager had already confirmed, "A review of the Stroke Care Pathway will take place". He also requested my verbal agreement that I would not progress my complaint (such as it was) through the NHS Complaints Regulations while these reviews were in progress. But there was then no communication from him for six weeks.

He next phoned on 30 June, not about the two reviews, but to say he was confused as to why Dr Peter had assessed Rita last October, when the PCT had only recently asked him to do the same thing in his position as Psychiatric Consultant to the clinic Rita would now be attending.

"Did Dr Peter write a report?" he asked.

"Yes, he did."

"Why didn't the PCT know about it?"

"I understood they did know," I replied. "A copy was sent to our GP by Dr Peter. I had been told that my point of contact with the PCT was through our GP. So far as I was concerned they had been informed."

"How can we make sure the PCT gets all the relevant information?" he asked.

"Easily. Have the PCT manager responsible visit us for an hour and I can provide Rita's history so far and answer any questions there may be."

Our next discussion was on 17 July when I telephoned to advise him I had just received a copy of the assessment made by the hospital social worker 13 months before from the county Social Services. This was the assessment commented on in Chapter 3, first page, which should have been given to me as part of Rita's discharge documentation when she left hospital. The Complaints Manager said he couldn't advise that I go to the Ombudsman about this, but he should be informed of that sort of failure. He added that things were "moving forward" at his end. Instead of two reviews, it had been decided to carry out one thorough investigation. I asked if this had begun and was given the strong impression that good progress was being made, though I should be getting a letter asking for my consent to the use of Rita's medical records.

On 22 July I received a copy letter sent by "our" PCT Commissioning Manager to her counterpart in Long-Term Conditions, at the hospital

PCT. This said that it appeared that Rita had not received a discharge plan when she left hospital the year before; could this be investigated? I phoned this lady to bring her up to speed with what I knew of the situation. She told me she had not seen the letter from the Commissioning Manager so had not yet investigated the matter, but it seemed that Rita had somehow slipped through the net. If this had in fact happened, it was very unsatisfactory and she would call me back when she had news. I heard nothing more from her.

I phoned the Complaints Manager on 1 September to ask about progress. He was moving to another post, he told me, adding that a senior manager from the PCT Patient Experience Team would be taking over his responsibilities. About four days later, I received a request for a "patient's written consent" for the PCT to pass on information concerning my "complaint". What this meant was that the alternative investigation on Rita's discharge had not even started. Four months had passed by since I agreed to suspend my "complaint" on the basis that two reviews would be completed by the end of May. To say I was displeased would be putting it mildly. I wrote a long and emotional letter to him, dated 7 September, expressing my views, knowing that he had moved on, but also knowing it would have to be picked up by someone else, presumably this senior manager.

It was. I received a letter from the Patient Experience Team, dated 15 September, apologising for the delay in responding and saying that the Head of Patient Experience, whom I will call Mrs Matthews, "will be in touch with you shortly".

The PCT's definition of "shortly" was not divulged. By the end of October, six weeks later, I had heard nothing further. My letter of 7 September had been copied to Sir Alan Haselhurst who, on his return to London, had written to me in early October to say he was "urged to intervene" by writing again to the CEO should I wish him to do so. On 30 October I asked him again to help, in whatever terms he thought appropriate.

Three days later, I received a letter from a Director of the PCT (not the Patient Experience Team,) dated 28 October, to say that she was now in receipt of the requested report written by the hospital PCT into the discharge arrangements for Mrs Guthrie. Adding that, "I am currently in the process of identifying an independent expert assessor to review this report to provide me with an opinion as to whether the quality of care and discharge provision was appropriate". I replied by return to ask for a copy of this hospital report.

This was sent to me on 23 November with a covering note saying, "... I have sent this report to an external expert for comment. I will therefore be writing back to you with our final response to your concerns as soon as I am in receipt of this expert viewpoint. We anticipate receiving the report back within the next 3–4 weeks and I will write to you again after that time". The report from the hospital was in the form of a three-page letter written by the, then, Chief Executive of the hospital.

This gentleman listed the facts surrounding Rita's discharge that were accurate enough, but he put a gloss on things. On 26 November, I replied to the PCT Director commenting on this hospital report (see Appendix A) to record how the same facts appeared to me, as a service user. I copied my letter to the CEO of the hospital, as he had said towards the end of his report, "We are keen to learn patients' views and use feedback to learn from patient experience". Nobody from the hospital followed up my comments. I was passed being surprised at this.

On 1 December, the PCT Director said that the expert assessor had requested Rita's medical notes. So it was necessary for us to provide written confirmation of our consent to this. This will mean, she added, a delay in obtaining a response from the assessor, but she would pass on my letter (Appendix A) to the assessor. This request implied to me that the "expert's assessment" was yet to begin.

As we moved into the year 2010, I received a letter from Mrs Matthews dated 7 January to introduce herself. She would also find it very helpful to meet. Fine. A week later, a letter came from Sir Alan Haselhurst to say he had now "extracted the enclosed response" from Mrs Matthews and he hoped I would take up her offer of a meeting. In her quite long letter to Sir Alan, she told him that her review of the file "... does clearly indicate that considerable time and effort has been taken by a number of staff at the Trust" to address my concerns. A lot of time and effort maybe, but no treatment for Rita. I couldn't seem to get the point across to these people that rehabilitation treatment for Rita was the be-all and end-all of what I wanted – not time and effort spent on side issues.

Mrs Matthews and I agreed to meet at our home at 3.00 pm on 20 January, Rita's seventy-first birthday. I had anticipated a meeting between the two of us, but she arrived on the doorstep accompanied by a newly appointed senior case manager. Did I mind if she joined the meeting? I could hardly leave her on the doorstep. This lady was deputed to take minutes. I spent a long time, at Mrs Matthews' request, retelling Rita's history since April 2008.

By the time the minutes were written up, Rita and I were in Fish Hoek for six weeks on our first visit to South Africa, so they were emailed to me. I considered them to be a poor record of our meeting, with many errors of fact. A few days later, an email from Mrs Matthews asked me, in bold type, to ensure that the minutes were an accurate reflection of what we had discussed, this being repeated twice. I found this an oddly specific request. There was no way I would sign those emailed minutes as they stood to be an accurate record of our discussion. I spent several hours correcting them to a state that I was prepared to sign as accurate, and emailed them back. Mrs Matthews had added that Rita's consultation with the urology department was being re-booked by her colleague for a date after March, by which time we would be back in the UK. In fact, when we arrived home, we found a missed appointment at the urology department for 22 February that we had not known about!

On 5 February, I wrote briefly to Sir Alan to confirm that Mrs Matthews and I had indeed met and to summarise the outcome, enclosing a copy of the letter I had written to Mrs Matthews in which I commented, among other things, that I was disappointed that she had viewed the *National Stroke Strategy* as "aspirational". On 27 March a short letter came from Sir Alan enclosing a copy of a letter to him [dated 19 March] from Mrs Matthews. She listed the actions she was taking and, in relation to the subject of "aspirationality" (sic), that I had taken her comments out of context. My recollection was that there had been no context. I had asked a simple question and received a straightforward reply. She did, however, reassure Sir Alan "… that a very strong commitment was made, and is being implemented, by the Trust to look into the care that has been provided to Rita in the past, and to establish what help is appropriate and necessary for the future". This sounds good and what one would hope and expect her to say. Unfortunately, I can identify no practical benefit that accrued to Rita as a result of her efforts or those of the Trust, specifically regarding rehabilitation, at any time after this letter was written.

There was one comment in her letter to Sir Alan that surprised me. She had "… requested an update from our Commissioning Manager with regard to the sourcing of a consultant … independent from the hospital Stroke Unit to provide an unbiased, expert opinion on this case". She continued that a suitable person had been identified and all correspondence had been sent to the consultant on 2 March. I had thought this assessor was appointed previously in November 2009, or was I getting confused? It would not be difficult. Sarcasm aside, there was a serious element to this long story. While this appointment of an assessor was ongoing, Rita had received no rehabilitation treatment whatever from the NHS from the date she left the residential clinic in September 2009, despite the strong recommendations from the therapists at the clinic that continuing therapy was most important.

Mrs Matthews wrote again on 15 and 29 April to say she was still awaiting the report and apologised for the delay. I replied on 3 May just to confirm that I would definitely like to have a copy of the consultant's report. I was disappointed that Rita and I had not been consulted. I knew the consultant had been given a copy of Rita's medical notes and he presumably worked from whatever other documents had been sent him by the PCT. But to write a report such as this without meeting the two people most closely involved, and getting their views, seemed extraordinary. It was not until mid May that I discovered his identity and that was via the "back door". I had thought it important that he meet Rita and me since I was the one creating all the fuss – or at least contact us by phone, letter or email. But no, he never met us and worked without knowing our direct opinions on the matter.

The "back door" was opened during a phone call from Dr Peter at 8.00 am on Monday 17 May during which he told me that the consultant appointed by the PCT was in fact a colleague of his; and he thought the report had been submitted already. This colleague and the Professor of Rehabilitative Medicine had believed there might be some issues that needed further input and had asked Dr Peter if he would consider visiting us again, but in the end he decided not to.

By 11 June, no report had arrived, nor had my letter dated 3 May to Mrs Matthews (asking for a copy of that report) been acknowledged. So I wrote again as a reminder of the existence of the Freedom of Information Act. Whether this had any effect I don't know, but a copy of the report arrived at last on 29 June.

Fourteen months had passed since the PCT Complaints Manager had told me that he was setting up two reviews of Rita's hospital discharge arrangements that would take an estimated month to complete. As most of this chapter has been about obtaining a report on Rita's hospital discharge – though different from the original ones planned – now that I have it I had better say what it contained. It is described and commented on in Appendix B.

22

May and June 2010

Frustration Leads to a Crisis

It was then the middle of May and two years since Rita suffered her haemorrhage. It was getting on for 13 months since the PCT told me, in a letter from the Complaints Manager, that the circumstances surrounding Rita's discharge from hospital would be investigated, with results expected in one month. Still there was no information about this from the senior manager of the Patient Experience Team, who now appeared not to be acknowledging my letters. I was not told the name of the independent consultant who had been commissioned to conduct the investigation into Rita's hospital discharge. I had not been given an opportunity to make my own submission to him concerning events. This was the aspect of the investigation that astonished me most. It seemed to me not the best way of doing things.

Meanwhile, Rita had received no in-community physiotherapy, OT or any other sort of therapy from the NHS since leaving the rehabilitation clinic the previous September, contrary to the recommendations in the final report from the clinic.

Despite the excellent six weeks in South Africa during February and March, Rita's behaviour had deteriorated again. She had become more confused and her incontinence and balance were worsening. The speed with which she ate meals was slowing. Around the 23 April, breakfast was again taking her 70 minutes to finish and I needed to prompt her up to a dozen times to resume eating. This was very wearing. On the evening of the 24th, I found she had wet her pants for the fourth time that day and, in acting immediately to change her and clean her up, I forgot I had put some rhubarb on to cook. This had burnt in the pan by the time I remembered it, of course. Around that time, three or more wet or soiled pads each day was quite common. For a change of activity, we joined the croquet group of SAS in early May, but Rita had difficulty understanding what was going on and about halfway through a session she was so tired she was almost falling over, so we gave up and returned home.

I was becoming more and more stressed and frustrated by the long hours of caring, with no professional support. I was upset by the length of time it was taking to complete the investigation into Rita's discharge from hospital, having been given no information on its progress. I still believed that the report would be critical of the PCT and that they would be morally bound, belatedly, to provide Rita with some of the missing rehabilitative treatment. For some time I had spent long periods lying in bed, awake, in the early hours, mulling things over. I decided I couldn't put up with any more of this, life was just not worth living for me, and Rita gave no indication that it was any better for her. I decided it was best to bring it to an end for both of us, but in doing so make absolutely sure that the whole sorry mess we were in, owing to the total lack of help from the NHS towards Rita's recovery, received national publicity. So, I worked out how this was to be done and refined it over several nights. Others would not be in any physical danger but the national papers should make a lot of it for some considerable time, I thought. This was all ridiculous, but I have to say, very real at the time.

There were two alternatives, just carry on with my plans, or tell the PCT the effect their totally unjustifiable inaction was having and give them a last opportunity to put it right. I decided to "play fair" and give the PCT one more opportunity to do something positive. This was the "correct" thing to do – it was better to let people know how one felt. So that is what I did and, soon after, was strongly criticised for my frankness.

On Friday evening, 21 May, I wrote out a rehabilitation programme for Rita, based on what the *National Stroke Strategy* said should be provided for stroke sufferers. This was to give to our GP as a demand. I set a date of 30 June for this programme to be put in place. The only appointment I could get with our doctor on the following Monday was at 5.20 pm so, at about 5.00 pm, I left Rita with a friend and drove to the surgery. I gave our GP a copy of the programme and explained why I was doing this.

Rita had received no NHS rehabilitation treatment whatever for eight months and the PCT had been investigating her discharge from hospital for more than a year. I regarded all this as unacceptable. The five weeks I had allowed for setting up my proposed programme was perfectly feasible as the NHS had all the resources necessary (no one had told me they were not available). I asked him if he thought this programme might be put in place. He shrugged.

If it didn't happen, I told him, he could expect the following.

As quickly as possible, I would finish a factual account of Rita's and my experiences since 20 April 2008 to the present day and attempt to find a publisher (most was already written). If, quite quickly, no publisher was interested, I would post it on the Internet. Secondly (or maybe firstly), I would appeal to the Secretary of State for Health to intervene with the PCT. I didn't expect this to achieve much but it was something that should be done. If neither of these actions achieved anything, I would kill both Rita and myself. Rita had little quality of life, certainly not compared with her previous capabilities, and I had none. I was not prepared to face doing what I was doing then for the rest of my natural life with zero medical support or advice on how best to take care of Rita. This was not a way of living that I was prepared to continue. This was not a bluff. I had worked out exactly how it would all happen. By then I had taken up more than the 15 minutes allocated for the appointment, so I left.

All then went quiet for a time. On 1 June, I had a call from a social worker I had not heard from before, based at an office 20 miles away. Could she come to see me the next day, Wednesday? Yes, she could; we agreed 1.30 pm.

She began by saying she worked at a level below Rita's senior practitioner, wanted to know more about our situation and whether she could help. This began to look unpromising. If she was at that level, then the likelihood that she could organise practical help seemed remote. I explained that my current argument was not with Social Services but with the NHS, in particular the PCT, and concerned the non-provision of in-community rehabilitation for Rita. I summarised the past 21 months once again. She looked very sympathetic, said she wished she could help but had no authority to do so (as usual, so had anything been achieved by our meeting?). But she would give Rita's social worker a full report. *She* was due to review Rita's progress on 9 June, in a week's time. This junior lady did mention that she had heard that a "meeting" was being arranged between our GP, Social Services, the PCT and perhaps others. Did I know of this? "I had heard a rumour", I said, "but had been told nothing through any official channels." The PCT had been having meetings for 13 months or more without achieving any progress of benefit to Rita that I could identify.

The following day I phoned my contact at a charity, Action for Family Carers, set up primarily to provide help to carers, rather than patients. She offered to come for another chat and we settled on the following Monday, 7 June. I brought her up to date with what had happened during the past six months, including the past week. She was concerned at the state into which I was getting and suggested that antidepressants might help in the short term, even though she had to agree they would be tackling symptoms, not problems. I declined the offer.

She also commented that she had had difficulty with some doctors at our local surgery and had been unable to make progress with them. They seemed to her to be unwilling to recognise that carers needed help. Surprisingly, she also knew about the impending "meeting" and added that I would not be allowed to attend even had I wanted to do so. She offered to attend the meeting on my behalf and act as my advocate, if I wished. I certainly did. I greatly appreciated that generous offer. She would tell me afterwards what was said. If the meeting was held on one of her non-working days, she would ask a colleague, who undertook work for the charity, if she could go instead.

On the 8 June, I phoned the district nurse about our conversation around four weeks before, when she had offered to make enquiries concerning some rehabilitation treatment for Rita. She reported that the view of the physiotherapists was that Rita's problem was not physical but mental; as a result she didn't remember the exercises she had to do. (This was a particularly invalid argument. A mentally damaged person can still have a very definite need for physiotherapy.) Apparently, the nurse told me, the resources to give Rita physiotherapy treatment regularly were not available and so nothing more would be done for her. This seemed more likely to be close to the truth. Why didn't they tell me this was the reason straight away and have done with it? A halfway house might be for Rita to attend our local gym under 1:1 tuition from an instructor. The district nurse would speak to our GP and, if he considered it safe, he might provide a referral to the gym. She added that she had asked our doctor for his suggestions on what might be done for Rita, but he hadn't come back to her. She had also requested a copy of the report from the physiotherapists. They had promised to send it, but hadn't done so by then. So, the only action so far as the district nurse could see was to get a referral from our GP for the gym, a desperately poor suggestion, given Rita's condition. I heard nothing more on this suggestion from anyone.

Did it not occur to any of these people that they were arrogantly playing around with people's lives and, when things went wrong or become too much trouble, washing their hands of the problem?

The next day, Wednesday 9 June, Rita's senior practitioner arrived as arranged. I said my main concern was still to get Rita the treatment to which she was entitled, the prime need being for a good case manager (using the description from the *National Stroke Strategy*) to set up a programme of rehabilitation long enough to determine whether or not rehabilitation *could* make a significant improvement to her condition. I said that if, after a "reasonable" period (however defined) it was clear that Rita could go no further, then I would accept that situation. We could, at that point, decide what to do from there, the probable outcome being residential care. But the therapy treatment had to come first.

For most of the discussion, the senior practitioner spent time explaining why it was so difficult to find the resources needed for therapy and arguing against my proposal, but I was not convinced with that approach. She did confirm that a "meeting" was arranged for 18 June, that it was for professionals only, and that I would not be allowed to attend. She gave me the impression that any action would be determined by rules – the medics might decide there was no future in providing rehabilitation for Rita because of her poor memory. Then it would be back to Social Services, whose only real option was to organise residential care.

As background information for our GP, who I then understood was to chair this upcoming meeting, I listed recommendations from the *National Stroke Strategy* on what rehabilitation services stroke survivors should receive, and compared it with the poor therapy Rita had actually had. I added a suggestion for a programme of therapy that I thought might now help Rita, two years after her stroke had occurred. And that was as much as I could do.

Had I been allowed to go to the meeting on the 18 June, it would have meant changing a holiday. We had booked flights to visit our elder son and family at their house in France for a week. Would I have changed the holiday dates had I been permitted to attend? Probably, because the only loss would have been the cost of two return tickets on easyJet. Had I known beforehand the direction the meeting would take, I would most certainly have attended (if I could), though it would have been an exceedingly difficult meeting for me.

The short flights to and from France went remarkably well. easyJet looked after Rita (and me) very nicely. In the eight years following Rita's stroke, we have flown with six airlines, all provided "disabled assistance" to an excellent standard. In our experience, disabled persons should have no worries about flying.

So what happened on the 18 June? On our return home a few days later, there were no notes or messages for me concerning what had transpired. I made an unsuccessful attempt to speak with our GP. It had been the colleague from Action for Family Carers who had represented me at the meeting, acting as an observer. She had not been in a position to act as an advocate since she knew too little of our long history – she and I had managed no more than a long phone conversation beforehand – but she did take almost verbatim notes of what had been said. She was away the week after our trip to France and her notes were not yet available so, as long as ten days after that meeting I was none the wiser about what had been concluded. The old joke came to mind about "feeling like a mushroom – being kept in the dark and just fed horse****". Needless to say, there were repercussions from the discussion which are described in chapter 23.

Two days after our return from holiday, there was a letter from our new Member of Parliament (boundary changes at the recent General Election meant that we had "lost" Sir Alan's help). Having been given Sir Alan's files on Rita's case, he told me he had written to the CEO of the PCT on Rita's behalf. I had not asked him to do this and did not know what he said, but was still very grateful for the support and wrote a thank you note.

23

June to September 2010

Repercussions From the Meeting – What Happened Next

The way things then happened resulted in me finding out about repercussions from the meeting before I knew what had been discussed and concluded. So that is the way I will tell it here; what the results of the meeting were before explaining in chapter 24 what I came to learn from the observer's report.

We returned from France on Tuesday 22 June, the "Professionals' Meeting" having taken place the previous Friday. I was somewhat surprised and disappointed to find no messages of any kind relating to its outcome. I phoned the charity's observer who had attended on my behalf, but she was on leave that week. She left a message to let me know that notes were following; also that she had passed the file on to an organisation based some 30 miles away because she believed I needed help from an advocate. I gave him the pseudonym of "Martin" and we met for the first time on 5 July.

A five-page letter from the senior PCT manager at the meeting arrived on 28 June. This gave me the first information on its outcome. Included with the letter, at last, was a copy of the consultant's report on Rita's discharge from hospital more than two years earlier (Appendix B).

I could have taken issue with several points made in the PCT letter, but I saw the importance of the conclusion. Part of it read "… the information

I have received from all the professionals involved in Rita's care is that any rehabilitation potential will not be sustained, due to Rita's cognitive impairment". In other words, everyone believed Rita was not capable of recovery. Further on, "… I can find no evidence to support the suggestion that there has been lack of appropriate support in terms of physiotherapy, occupational therapy and continence care". The inference I drew from this was that the health and care professionals had convinced themselves they had acted properly and had given Rita all treatment that was warranted. No more would be authorised in the future – to do so would be a waste of scarce resources as she would not benefit from further therapy.

In her letter to Sir Alan Haselhurst the previous March, this same PCT manager had explained, among other things, how carefully Rita's treatment had been reviewed and that if she had needed treatment, it would have been unacceptable not to provide it. My contention was that Rita's treatment, when compared with that recommended by the *National Stroke Strategy*, could be seen as wholly inadequate. Impasse had been reached; time and money were disappearing and no progress was being made. (Yet a few months later, in South Africa, a nurse and two therapists assessed Rita as being in need of rehabilitation therapy, immediately set up a course for her, and were immensely successful. How this happened is described in Part 2.)

How could two people have such different views on the adequacy (or not) of a course of treatment as this senior PCT manager and me? One answer, I suspect, lay in the methods of measurement. The manager clearly spent considerable time investigating the matter and accepted what she was told by colleagues and the professionals who had seen Rita. In the letter to me she referred to the written notes held by the PCT: "… it can be seen that there are in excess of 40 entries detailing telephone calls and visits by the occupational therapist between the dates of 10 October 2008 and 13 January 2010 and spanning 39 pages". It sounded like a lot of contact with Rita, and that is what she wanted it to sound like, I suppose.

My method was to count the number of practical therapy treatment sessions that Rita actually received from NHS therapists during two years. This totalled a six-week course of OT and three physio sessions of about 45 minutes each. There was, in addition, the 12-week residential course during which Rita made progress, but it was not followed up in the way the clinic's therapists had said was important. And there was never a formal programme of rehabilitation, as outlined in the *National Stroke Strategy*. It was probably not surprising that Rita made little progress because successful rehabilitation needs guidance by trained therapists, as I later learned all too well.

So what else had happened? The GP had phoned on Monday 28 to say that he and the senior practitioner would accompany Rachel, the CPN, to a meeting she and I had arranged for the following Wednesday 30 June, at 9.30 am at our house. I asked about the outcome from their meeting ten days earlier, but he said that would be better explained when they arrived. The three of them came at 9.30 am as promised, and I did wonder why three were needed for this seemingly simple task. Had I received the observer's notes by then I would have known the answer to that one, but the arrival of the notes was still two days in the future. The gist of what the three of them told me confirmed the PCT letter. "Those at the meeting had not acceded to any one of my requests. It had been decided that Rita had got as far as she could go – there was no more rehabilitation to be done – and they would not accept that, because Rita's discharge from hospital had been so poor (as confirmed in the consultant's report sent to me with the PCT letter – Appendix B), the NHS had any moral responsibility to do more."

It then quickly became clear these three had come to invoke SOVA (the Safety of Vulnerable Adults). They saw Rita as being in a vulnerable position, because I might take the negative decisions from the meeting the "wrong way". So, that night she was to go into a local care home for an undefined period, for safety. Did I have an option to appeal against that decision? Not really, as it almost certainly would have been enforced one way or another.

"Who is going to pay for that?" I asked, fishing around for something to say. "You are." Why was I not surprised? They soon departed with Rita in tow. Later, I packed a case of clothing for her and took it to the care home.

This SOVA business didn't appear all that stringent. The next day I visited the care home, took Rita for a session of swimming with SAS, then home for lunch, not returning her to the home until the late afternoon. It all seemed rather odd.

Two days later, Friday 2 June, a letter arrived from the observer who had attended the meeting on my behalf, enclosing her notes. I was amazed by what she reported (chapter 24).

Then, on the Monday, Martin, the advocate to whom she had forwarded her file, and I had our first meeting. Martin told me his job was to be impartial, not take sides, but work to the evidence. So I once more I related our history – taking the best part of two hours now – while he listened, straight-faced for the most part.

I did feel he was becoming sympathetic to my point of view and what I had attempted to do. On one occasion he said "Good" when I related something I had done then grinned sheepishly, remarking, "I shouldn't have said that". He did comment that I had "put the cat among the pigeons" by my threat on our lives and it would take some getting out of that. He listened carefully; thought the consultant's report (on Rita's hospital discharge) was really strong; and told me he had been given false information about me refusing things.

Martin was immensely supportive during the next two or three weeks. He was instrumental, I believe, in obtaining a copy of the "official" minutes of the Meeting. He had first been informed by a secretary there were none. I knew they did exist because by then I knew an NHS secretary had attended and from that information he insisted copies be released (they did not reach us until early September!). He spoke to the senior professionals involved to get their views. He told them that whenever another meeting was arranged, both he and I must be informed and invited to attend. We corresponded regularly by email during the next two weeks. On his recommendation I outlined two "projects" that should persuade those professionals that Rita would be safe if SOVA was lifted. One project was to invite a private company to provide rehabilitation treatment for Rita; the second to take her to South Africa again in the near future and for a longer stay.

The next meeting was held at the surgery on Friday 16 July with our GP, the senior practitioner, the CPN, a PCT minute-taker, Martin and me attending. My two projects seemed to satisfy the assembled party and it was agreed that SOVA would be lifted on 11 August, following my return from Cape Town (just to make sure I went? Chapter 25). The GP offered to send a referral for Rita to the private rehabilitation organisation (chapter 26). Towards the end of the meeting, the social worker leaned forward to tell me that I could expect to be contacted by the police who would want to interview me concerning my threat.

"Good," I said. "There is a lot I would like to tell them about what I regard as the inadequacies of both Social Services and the PCT in this region, which I believe caused me to issue that threat" – or words to that effect. I was mildly disappointed that the police never arrived.

At the end of the meeting, Martin offered the senior practitioner a copy of the consultant's report on Rita's discharge from hospital in June 2008, having ascertained she had not seen it. She immediately refused the offer. Why should she do that? She had previously made it clear to me that she was responsible for Rita's well-being, so why should she refuse authoritative information concerning facts that had seriously affected Rita's life? I could think of several speculative, but no rational reasons for her refusal.

So, by mid August Rita had spent her six weeks of enforced stay in a residential home (which cost me about £3000; that was a cheek too) and I had been to South Africa for two weeks to furnish our holiday home there (chapter 25). We were back together at home with carers coming in for about half an hour each morning to help Rita dress, and Rita went to day care four times each week. What had changed? Nothing. Had anything beneficial occurred in Rita's treatment? No. Had anyone believed my threat? I can't say, but they should have because it was real at the time. Was the threat still there? Not in the immediate future. Why not? For two reasons. Firstly, I was quite enthusiastic about what the private rehabilitation organisation might offer, based on the statements in their brochure. Secondly, the planned ten weeks' holiday in our own home in South Africa was not far in the future and I was certainly going to give that a go.

24

June and July 2010

The Professionals' Meeting, 18 June

The events following this meeting have been described in the previous chapter. During most of that period, 19 to 28 June, I had no knowledge of what, exactly, had been discussed by the attendees and what conclusions and actions had been decided. Pretty well everyone I met during those ten days was better informed than I was.

A copy of the excellent notes the observer had made – six typed A4 pages of them – arrived by post on 2 July. They appeared to be close to a verbatim account of the discussion so, now that I knew the nature of the meeting, it is an appropriate time to return to it. I have to say I was appalled at much that had been said about my actions and character. In addition to these "unofficial" notes, I also wanted to see the official minutes that I knew existed, since a secretary had attended. These were more difficult to access and the best part of three months passed before I was sent a copy (with help from advocate Martin). One of the excuses for the delay was "patient confidentiality". Rita had been my wife for 48 years, for goodness sake, but her written permission still had to be given for me to see these minutes. The social worker was not unintelligent and would have known as well as I did that Rita's confusion was such that she could not have understood what she was giving permission about. There was a clear implication here.

So, three months later, I had two reports on what had been said. At least they tallied reasonably well, both clearly reporting on the same meeting, though the observer's notes gave me far more information. Both suggested a similar "flavour" to the meeting, though the official minutes were, in parts, a pretty unimpressive attempt at recording. Some sentences were left unfinished and the record of one whole section of the discussion was so obscure you would need to have been there to understand what the minutes were trying to say.

Returning to 2 July and the observer's notes. Firstly, I had had no idea I had become such a *persona non grata*. I was clearly unpopular with all Rita's care and health professionals present at the meeting and criticisms of me and my actions were voiced constantly. If I chose one adjective to describe their unanimous view of me as a carer, "incompetent" would seem to fit the bill best. That could well be an accurate assessment since I had received no training (apart from some training provided by three charities) for what was a very difficult job, but all I was trying to do was both organise an effective in-community rehabilitation programme for my wife and care for her as well as I could, effectively full time!

So who were the attendees? There were just three who knew both Rita and me well: our GP (acting as Chair), the senior practitioner (Social Services) and the community occupational therapist (who had given Rita the six-week course some 18 months earlier). There was the community psychiatric nurse (CPN, who knew me but not Rita). Then there were the following who hardly knew either of us, so far as I am aware: a senior manager from the Patient Experience Team (PET, a section of the PCT), who had met me once, but not Rita, the senior complaints manager (PCT), the manager for the Community Therapy Team (NHS), and the community physiotherapist (NHS). Plus, of course, an NHS secretary and the observer from the charity.

There was no one attending who was able to give my point of view. This was extraordinary since I was the reason the meeting was being held.

There was no written agenda. Our GP introduced the meeting. To paraphrase his opening comments – "He felt a lot of people had been involved with Mr and Mrs G but they don't always communicate well … matters were now at a head due to my threats … concerns for Mrs G's welfare … I had given him a list of demands … need to see what has been provided and what more can be provided". This was fair enough. The meeting then became a general discussion that appeared largely to consist of a series of anecdotes concerning Rita's incapacities dating back the best part of a year (or more) plus my incompetence as a carer. Unsurprisingly, I did not find this at all satisfactory.

In the first draft of this chapter, I tried to analyse that discussion and comment from my point of view on the various points made. This was soon 13 pages long and going nowhere that would interest anybody. So I pressed the *Delete* button on that and instead analysed the observer's notes from a different perspective.

These notes provided many specific examples of individuals' comments. The comments fell into a number of categories: (1) Those that I agreed with; (2) didn't understand; (3) needed challenging; (4) were misleading without my explanation of events being put forward as well; and (5) ones that I regarded as downright wrong. So I decided, first, to list the adjectives and phrases that were applied to me, divided into negative and positive categories.

Negative: I was described variously through the meeting as: frustrated; brusque; doesn't understand therapy; refused an offered visit; stresses his wife (repeated three times); puts pressure on her; turned down a carer's assessment; fixated on rehab; dismissive; does things more quickly than Mrs G can cope with; will only do things his way; wants rehab or else; goes to different doctors and social workers till he hears what he wants to hear; missed appointments; declined intervention; he has failed in his "mission"; reality and his perceptions don't match; keeps charts and tables instead of working with emotions; he is wrong about the care she needs; did not get on with the carers.

Positive: These were more difficult to find. The only two I could locate were: "determined" and "intelligent".

I was amazed at the negative picture of myself and disagreed with most of it! I was most certainly not wrong about the "care" (should be "treatment") Rita needed as subsequent events would show. And, generally, I got on well with the carers, those I didn't get on with were the managers who mismanaged the carers and allocated them jobs that were impossible for them to do.

The categories for Rita were rather different:

The problems she has and her incapacity: cognitively damaged; tends to wander; doubly incontinent; problems processing information; distractable; needs to be prompted; can't orient; ignores signs; has been rehabilitated to a point where she can't do more; is stressed by too many people; won't [*can't?*] learn; her damaged brain won't regenerate; suffers from fatigue; has complex disabilities; has high-level balance issues; repeats actions due to no memory.

Capabilities: independently mobile [*which, given her cognitive problems, was a potential hazard in itself*]; improves temporarily with intervention; improved greatly in South Africa three months ago; goes to toilet with minimum help at day care; easy and pleasant to look after. They could have added, but didn't, that her speech, eyesight, hearing and sense of smell appeared unaffected by her stroke.

The picture of me was far from the truth (that's my view, of course) because questionable statements and claims were made that should have been challenged. Other comments needed an explanation from me that might have provided a different interpretation.

The OT had seen more of Rita and me than any of the managers or other therapists, though only during a short period, from October 2008 to January 2009. One of her claims was that, "Mine was a mission that had failed". I had to agree she was right, and no one took issue with this claim. As my "mission" had been to obtain the best treatment I could for my badly disabled wife, I was still sad to know it had failed!

The meeting on 18 June seemed a good example of what psychologists sometimes call "groupthink". It seems to me that all the NHS and Social Services staff accepted any evidence they could find that they had provided Rita with the correct and full treatment after discharge from hospital. They agreed she was so disabled that to provide more would be a waste of resources – since she was unable to benefit from therapy.

The only evidence that the treatment provided was at best inadequate and at worst didn't exist was in the documents I had provided to our GP prior to the meeting. The general agreement was that I was wrong in these claims. The meeting seemed unbalanced; there was no one present to question many of the claims made, or to raise the issue of what the *National Stroke Strategy* required, for example, and compare it with Rita's past treatment. I could, and would, have provided much of this evidence, but had been excluded from the meeting.

What items would I have added to an agenda, had it existed and I had been given the opportunity? There were three.

The **first** was my main demand, clearly identified in the papers I gave our GP at the end of May, for the appointment of a Case Manager as defined in the *National Stroke Strategy*. Such a person would identify what medical treatment Rita needed, prepare a treatment plan, integrate the work done by various professionals, monitor progress achieved and amend the ongoing plan as necessary. This is perfectly straightforward and need not be expensive or time-consuming. But it had not been done. There was nothing special about providing this – it is a summary of the recommendations in *the National Stroke Strategy*.

It was, of course, possible, at that time, that any further treatment given to Rita would have been wasted because the likelihood of producing a significant improvement was too small. My view remained that she *might* be capable of recovery; the NHS and Social Services seemed to have come to the decision that she was not. But nothing had ever been proven either way, only speculated upon. A case manager should get to know a patient well enough so that, with his experience, he could make an educated prognosis. I wanted Rita to be given enough good quality therapy to establish the answer one way or the other.

The **second** item would be a consideration of how far Rita's treatment fell short of that suggested in the *National Stroke Strategy* and other similar documents. I had identified some differences in my letter to our GP of 11 June, but it would have been a discussion that needed my presence. In fact, the observer did read the points I had made to our GP to the meeting, but noted, "Virtually every allegation was denied". In my opinion this was a perfect example of "groupthink". If these health professionals were actually familiar with the *National Clinical Guideline for Stroke* and the *National Stroke Strategy*, they could not honestly claim that the requirements had been met. Was there a written programme of treatment for Rita? Or a named team of therapists? Or a nominated person for me to contact? Or training for the main carer? There were none of these.

The **third** item I would have added should have been the first on the agenda – the all-important analysis of the reason for this meeting being held in the first place! This was not considered at all. The chairman should have asked why a 73-year-old, intelligent and stable man, who had been happily married for 48 years and with a close family, should "suddenly" seek an appointment with him in order to threaten to take his own life and that of his wife. There must have been a reason. This doesn't just happen out of the blue. It is dangerous to come to conclusions on future action until that reason is identified. It was not even mentioned by anyone.

The reason was obvious; to me anyway. It was owing to the situation I was in (as the CPN agreed, some months later). If this situation had been removed, the threat to the wife would vanish. Was there anything they could do about improving the situation? Yes, there was a lot they could do. For a start, someone sensible from the PCT could talk to me on the basis that they had not met the recommendations laid down in the *National Stroke Strategy* (they *must* accept this fact because it was so obviously true), but that limited resources meant that those recommendations could not be met in full at the present time (which I could understand, if reluctantly). So could we talk about how, within the resources that existed, something could be worked out that helped Rita?

I would have accepted that way forward, in principle. I know that resources are not unlimited. It would not have been a guaranteed way of finding a solution, but it had a reasonable chance of success and was certainly worth trying, given willing negotiators. But by now the two points of view were poles apart.

To go back to The Meeting. My cynical assessment was that they all found anecdotes to build up a feeling of self-justification that they had done everything possible within the resources available. Rita was just incapable of further progress, they agreed. There was no justification in ploughing resources into someone who cannot progress, they said. The best solution was to put her in a care home – it would come to that eventually anyway. Nothing was done to remove the basic cause of the problem – not surprising since it had not been recognised. In effect, the cause was still there, as the CPN pointed out at a final meeting she and I had in December 2010.

I could see why they didn't want me to attend the meeting and why it was so difficult to get hold of the minutes. As an even more cynical analogy, I saw the meeting as a kangaroo court. The only attendees were the prosecutors who built up a case from one-sided evidence. The defendant was not allowed to attend, nor was there an advocate who could speak for the defence. I hope not many NHS meetings are set up in this manner.

Lastly, how was I feeling now, after reading all that had been said in the Meeting and negotiating the repercussions discussed in chapter 23? Actually, surprisingly good. Everything was now out in the open. I knew where I stood. There was no point in wasting any more time in attempting to persuade the health and care authorities in this country to provide good rehabilitation for Rita. There was no chance of it happening as she had effectively been "written off" so far as recovery from her disabilities was concerned. It was all up to me now.

Yes, I know, my criticism of the professionals' meeting has been harsh. This despite my being happy to accept that the attendees acted honestly and with the best of intentions. But from the way the discussion went and the one-sidedness of it, the end result soon became obvious. The absence of an advocate for me became an important omission. He could have challenged some statements and demanded an explanation or back-up to many of the claims made. No such person was present to balance the discussion.

The final agreed conclusion was that Rita had no capacity for recovery owing to severe cognitive disability. I was informed of this as described in chapter 23. To then suggest she would be best served in a care home was one certain way to ensure she never could recover, however good the home.

They might have been correct in their conclusion, but it had never been proven, only speculated upon. My view for a long time was that Rita first needed a proper rehabilitation programme as define by the National Stroke Strategy to decide in practical terms whether or not she was capable of a recovery. With the results of that work we could discuss her further treatment or care with some authority.

Luckily I had the freedom allowed by our savings to do as I thought best. I took her to Cape Town to give her a sunny climate, away from the UK winters. It was purely fortuitous that we quickly found a form of in-community rehabilitation programme which was exactly what Rita needed.

25

23 July to 8 August 2010

Winter in Cape Town

While Rita was held in the care home under the SOVA rules, I booked a flight to Cape Town and gave myself 17 days to furnish our South African house. Would that be enough time? It was easily enough. I landed in Cape Town on Friday 23 July at 10.40 am, about 40 minutes late. I picked up a small Hyundai instead of the Volkswagen I thought I had booked. Our new neighbours, Dickie and Monika, let me in to the house as they had the keys, having been looking after it for me since the end of May. Everything looked fine and cleaner than I had expected – Dickie and Monika must have been in with their dusters and vacuum cleaner, I guessed, and felt guilty about that. They soon became very good friends.

I drove to Simon's Town for a late lunch and then to Fish Hoek to begin a search for furniture and all the other things needed. Good news! As it was July, the winter sales were on. I had a look in several shops at what was available, but left making final decisions till the next day, though I did indulge in a large shop at the Pick n Pay supermarket both for food and a start on the kitchen and other utensils that would be needed. I made myself a light meal and went to bed early.

I had a terrible night trying to sleep on the second-hand three-seater sofa we had bought from the previous owners. I'm too old to sleep curled up on a sofa and made a firm decision not to attempt that again. From the previous owners, Rita and I had also bought a remarkably old dishwasher that still performed very well, a huge microwave oven that doubled as a conventional oven and grill, and an electric cooker with a gas hob, powered from a gas bottle. The rest was up to me.

Rita and I wanted family and friends to visit us, so we had decided to furnish all three bedrooms and equip the house to cater for up to six people. Realistically, I could only buy what was available in the shops for immediate delivery, but I still had a good day on the Saturday, ordering two double and two single beds and a large dining table with eight leather-covered chairs (40% off in the sale). We didn't need eight chairs, but the spare ones could be used in the bedrooms. I also purchased a washing machine to be installed in the garage and a fridge/freezer that fitted the space in the kitchen. It was pleasing to find the shops would deliver the goods when I wanted them and not at their convenience.

I also bought a thin mattress that I could fold up and stuff into the Hyundai, plus a single duvet, pillow and sheet, and for the next few nights enjoyed a much more comfortable sleep.

The next thing was paying for all of this as I had no current account in South Africa. One service the attorney offered to "Swallows", the name given to Europeans who flew in for the summer months, was to act as bankers. This included looking after the payment of all bills that became due while we were in the UK. I had already transferred a reasonable sum to my client account with the firm, so on Monday I arranged for electronic payment of the major invoices and a lump sum of 10,000 Rands in cash for my immediate use. That released the furniture for quick delivery.

I had a bit more luck with the purchase of all the bed linen I would need for six people. The department store in Fish Hoek started its winter sale on Friday 30 July. Two days before that, I went to browse through the linen department (discounts of 30% to 50%) and was soon accosted by a member of staff – could she help? I explained what was needed and said I would return on Friday to buy everything.

"Oh, we can do better than that," she said. "Give me a list today of everything you want. I will put it together for you, then on Friday, come in at 9.00 am when we open and go straight to the check-out."

So I did that and, of course, was the first customer at the check-out desk. There was a large pile of packages marked for me; these I paid for and a member of staff helped me carry everything to the car and wedge it in. Already a highly successful day and it was only 9.30 am!

I switched on the solar heating panels for the swimming pool and it took only about five days to lift the water temperature from 14 °C to 21 °C. For me that was (just) warm enough to swim in so I paddled backwards and forwards for 10 or 15 minutes. It was amazing to go swimming in an outdoor pool in midwinter.

Considerable quantities of cash were spent on all the little things needed, from doormats to light fittings. What a lot of bits and pieces. I also made a list of small things we had spare at home and could bring over when we came. The sun shone from the north, of course, and I noticed it had cracked the putty around most of the windows in the direct sun, so I obtained a quote for repair from a local handyman; this he could attend to when we arrived around six weeks later.

It occurred to me that renting a car for 10 to 12 weeks regularly would become expensive – I was enjoying being on the Cape Peninsula again and beginning to think long term. So I looked round for a suitable second-hand car. Old cars are one commodity that was relatively expensive in South Africa at that time, when the Rand was stronger against the £ than it became five years later. I began by looking for a small silver VW and ended up buying a five-year old black Renault Clio with a tiny engine. I knew Rita's folded wheelchair would fit nicely into the boot. As it happened, this car served us well for the next six years.

So, only about ten days after arriving in our new home, I had a decent bed to sleep in. All the furniture and white goods were delivered and, where necessary, installed. There was plenty of time for me to do more exploring around the Cape, including wine tasting in the Constantia vineyards. It was a great holiday and I returned to the UK on 8 August well refreshed, pleased with what I had achieved and feeling more positive about the future.

26

June to December 2010

The Possibility of Private Therapy is Explored

Earlier in 2010, our daughter Sue had done some research on her own in Birmingham and found a national rehabilitation organisation that I will call the UKRSTC (the UK Rehabilitation Services and Treatment Centre). She spoke to one manager in Birmingham and found her to be very helpful. Sue suggested that I got in touch with them. I read the glossy brochure and, certainly, their approach appeared promising.

Comments in the brochure along the following lines seemed very relevant to Rita's needs: *"More people are now surviving a serious stroke as a result of medical advances and need rehabilitation. The purpose of this is to help disabled patients re-learn lost skills. It is important to understand that brain injury usually affects the whole family. Good training for our staff is a high priority. Everyone who uses our services has access to all the support they need. The rehabilitation programmes we set up are designed to meet patients' needs, such that they are treated while living in their own home."*

I could see nothing in the brochure that excluded Rita, so I phoned the people Sue had spoken to and was encouraged by what was said. So this was one possible line to follow to help Rita.

A second was to spend more time in South Africa. We had really enjoyed our six weeks there earlier in the year. At the very least it would take us away from the UK winter into warm sunny weather. This could only be good for Rita. Being able to spend time outdoors might help her significantly.

In my discussions with Martin, the advocate, I told him of these two options I was considering. He thought them both good and we built them into my plans to put forward at the review meeting held on 16 July. Both were well received. They particularly liked the "support in the community" aspect. Our GP offered to refer Rita to the UKRSTC. As I was then planning to go to Cape Town in the near future, I asked if he could try to arrange an assessment for Rita in the third week of August.

On my return home on 8 August from the two weeks in South Africa, I followed up the referral. It had apparently first gone to the wrong address, but that had been corrected within a few days. Unfortunately, when there was no reply, no one from the surgery had followed up by contacting UKRSTC to arrange an assessment date. I phoned the local UKRSTC centre. The referral had been received, but nothing had been done about it. After some pushing, the 10 September was agreed as a mutually convenient date for a neuropsychologist to assess Rita at home. This was barely two weeks before I had booked our flight back to Cape Town, but there might just be time, I hoped, for them to provide some advice on suitable therapy, based on what they learned about Rita's condition, that I could take to South Africa with us.

On the morning of 10 September a neuropsychologist from UKRSTC (I will call her Dr Alison) arrived to assess Rita and stayed for about two hours. She was pleasant, friendly and seemed very competent. She asked questions of Rita's history before and since her injury and ran a number of tests. She concluded that Rita needed medical treatment and said that she would write to the PCT herself. Whether she did or not, separately from her report, I did not find out.

We didn't hear again from Dr Alison before Rita and I left for Cape Town on 23 September, so I was not able to take any suggestions concerning how best to look after Rita to Fish Hoek Home Nursing.

Dr Alison emailed me on 3 October to say her report should be with me shortly, via email. She also included examples of a morning routine prompt sheet, plus a monitoring form used for ADLs (Activities of Daily Living). The latter was a check sheet for carers to confirm they had provided all the prompts that a patient required to perform a task. It covered a period of a week. She suggested documents similar to these might help Rita with repetitive tasks.

On 19 October, Dr Alison emailed again to say that she had received permission from the Exceptional Cases Panel to refer directly to the community team for OT and physio to come into the home to reassess my wife (except we were not there. There seemed to be confusion arising).

She added, "I will also request a neuropsychology assessment so as to provide the therapists with more detailed information about her current strengths/difficulties, but it sounds like this might be difficult to access unfortunately due to lack of provision – in any case I think OT and physio programmes will make more difference to your wife in terms of meaningful change."

I thanked her for the information, said I would reply in detail when I had read the report of her assessment (when it came). This five-page report, addressed to our GP and copied to me, arrived by email on 27 October, something over six weeks after the actual assessment. It opened by stating what the referral (that I hadn't seen previously) had requested: "Advice on whether further rehabilitation would be beneficial for Mrs Guthrie and, if so, in what form this should take". I had expected, and hoped for, a report that first described Rita's current status. That would then go on to say how the expertise of the UKRSTC could help, what form the optimum programme might take, with an indication of cost for the first period. It was not quite like that.

The first two pages were a summary of Rita's medical history since her haemorrhage and our experiences of subsequent treatment. I was pretty familiar with this! Dr Alison then went on to describe Rita's current presentation. Under "Observational Assessment", which was described in some detail, she said, "Mrs Guthrie presented with marked cognitive difficulties". This was all unexceptional.

But under "Opinion and Recommendations" there were nine paragraphs of comment. I read these a good many times and found it difficult to identify, exactly, what Dr Alison considered the best course of action to be. Examples of suggestions were:

"… If Mrs Guthrie is going to be living in her home for the time being, she would benefit from a review of the therapy going into the home as opposed to a period of residential rehabilitation. Community rehabilitation intervention may be beneficial to assess her current presentation. … I do feel there is potential for her to gain more independence in this task [of making a cup of coffee] using a structured PADL approach with errorless learning."

"… It would be imperative that those supporting Mrs Guthrie with such rehabilitation strategies are involved in training around identified goals in order to support her to the best of their abilities. … It appears that she would benefit from a review by physiotherapy … Mrs Guthrie would not be unsuited to a period of residential rehabilitation … community intervention should therefore be the focus on intervention at this stage."

This last opinion at the end of the nine paragraphs was, to me, the nearest that any of her comments got to a statement of positive intent. Did these suggestions answer the two questions posed in our GP's referral? I found it difficult to decide.

The "Opinions and Recommendations" section was all written in the "possible" tense, including such terms as *could, might, possible alternative.* Why? Dr Alison was the neuropsychological expert that others, including me, looked to for guidance. Surely she should have stated clearly the best course of action to follow for a patient she had examined carefully. Who was going to pick out the best course of action from all the suggestions and alternatives that she had talked round? The short answer was "nobody", which possibly was part of the explanation why nothing much happened.

There was one telling remark in the eighth paragraph of the nine. "I have suggested to Mr Guthrie that he wish to investigate private therapy provision." I thought that was where we were going by involving UKRSTC! My mistake, perhaps, for accepting the GP's offer to refer Rita. If I had self-referred maybe it would have been clearer that I was, in fact, expecting to "go private".

It was a pity, because the PCT managers then became involved once more, Dr Alison's report having been sent to the NHS. Without going through the details, I lost contact with Dr Alison, and the physiotherapy and OT assessments she had suggested didn't happen. To be fair to the managers who might possibly have been trying to set them up, one reason was that we were not in the UK at the time, though I had informed those involved of our dates in South Africa. When we were back in the UK at Christmas 2010, I did try to move things forward, but made no progress. As Rita was by then doing so well in South Africa, I dropped any idea of going forward with UKRSTC and wrote to them no more. Nor did I hear anything further from them.

27

September 2010

Last Words for Part 1

On 13 September, just three days after the assessment by Dr Alison, Rita was due to have a routine assessment by a stroke consultant, to check her status relative to the earlier one performed in April. This was carried out in the local hospital stroke unit.

About 40 minutes were spent completing a variety of tests. We had a discussion on the range of medicines Rita was taking; the consultant decided to make no changes, though he was concerned at Rita's rather high blood pressure. He wanted me to check it regularly (we have a small Omron BP monitor at home, so it was easy for me to keep a record of how her blood pressure varied).

At the end of the meeting, the consultant told me that he considered Rita to be as good as she would ever be, but that I should expect a steady decline in her condition and abilities into the future. This was yet another (the ninth) negative prognosis concerning the possibility of Rita being able to recover from her physical and cognitive disabilities.

There are both frightening and sad aspects to this affair. The frightening aspect is that I have no doubt, if Rita had stayed in the UK, she would never have recovered. This was because there was no reason why she should have got better. By now she had made little progress during two years and six months since her stroke in April 2008, despite all the treatment (if the PCT was to be believed) she had received. She would certainly receive no more rehabilitation from the NHS. So her lack of recovery from that time on, had we stayed in the UK, would have "proved" the health professionals to be right in the negative prognosis they had unanimously given Rita. Thus their views of what was possible and what was not possible would have been strengthened, including their ability to assess patients accurately. (The sad aspect is commented on in chapter 40, at the end of question 5).

We did not have to spend long in South Africa before it became evident that all the UK professionals had been wrong in that pessimistic assessment. All the negative prognoses Rita was given were incorrect. It became apparent that, despite Rita's lack of progress towards recovery during two-and-a-half years, in 2010 she did still retain an innate ability to recover *if* she was given appropriate treatment. Remarkably, she was to be given this straight-forward treatment in Fish Hoek and, as a result, recovered from all her several disabilities with the exception of one. How this happened is the subject of Part 2.

Two weeks after the consultant's prognosis of "a continuing steady decline in Rita's condition", we flew to Cape Town for our first long, 10-week stay there. We didn't know it then, but it would mark the beginning of Rita's recovery from her disabilities.

Part 2

Recovery – How it Happened

October 2010 to April 2013

28

23 September to 22 October 2010

Ten Weeks in South Africa – The First Four

Rita and I had spent six weeks in an apartment in the seaside town of Fish Hoek, south of Cape Town, during February and March 2010 (chapter 19). My hopes of this rather risky enterprise had been more than met – rather surprisingly as it was more frustration at life in the UK than certainty that South Africa would be right for Rita that had pushed me into taking her there for a holiday.

Rita had liked the climate and the seaside environment as much as I did. She got on well with the carers provided by Fish Hoek Home Nursing (FHHN). It had seemed almost automatic to look for a small house that could act as our future base during the UK winters. By the end of July, all the stress and frustrations during the first half of the year added to my keenness to go back to South Africa earlier rather than later. Apart from this, I was committed to returning to Fish Hoek, if just to get Rita back with me after the SOVA interlude!

During previous years we had never left our home in England empty for more than three weeks at a time. It became apparent that a period of 42 days was critical but this was much less than our intended "holiday" of about 70 days. Neither our house insurance company nor the travel insurance companies liked absences of more than six weeks. However, I found a company which would insure Rita for that period of travel, paid an extra premium on the house insurance to cover it being empty long-term, re-directed the mail to our daughter-in-law and tried to make arrangements to cover anything that might have to be dealt with during our absence.

A taxi took us to Heathrow on Wednesday 22 September for the overnight flight to Cape Town. The flight went round, rather than over, France owing to an air traffic controllers' strike, but still landed at Cape Town only ten minutes late. The flight captain told us he had "turned the wick up a bit". We were met by another taxi for the 45-minute drive to Number 59, our home for ten weeks, arriving about 11.30 am. Elizabeth, the carer for the day, was already waiting by the gate; she would take care of Rita for a few hours while we got settled. Another welcome was inside the house. We found a large bunch of colourful proteas and a bottle of wine from Monika and Dickie, our new neighbours, on the table.

Rita's shower was delayed a while by the need to heat the water. I could have asked Dickie or Monika to switch on the geyser, had I thought of it. Proudly, I showed Rita round the now-furnished house; she was delighted with what I had been able to do. We unpacked with Elizabeth's help. I went shopping. We all had lunch and, at 3.00 pm, Nicola, a FHHN staff nurse, arrived to check everything was OK, agree again what the carers' responsibilities should be and write out instructions for them.

It took no time at all for Rita to settle. Within days she was doing better than she had at home and the carers, as before, did their job effectively and with good humour. I, too, immediately felt more relaxed which, unconsciously, probably helped Rita. The carers arrived at 7.30 am with Rita still in bed. I had got up at 7.00 am and was dressed by the time the doorbell rang. The carer for the day showered and dressed Rita while I prepared breakfast, sorted out Rita's several pills, pottered around the garden and de-leaved the swimming pool till they were ready. We all had breakfast together, after which the carer took charge of Rita for the rest of the morning.

We began with Elizabeth and Zolie, more or less on alternate days. Then Doreen put in an appearance. This pleased us greatly as Rita had got on particularly well with her during our earlier stay. Doreen seemed as pleased to see Rita as we were to see her. Soon there were more changes and, after a couple of weeks, we settled down with Doreen three or four days out of seven, the other days being covered by Brenda and Welekazi who was delightful but a little diffident, being younger than the other two. Needless to say, all carers were varying shades of black.

Fish Hoek Home Nursing differed from the caring services we had experienced in the UK in that it ran what was an effective quality control system. The service was headed by five qualified nurses and, during the first few weeks we were visited regularly, without warning, by the "duty sister" or another nurse to check we had no difficulties or queries and that the carers were doing everything that had been agreed. The carers were very aware that these visits would happen and knew that if things were not as they should be, there would be words said. A regular visit from management, not requested by us, had not been part of the system for any of the caring companies in the UK with which we had had dealings.

Sister Jenny arrived at 11.30 am on 1 October, visiting for the second time. She told us she would probably be called a community nurse in the UK. She thought the house was just right for Rita, though recommended buying a non-slip mat for the shower and a stool on which Rita could put her feet and rest her slightly swollen ankles. We agreed that the carers should be asked to help and supervise Rita with household tasks rather than, as was usual, do all the light housework themselves. Jenny thought Rita had improved during the six months since she had last seen her in March and was dismissive of the NHS view that Rita was not capable of further progress. "Use it or lose it," she said, adding that what Rita needed was gentle stimulation. She promised to organise the carers to help Rita regain her lost skills.

Jenny came yet again a week later and stayed for an hour. She helped Rita with a small jigsaw while chatting to her, then recommended that Rita lose some weight and gave us suggestions for a suitable diet. She also left instructions for the carers that, every day, Rita should be taken for a short walk, weather permitting (which it did).

"What your wife needs most," she told me, "is rehabilitation." Then she added what were to prove the most important words I had heard for two-and-a-half years. "If you like, I can find you a couple of therapists in Fish Hoek who should be able to help her." That was the start of a week that was to see a rehabilitation programme established.

The next day, Jenny had called in briefly to leave me the names and phone numbers of an occupational therapist and a hydrotherapist. I contacted them immediately and, within a few days, both had been to see and assess Rita. Both also agreed to begin a therapy programme. That was all that was needed to start Rita's rehabilitation programme that was to run for over three years.

The hydrotherapist turned out to be Adele, a very capable physiotherapist with an indoor swimming pool. Amazingly, her clinic was a mere ten-minute walk from where we lived at No 59. That first session with Adele had been given over to an assessment of course. When she left, Adele said she would think over what she had found concerning Rita's disabilities and, at the next session, would tell us what she planned.

A week later, Adele said Rita's main problem was that she had lost her sense of balance. "Get that back," she said, "and everything that follows should be much easier." But she commented that Rita's muscle strength was poor because of the little exercise she had had over more than two years. So there would need to be a lot of exercises to restore both Rita's core body strength and her musculature. The therapy began immediately and, at the end of the session, Adele wrote a short list of exercises that she gave to the carer (who had watched what was going on), making sure they were understood. Adele's instructions for the carer were that Rita was to be given these exercises for about 20 minutes every day, until the next session. I passed these instructions on to the other two carers who, despite having no rehabilitation training, were keen to be involved and were actually excited about being given more responsibility to help Rita. The use of supervised carers was the one major difference between the South African programme and the recommendations of the *National Stroke Strategy*.

The OT's name was Estie. I was surprised how young she looked, but she must have been older than she appeared. She told us she had worked for several years in both France and the UK. Her main job in Fish Hoek was working for an organisation that helped retarded and disabled children. Having also assessed Rita's problems, Estie followed two lines of attack that were both rather easier for the carers to help with than the physiotherapy exercises. One was to tackle Rita's weak left side and her disinclination to use her left hand. Rita often tried to eat using her right hand only, letting her left hand hang, unused, by her side. Estie gave her a series of repetitive physical exercises to do. These were simple, sensible, and one could see why they would help. Just as an example, with a dozen clothes pegs and an empty 1 kg yoghurt carton, Rita had to clip all the pegs onto the side of the pot with one hand only, then off again one at a time, then on again, for five minutes. This was then repeated with the other hand, then she went back to the first hand again. After 20 minutes of this Rita was very bored, but was willing to do as she was instructed by both Estie and the carers (but not by me!). Other exercises were similarly repetitive, but clearly effective.

The second line of attack was to treat Rita's cognitive limitations. This was done mostly with a variety of children's games, some of which involved memory such as the card game we used to call Pelmanism. A number of paired cards were placed face down at random on a table. Each player turned over two cards. If they were a pair they were kept by that player, otherwise turned face down again in the same locations. Later on, when the second "donkey" was turned over – where was that first donkey seen a minute before? The player with the best memory generally won. Estie also had cards with simple pictures, such as a duck pond with a farm in the background and a few trees. Rita was allowed about 15 seconds to study the picture, then had to answer questions about it. How many ducks were in the water? What was the colour of the farm roof? Was it a sunny day? What else can you remember in the picture?

Estie lent us several games and Rita and her carers had a lot of fun playing these together with the dominoes, UNO cards and jigsaws we had brought. During that visit and the next one we made to South Africa, in early 2011, I attended all the therapy sessions, as did the carer whenever the sessions were in the morning. Especially when I was watching Adele, I saw how important it was that a trained therapist worked with Rita. To begin with, the exercises were simple but Rita still struggled to do them. I was impressed how quickly Adele could see why Rita had difficulty. Her posture was wrong, or a limb was slightly in the wrong position. Or Adele needed to simplify the exercise. As soon as Rita managed to complete an exercise successfully, Adele shouted "Well DONE Rita", immediately followed by high fives. Rita responded well to this encouragement. The next exercise was immediately just a little harder. The result was that the list of exercises given to the carers changed each week and Adele made sure at least one carer understood what was required by the new list.

Regularly, neither the carers nor I could get Rita to do one or other of the exercises on the set list, so that was left aside without a fuss being made. At the next therapy session, Adele asked, "Any problems?" "We couldn't get Rita to do exercise 4." So Adele then demonstrated how easy in fact it was. Jenny returned later in October to see how things had started. The answer was, "Very well".

So, around three weeks after we had arrived on the Cape, we had a routine established that, each day, involved carers giving Rita simple

OT-type exercises, plus physiotherapy, plus a walk of a half to three-quarters of a kilometre. There were also the formal physiotherapy and occupational therapy sessions every week. The carers also helped Rita complete household chores such as vacuuming, preparing drinks, peeling vegetables, making the bed, even ironing (which Dr Peter had told me was a no-no), and playing games. It was just as well we had the carers for four hours each day – the rehabilitation programme had become so extensive that very soon most of the time was taken up.

Early in the ironing sessions, Rita had been doing well, apparently, so the carer gave her several hankies to iron and went off to do something else. Ten minutes later she returned to find Rita still ironing the first hankie, turning it over and over. By then it was the colour of lightly done toast. We decided that, until further notice, carers had to stay with Rita while she was ironing. They would position the clothing while Rita ironed it.

So, only a few weeks into the first regular treatment regime Rita had ever been given – one that could truly be called an in-community rehabilitation programme – she was making as good progress as could possibly be expected. How far could it go? A long way seemed entirely possible.

How was I feeling now? As if an enormous weight had been lifted from my shoulders. There were no battles to be fought. It was wonderful for me to have the support of a small group of three "health professionals" who all had a positive approach to Rita's problems. They believed she could get better – perhaps not fully better, but much further than her present status. What a change from the universally negative attitude I had met from the health managers in the UK who made the decisions on what Rita could and could not have by way of treatment. For whatever reasons, these people had decided that Rita's was a hopeless case and no more NHS money was to be spent on her rehabilitation – it would be a waste of scarce resources. The approach to Rita's disabilities was negative in the UK, positive in South Africa. I much preferred the latter.

There was also the regular advice from an experienced nurse who was keeping an eye on how it was all working. I had not asked Sister Jenny to do this; she took it upon herself as part of the complete service the FHHN provided. As we shall see later, Rita made more progress during these ten weeks than in the whole year previously. Just how much was due to this regime we had established, and how much to the equable climate and the beautiful and stimulating surroundings, it is difficult to be sure. But I had no doubt that the therapy and care regime counted for a very large part of it.

We paid for these services ourselves, of course, but it was not expensive in UK terms. The 28 hours of caring each week plus two sessions of professional therapy were costing me in Rands the equivalent of £130 or thereabouts. The programme had the huge advantage that, if I wanted it to continue, then it continued as time-unlimited therapy, exactly as the UK *National Stroke Strategy* document recommended.

29

October and November 2010

Newsletters Home

Several family and friends had been concerned that Rita and I were disappearing off to South Africa, 6000 miles away, for as long as ten weeks. Was it safe? Could we find medical treatment if something went wrong or Rita fell ill? So, during the first two months, I wrote five newsletters describing what we had been up to and how Rita was doing. These were emailed to quite a long list of family and friends to calm nerves. The following are extracts from these newsletters to describe how we found living on the Cape Peninsula, quite separate from the important therapy already described.

Written on 3 October

"Rita appears to have no problem whatever with settling here. As we found the last time we came, in February, there seems to have been an immediate stepwise advance in her progress. She has been getting up from a sofa with no help and appearing in the kitchen offering to wash up or do the vegetables. She has walked around the local Pick n Pay supermarket, which is all of five times the floor area of our local one at home, pushing a trolley, with no sign of getting tired, but lifting anything that takes her fancy off the shelves, which is less helpful!

"The weather has been mixed. We had one-and-a-half days of rain early on which was described by our neighbours as "unseasonal". We have also

174

had cloudless blue days that are beautiful. Last weekend there was a south-easterly gale for two days. The Western Cape is a very windy place, but it has not been cold. Our stoep (covered terrace) faces north to north-west so was sheltered from the wind and we could sit comfortably in its shade looking over the garden. There were clouds sitting on the mountains both sides of us, but in the valley, where we are, it was almost uninterrupted sun – hence its name, Sun Valley."

Written on 9 October

"Wednesday was cloudy/bright – good weather for visiting the Cape of Good Hope National Park whose entrance is about 15 miles south of where we live. We took Doreen with us, partly because she was so excited about going there. She is in her late 40s and has been "caring" for years, yet no one has ever taken her down to the Cape before. She took Rita for a long walk at Buffels Bay, after which we stopped off at the car park below the Cape of Good Hope for a while, though Rita just wanted to sit in the car and watch the sea. Lunch was at Cape Point where we ate outside, with a "baboon warden" hanging around a couple of paces from us. Speaking in the native Xhosa language, she told Doreen that she didn't want a baboon stealing our salads! (Doreen claims to speak three languages well and can get by in two others). We then watched a baboon hang around on the roof of the cafeteria with no apparent interest in anything until it suddenly picked its moment and shot into the cafeteria while a group of tourists were going through the door. A few seconds, and quite a lot of screams, later it emerged at high speed hugging packets of crisps and chocolate and escaped up the hill.

"We spent the afternoon driving around the little back roads of the Park where coaches rarely go, including the long track to Oliphantsbos Bay on the Atlantic coast where we took another short walk. On the way back, I stopped the car abruptly twice. The first for a red creature crawling across the road. This turned out to be a locust or cricket, about 4 inches long and patterned all over in black and scarlet. The second was when a Cape Cobra, four or five feet long, slid across the road in front of us. It raised its hood momentarily at the car, then disappeared rapidly into the fynbos vegetation at the side of the road.

"I bought tickets for a choral concert at the Fish Hoek Civic Centre – doesn't sound much except that the advance publicity was promising.

The choir was the almost 100-strong Stellenbosch University Choir. We were told in the introduction that, a few months ago, the choir had been in India where it won at an international choir festival. Also that "Musica Mundi", that ranks the world's best 1000 choirs, then placed the Stellenbosch choir at No 2. (By 2016 it had achieved number 1 spot!). The evening was astonishingly good. I had no idea singing could be like that, and Rita enjoyed it hugely. It was all multi-multi-part singing with the "voices" all mixed up in the group instead of having the tenors standing together, for example. There wasn't a musical instrument to be seen, nor a sheet of music. I knew none of the music but it was all wonderful to listen to, varying from a single voice for a few notes changing suddenly to enough noise to challenge a big orchestra. Freddie Mercury's Bohemian Rhapsody was extremely complex and received the biggest ovation, but I particularly liked the three witches from Macbeth in "Double, Double, Toil and Trouble". A storm was raging, the witches cackling and shrieking, yet the names of all Shakespeare's ingredients going into the brew could be clearly heard. Without a shadow of a doubt, I shall never hear a better choral concert. How does little Fish Hoek put on a show like that?"

Written on 16 October

"Yesterday (Friday) the weather was a bit iffy, but I had booked Doreen for the day so we drove over to the Kirstenbosch Gardens (16 miles) and spent the day there – and it didn't rain. I needed Doreen's help because the gardens are not wheelchair-friendly, being located on the lower south-east slopes of Table Mountain. The Gardens, claiming to be the "best in Africa", were established in 1913 when the needs of disabled people were hardly considered. The whole place is on a slope, there are paths made of small boulders laid in mortar over which it is difficult enough to push an *empty* wheelchair, and many short flights of stone steps built of roughly cut granite blocks. We climbed to near the top of the gardens where most of the proteas are – in full bloom and beautiful. Almost none of the claimed 600-plus varieties of Erica were in flower, it being too early in the summer, but there were plenty of other plants that we had never seen before. We stayed for just over four hours and Rita did really well. She walked everywhere, not using the wheelchair once. Of course, she needed help up and down steps, and regular rests, but there were plenty of benches scattered about. She turned down all offers of a ride. And that was much better than on our previous visit seven months before."

Written on 27 October

"Last weekend, 23 and 24 October, saw Africa's largest Kite Festival (allegedly) at Zandvlei Park. As Zandvlei was only nine miles away, we decided to go on Saturday despite a poor forecast. It had rained heavily during Friday night and was still doing so at 7.00 am but, by 10.00, the clouds were breaking, so we risked it and were lucky. The festival was organised as a fund-raising occasion for the Cape Mental Health charity – which seemed appropriate for us – and several thousand people were there. It was a very family-oriented affair; all the children were encouraged to bring their own kites to fly, or to buy one of the many available, so all the time we were running the gauntlet of crashing kites and being strangled by thin string!

"There were some fine professional kites. Some were huge, 100 feet long or more. Most were designed as animals, fish or dragons. There was only a gentle breeze so some of the biggest were struggling to get off the ground, but two colourful and ornate dragons were flying one above the other, held up by at least ten kites sent up first on the same cord, one above another until the highest was almost out of sight. Rita managed well walking across lumpy turf and avoiding obstacles and altogether it was a good day's entertainment for under £20, including three lunches, as we took a carer! We found a stall selling spiral crisps. They pushed a long wooden skewer through a large potato, cut it into a spiral on a machine, then fried it so it came out as a foot-long spiral crisp stuck to the skewer. Hot and tasty."

Written on 8 November

"The weather continued quite mixed. On Saturday we thought we would visit the African penguins at Boulders, near Simon's Town but, for the first time since we have been here, our plans were rained off. We made two attempts to leave the car but each time a sudden shower arrived so we gave up and, instead, drove to our nearest vineyard to sample their wines. Cape Point Vineyards are still in Noordhoek, but at the north end of the village on the slopes of Chapman's Peak mountain. It claimed that vines were planted there well before 1700, but the enterprise fell on bad times and was only re-started as a modern vineyard six or seven years ago. We felt quite under-dressed as the presentation of the wines was very formal. Anyway, it was fun to try them and, as I liked the cheaper wines as much as the more expensive, we came away with a few bottles of very drinkable everyday wine. The name given to this brand hardly went with the opulence of the tasting room – "Splattered Toad". It was a nod in the direction of the most distinguished amphibian of the Noordhoek wetlands, the endangered western leopard toad. As the vineyard is sited just above the wetlands and a significant number of toads get squashed on the road running between the vineyard and the wetlands, they are supporting efforts to protect the creature. Oh yes, it seemed odd to be drinking 2010 wine already, in November, till I realised it had been produced around last March.

"We enjoyed one fine day, then on Monday it rained again, all morning, only clearing up around midday. After lunch we drove south down the Peninsula to call in at a big ostrich farm. Mondays are probably not the best day for them as they were short-staffed and couldn't organise a tour for us, but they were very welcoming nonetheless. We were taken in hand by an extraordinarily loquacious German lady and, not only did we learn a lot about ostriches, but we heard all about her divorce and her new life in Scarborough (on the Cape, not the Yorkshire coast). How that came up in the conversation I don't remember. She talked about a wide range of things totally unrelated to ostriches.

"Just as matters of interest, some claims she made were that you can stand on a newly laid ostrich egg without it breaking; ostriches are the fastest growing large animal in the world – it takes them only 14 months to grow from a 1 kg chick to a 150 kg full-grown adult; ostrich leather is the second most expensive of any and, judging by the prices in their shop, I can believe it; and this year summer is very late arriving. A female ostrich will only lay eggs when the weather is warm enough. Their season at the farm normally begins in September but, this year, they had their first egg only last week. That may explain why the ostrich farms started in the UK never seem to survive very long.

"Anyway, Rita and I came away with a white feather duster that is rather nice and very soft. We made it a circular tour and drove back through Scarborough, up the Atlantic coast through the village of Misty Cliffs, and back across country to Noordhoek."

Written on 12 November

"Yesterday, Thursday, started reasonably well but clouded over soon after lunch with heavy rain for just a couple of hours in the early evening. Rita had her hydrotherapy in the morning with more advanced exercises now and she looked forward to going. But was tired afterwards and was happy with a quiet day at home. The weather forecast *sounds* as though there will be little rain over the weekend, with temperatures reaching 32 °C early next week – about time!

"As an example of how Rita's manual dexterity is improving, today we went for lunch to the Blue Water Café on the Kommetjie road. From the café's terrace (with peacocks wandering around the tables) there was a panoramic view over the wetlands and Noordhoek beach, with a backdrop of Chapman's Peak and the range of mountains to the north. We both ordered spicey duck salad and this came with chopsticks as an alternative to a knife and fork. Rita chose the chopsticks and completely cleaned her plate using only those. There is no way she could have achieved that three months ago."

Written on 28 November

"Rita has at last started to regain her interest in books and enjoys being read to for an hour or so in the evening. This interest in reading has now transferred across to magazines and newspapers that she looks at with obvious interest. This can only be good.

"Nowadays she is taking herself to the loo during the day more often than not, and needs no help at all with dressing herself again most of the time. It is just when she is tired that her clothes don't always finish up in quite the right places. Yesterday we went to a rather pricey restaurant in Noordhoek and, as we left, Rita, as usual, needed the loo. I made to go with her but "I can manage all right," she said. And did so. I am sure that will be the start of much more independence for us both.

"Things can happen very quickly when you're dealing with one of the small local tradesmen. Last week I thought we should get in more fuel for the wood-burning stove. I had seen that a local fruiterer had stacks of wood in his yard, so I phoned to ask if he delivered. Yes, he did, and if we came round in 20 minutes he would be there and we could decide what we would like. So we drove there; about two miles, give or take. We decided on a crate of hardwood, whereupon he promptly whistled up two lads, a fork-lift loaded the pallet precariously onto his "bakkie" (pick-up truck) and he followed me home, with the two lads sitting on top of the wood to stop it falling out and the tailgate swinging free in true South

African style. It looks horrendously dangerous and illegal to English eyes. He backed into the empty half of our garage, the two lads unloaded it all, and just 25 minutes after we left home we had around half a ton of wood locked away in the garage!

"We had another dose of culture on Friday evening at the Civic Centre. There was a piano recital by the claimed "international pianist" Valda Fuhr. Her ability to play about 20 notes per second was astonishing and she must be a top pianist, but I am not enough of a musician to appreciate the intricacies of Debussy, Bach, Beethoven and friends, even when played well. I still enjoyed the evening though and Rita loved it. The applause was loud and long, enough to encourage an encore. This was five minutes of fast ragtime which was fantastic; the best part of the evening for me. There is a lot going on in the evenings that we haven't made the most of. We didn't go to either the Kalk Bay Theatre or the Masque Theatre in Muizenberg, largely because of the continence situation, but maybe that is nearly resolved. Throughout the summer, there is an outdoor concert every Sunday evening at the Kirstenbosch Gardens, plus evening talks that might interest me more than Rita. Lots to look forward to on our next visit."

30

23 October to 2 December 2010

Six Weeks of Progress

It was in early October that Rita's South African in-community rehabilitation programme was put together (yet its format changed little in concept right up to April 2013, by which time Rita had received close to 18 months of therapy over six visits to Cape Town). The way it was set up was just straight forward, sensible and simple. It was also economical cost-wise (chapter 42). Eventually, when it was clearly such a successful rehabilitation programme, I wrote a formal account of how it was put together and managed, and how it worked for Rita (chapter 38).

Why could something like this not be set up back home? Well, of course it could be. There was nothing in Rita's programme by way of technical knowledge or therapist training that was not already known in the UK. So why isn't a similar programme offered? It may be an unfair criticism, but based on our long experiences, my explanation would be "management attitude and money".

As an example of the difficulty, and slowness, of getting things organised in the UK, my earlier attempts to set up private therapy for Rita illustrated the point. The idea was first agreed with health and care professionals during the 16 July 2010 meeting at our local surgery, but Rita's assessment by the UKRTC didn't happen until 10 September. The report on this was emailed to me on 27 October with a request from Dr Alison to let her know what I thought. I emailed back within a few days and included an outline of what had been set up in South Africa, asking whether something similar could be established at home as it seemed to work well. I sent a reminder on 17 November, both of these being copied to our GP. By the time we returned home on 3 December, there had been no further reply from either Dr Alison or our doctor. By then, six months had passed by with no evident progress towards Rita being given private therapy, paid for by me. Yet it had taken only a week to set up a therapy programme for Rita in Fish Hoek!

But enough of complaints.

The sixteenth of October became another "first" for us, resulting from a decision to drive into Simon's Town after lunch, as a small outing. Going south out of Fish Hoek, there was a crowd of people standing by the side of the road, looking out to sea. We stopped and joined them. There were two southern right whales floating close together roughly 50 yards from the rocks, occasionally blowing a fountain of wet air straight upwards. It was Rita's first sighting of these huge creatures that reach 45 tonnes when adult and can achieve 60 tonnes.

Rita's mobility, in terms of her walking, was improving steadily, but while this happened, an unexpected cognitive problem surfaced. In October, the carers had begun by pushing Rita out in her wheelchair, with Rita taking short walks and then returning to the chair. Soon, the walks involved Rita pushing the chair as a support, stopping fairly regularly to sit in it and recover her strength. After not many weeks, a big step forward, for short morning walks, was to leave the wheelchair at home and walk hand-in-hand with the carer. The hand-in-hand aspect was necessary owing to Rita's difficulty with perception, mentioned in Part 1. She could see obstacles such as kerbs well enough but continued as though they were not there, either falling down them or tripping over them. We discovered that any obstacle needed to be pointed out to her verbally. It took a long time before she overcame this difficulty and I am not sure that she ever has, totally.

Many months later, Rita and I were walking along Fish Hoek High Street. The pavements mostly had canopies at first floor level to protect pedestrians from sun or rain. At one point a few supports for the canopy were anchored at ground level by circular blocks of concrete about three feet in diameter and eighteen inches high. As we approached these, I moved well over to allow Rita plenty of room to pass them by, but I made no comment. Rita walked straight into the first one and went sprawling on the pavement. No damage done luckily, apart from grazed hands. "Didn't you see the concrete block?" I asked. "Yes." "So why did you walk into it?" "I don't know," was her reply.

Around the end of October 2010, only a few weeks after the therapy programme got underway, a really important change to Rita's condition became apparent. Her incontinence began to improve! This first showed itself during the night. The first two weeks were much as they had been for around two years in the UK. Rita stayed in bed all night and woke in the morning almost always with a wet pad. During the next three weeks or so she began to wake up in the middle of the night, needing the toilet. This was a good sign, showing she had an awareness that she needed to "go". Even so, she was often too late and the pads were wet at least once during the night.

Later on things improved further. She usually made it to the toilet in time and it became rare for any pad to be wet. This awareness of needing the loo read across to the daytime and Rita became much better at deciding to go to the toilet when she needed to – much better than me guessing when it was time to take her. Neither of the therapists had made any direct attempt to cure her incontinence, so I could only put it down to a general improvement in her cognitive function as a result of all the hours of daily physical therapy. This had the potential to be a major bonus, resulting directly from the therapy programme.

Our first stay of ten weeks on the Cape Peninsula in our own home was delightful. Rita missed her walk on only one day, and often walked considerably more than a kilometre. It did rain, quite a lot, but never for long. The sun came out and, within half an hour, the ground was dry. After the carer left at 11.30 am each day, we either had lunch at home, or drove to a nearby café or restaurant. Although food prices in the supermarkets did not appear much lower, on average, than those in the UK, eating out was relatively inexpensive because of the low cost of labour.

This visit to South Africa was the first of many during which we lived in our own house rather than a rented apartment, but no difficulties arose. The great majority of people we met were friendly, welcoming and helpful. Our neighbours, Dickie and Monika, went out of their way to help and make sure we knew where to find anything we needed.

The country was just as beautiful as it had seemed on my first visits, the coastline just as spectacular, the winds just as strong! Almost every time

Rita and I drove back home after an outing, she would comment, "What beautiful mountains!", these being the ones either side of the Noordhoek valley where we lived. When the time came to return to the UK in early December, she was reluctant to leave and needed reassurance that we would soon return in the New Year.

31

3 December 2010 to 12 January 2011

Christmas 2010 Back Home in England

We landed back at Heathrow ten minutes early, just before 7.00 am, after a good flight, though I think Rita slept hardly at all once again. Our reliable taxi driver Steve was there to meet us and we had a good drive home, arriving at 9.15. We had missed the worst of the first snowfall, but there were still about two inches of melting slush on the ground. Our son Duncan had put on the heating in the house, but at a low level (that I had requested, not knowing the conditions) and the house seemed very cold. We soon got one room warm by the use of electric fires as well as the central heating and I began to unpack.

An important outing was to the supermarket to restock the fridge and kitchen cupboards. This was a little fraught because Rita was under the impression we had four to six people in the house and tried to over-provision by a substantial factor. She objected to me putting things that she had chosen back on the shelves. As soon as we were home, I lit the wood-burning stove and, after lunch, we both fell asleep in front of this till Duncan and family arrived to see us later in the afternoon.

It took me a little while to recover my wits. I mis-set the alarm for the next morning, Sunday, so it didn't go off at 7.00 am and I left the carer standing outside for ten minutes in the cold. The stove was lit immediately (it should, but didn't, stay in overnight) and we stayed indoors. I checked a pile of mail, reacquainted myself with our bank accounts and made a few phone calls. Rita did not get her walk, but completed the medicine-ball exercises well.

On Tuesday afternoon, 7 December, we had an appointment with the doctor. He checked Rita's blood pressure that was OK – just. He said to stay with the daily 10 mg of amlodipine that had been prescribed in South Africa. I suggested that, as Rita had not had a urinary infection for some months, maybe we could drop the prophylactic antibiotics. He agreed and said to stop immediately. It might also be possible to stop the desmopressin, and this could help with the swollen ankles, but we were advised to wait till some time after Christmas. Once the desmopressin had been stopped without any resulting problem, I could reduce the oxybutynin by half (to a pill every other day) for a few weeks. If things were OK, I could stop that too. Briefly I explained the regime we had running in South Africa and said I would like to have it set up in the UK, if possible, when we returned home around Easter. He agreed that it seemed a good system that should work well. He would speak to a senior nurse and come back to me within a week. This didn't happen. I couldn't resist pointing out how well Rita had done in Cape Town despite the "no further progress is possible" prognosis from the June meeting that he chaired. That might have been an unwise comment.

The next day I attempted to phone Dr Alison of UKRSTC, but without success. For lunch we joined the SAS swimmers' Christmas dinner, generously hosted by one of the member's wives and helped by several others. They put on a superb meal. That evening there was an annual Torchlight Procession and Carol Singing in the local town. It was much too cold for Rita to walk through the streets and stand for an hour in the public gardens, but we did accept an invitation to the Mayor's reception afterwards, with drinks and nibbles. Rita stood up well to all the day's activities.

The 10–12 December was a busy weekend. Sue and her two girls came down from Birmingham, Gary flew in from France and our two oldest grandchildren came down from Edinburgh for a get-together. Only Gary's wife couldn't make it as she was convalescing after an operation. The get-together consisted of a Christmas lunch at an old coaching inn that Duncan had organised. All his family were there too, of course, so it was one of the rare occasions when nearly all of us were in one place. Rita loved it and sparkled in the company. How much she had improved during the ten weeks in our home in Noordhoek became very evident.

She could look after herself, go to the loo unaccompanied and join in the conversation. It was really just her short-term memory that remained very poor. She remembered little of what had been said, what had been decided and what we might be doing in the future.

On Sunday morning Gary, Duncan and I drove over to Duncan's new small factory that Gary had not seen. It was impressive and we had an interesting discussion about what the company was doing and its prospects. It sounded encouraging for the minor shareholders, Gary and me!

The Community Psychiatric Nurse (CPN) came on Wednesday for a chat; one of the very few occasions she saw Rita. She was astonished at the improvement in her compared with the last time she had seen her. Again I pointed out this was after she had effectively been written off – so far as her potential for recovery went – by those at the meeting on 18 June, six months earlier, as well as by a stroke consultant the following September. I had intended saying I was disappointed in her own lack of contribution at the June meeting, since she knew me much better than any others who were there, but didn't have the heart as she seemed such a sympathetic person. She did say she would write to our GP and others to emphasise how important it was that Rita should receive continued therapy. She would let me see a draft of the letter after Christmas. She told me the Mental Health Group was "signing me off" as a client. According to the letter she wrote to me, I clearly had no mental health problems, as I knew! If, and when, I became depressed it was not clinical, but situational depression. No mental problems were ever really suspected, of course (so far as I know). The involvement with the group only began after our GP asked me whether I would like to make use of the consultation service the practice was then offering, some 14 months before.

By 15 December, I had become irritated with the agency supplying the afternoon carers. They were supposed to work with Rita on a kind of amateur OT basis and supervise her doing household chores as well as go through the list of exercises we had brought from South Africa. But for four successive afternoon sessions, we had had a different carer and I had to teach all of them what to do for Rita. I might as well have done it all myself as pay them to come. But a phone call to the supervisor then improved matters.

The Thursday evening, 16 December, was the night of the biannual "Carol Concert", the main fund-raising event for Success After Stroke.

It was held in a big church capable of holding a congregation of about 600. It was always packed and the service included readings by TV and radio celebrities, with professional singers. When Rita and I arrived, it was already snowing. We parked on the large sloping meadow below the church. I did an experimental attempt at driving up the slope to park but the car clearly wasn't going anywhere uphill on snow-covered grass, so I ran it backwards downhill to turn, and parked facing towards what I hoped was a second exit in the distant bottom corner of the field.

The concert was as good as expected. Coming out of the church it was very Christmassy with 2 cm of snow on the ground, though it had stopped falling by then. There was no difficulty getting off the field and we were in bed by 10.00 pm. Rita hadn't needed the loo, fortunately, as there wasn't one within convenient reach of the church. I am recording all these Christmas activities to show how much better Rita's incontinence had become and how we were on the road to leading a nearly normal life again.

It was on Saturday afternoon, 18 December, that the snow set in steadily. By late evening there was a level 15 to 17 cm around the house, with very little traffic using the road. I had cancelled the carer for the morning, so showered and dressed Rita myself. The Day Care Christmas Party had been organised for Sunday afternoon but the manageress phoned to say it was cancelled. Cars were unable to get up the road to the centre.

The carer and day care were cancelled on Monday, too. The house was cold when I went down for breakfast and I found the oil-fired boiler had cut out and refused to re-start. I rang Bob the Boiler Man at 8.00 am. He said he would see what he could do. Surprisingly, and very pleasingly, Bob arrived about mid-morning. He said the temperature the previous night had been -11 °C. It took him an hour to clear the fuel line outside that had become blocked with sludge and ice. After this the boiler fired up and worked perfectly.

Two planned visits were cancelled, including one to some old friends near Oxford. The next day, I picked Rita up from day care, but then couldn't get the car up our sloping driveway. My bag of builders' sand was of no help, but the farmer gave me some "winter grit" which did make a difference. It still took 20 minutes to get the car high enough up our drive to turn it, then roll it down into the garage, just in time to let a carer into the house to look after Rita for an hour.

The cold had eased the next day, so we did get to visit our friends, then continued to Birmingham to stay with our daughter Sue and family over Christmas. It was a happy family occasion. We all mucked in with the preparations and cooking, the girls didn't squabble as sometimes happened, and Rita was bright and did her bit, though had trouble finding her way around a strange house.

One of the middle-term options I had been considering for Rita and me was to rent out our own home and possibly rent a smaller place near Sue and family in Birmingham. This would allow us to keep our options open while we found out if the idea of moving to the Midlands, which Sue wanted us to do, might be workable. We spent some time looking on the Internet for small bungalows or houses to rent within a few miles of the family, but found nothing that looked at all suitable or appealing.

We returned home on 28 December on a damp dark morning but with the temperature a little above zero for a change. The journey was murky all the way, but with little traffic we were home before 1.00 pm. So we had been fortunate and not badly affected by the weather that had caused so much havoc at the airports before Christmas.

On 4 January 2011, a Tuesday and the first SAS meeting of the New Year, I had a call just after noon from one of the volunteers at SAS to say they had "lost" Rita; should they call the police? At the end of the meeting she had apparently walked out without her coat, but carrying her bag of spare clothes, unnoticed by anyone. I said I would go straight over. Several of the volunteer staff had gone out to search and, more or less as I arrived, Mark returned with her. He had found her about half a mile away, walking determinedly towards the town centre, so as to meet me, she said! How she thought I would know what she had decided to do she couldn't explain.

Because the weather during December had been so cold and miserable, I saw no reason to prolong our stay in the UK and booked tickets back to South Africa on the earliest date I could, leaving Heathrow on 12 January.

32

13 January to 7 April 2011

12 More Weeks in South Africa

A few days before we left home, I had emailed the therapists and Fish Hoek Home Nursing so that we could slot straight back into the regime of therapy and care we had left in early December.

It was our third London to Cape Town flight together and was almost becoming a routine. Arrival in Cape Town was on time on 13 January. The usual taxi met us for the 45-minute drive to Noordhoek and home. Doreen arrived 40 minutes later to take charge of Rita while I unpacked and shopped. All efficient, easy and routine.

A few things needed to be put right. The "trip" on a lighting circuit refused to switch on, but that was down to a light bulb that had short-circuited. The broadband worked as soon as I had typed in a long code that appeared in a dialogue box on the "investigate the problem" menu. The carer next day told me that the vacuum cleaner had stopped working; this was put right by cleaning the HEPA filter.

We were immediately back in the regime of the previous autumn with Estie, OT, and Adele, physiotherapist, giving Rita weekly sessions. The weather could hardly have been more different from that we had left behind. The daily temperatures were in the upper twenties, the sun shone every day and the pool water was up to 30 °C, thanks to the solar heating. Rita settled so quickly that on the third day her blood pressure was the lowest since I had been measuring it, 128/80, though it did not stay as low as that. There was a lot of wind; we were told it was the windiest summer "for years" with seven gales during the first two weeks we were there, obviously all short-lived. The worst the wind did was dump leaves and sand into the pool – though I was concerned at how often I needed to top it up with fresh water. Was there a leak? Rain did not help to refill it, of course. The only rain during the first two weeks was just sufficient to wet the ground; after that there was none for two months.

So I gave myself a little project – to determine whether the pool system was leaking water. By inspection I could see the glass fibre pool itself was sound, no sign of a crack or loose joint. But maybe there was a leak in one of the several underground pipes that carried water between the pool, the pump, the chlorinator and the heating panels? There were several ways I could check for this, but having a preference for simple ideas I acquired a large shallow plastic container. This I put on the side of the pool, filled it to the brim with water, marked the surface level of the water in the pool and left things for three hot and windy days. After 72 hours, the water level in the container had gone down nearly 30 mm and, within 10%, the pool had gone down by the same amount. There was no leak, or if there was, the loss by evaporation greatly exceeded it. Knowing the surface area of the pool, a quick calculation showed that during hot windy weather, the pool was losing approximately 60 gallons of water by evaporation each day! Moreover, the heat needed to evaporate all this water had to be coming from the pool itself, tending to cool it.

So I purchased an inexpensive cover that floated on the surface and could be wound out of the way when swimming was planned. This did little to prevent sand and leaves getting in the water, but it reduced evaporation by 90% or more. It also meant that, during hot summer days, the water temperature reached 34 °C, at which point it was becoming uncomfortably warm and the heating was turned off.

By now Rita loved to swim but being in the pool emphasised her continuing poor sense of balance. During hydrotherapy classes, Adele worked on this with Rita sitting on flotation "noodles" to lift her feet off the bottom. She then had to balance herself using hands and arms and was very bad at it! She couldn't stop herself tipping over. In our own pool she was never out of her depth; at the deepest point the water hardly came up to her chin. But, despite having her feet on the bottom, Rita regularly "turned turtle". Her legs came to the surface, her head went under, there was much thrashing about and a need for a quick rescue. Rita didn't seem concerned by these episodes – but they worried me considerably. I quickly made the decision that Rita must never be left on her own in the house in case she took it into her head to go into the pool. There would be no one to provide a rescue service.

Interestingly, not one of the carers who came to us could swim. It was just not something they thought of doing although the sea was never more than a few miles away. We suggested they might like to learn, and one of the nurses said she would teach them, but they just gave an embarrassed smile and declined the offer.

Both Estie and Adele said how pleased they were with Rita's steady progress and the fact she had lost nothing during the six weeks in the cold UK over Christmas. The split of work between them was rather different from what pertained in the UK on the infrequent occasions when Rita saw OTs and physios there. During the six weeks at the end of 2008, when the OT had worked with Rita, she had concentrated on Rita's moving around the house, getting in and out of bed, for example, as well as simple household chores. Here in South Africa, that fell much more into Adele's field. Estie concentrated on two aspects of Rita's shortcomings – manual dexterity and cognitive dysfunction. As already mentioned, each week she brought exercises to improve Rita's ability to handle small objects, especially with her weaker left hand. In addition, she brought a variety of games involving memory, a surprisingly wide variety of them, that she showed Rita and the carers how to play, plus written homework for Rita to complete, rather reluctantly.

Adele continued to concentrate on a wide variety of exercises that involved balance, that having being identified as Rita's main difficulty. Adele's view remained that when Rita got her sense of balance back, everything else would fall into place, including posture, walking style and stamina. Her persistence eventually demonstrated she was correct in this diagnosis. A medicine ball was one of the most favoured accessories – there is so much you can do with a medicine ball. If Rita had difficulty with an exercise or was getting frustrated at her inability, Adele was astonishingly quick at picking up her mood and subtly modifying the exercise such that Rita *could* do it. Adele also made it clear to me, and whoever happened to be the carer that day, exactly what she was trying to achieve, and how to put right probable failings, so that we could do the exercises with Rita for the remaining six days of the week. This all worked very well and if we had particular problems with anything, we told Adele at her next weekly meeting, when she found ways round the problem. Adele was always greatly encouraging Rita, emphasising how well she was doing each time a small target was met. Possibly this was a bit OTT, but Rita liked it and, certainly, Adele regularly upgraded the difficulty of the exercises for the next week. In the swimming pool, Adele continued to concentrate on balancing exercises, which included walking with long strides forwards, sideways and backwards. But the main balancing exercise in the pool was still the use of a "noodle" to lift Rita's head above water and feet off the bottom, maintaining balance by just the use of her arms. Rita always found this extremely difficult and had not mastered it by the end of February. It seemed even more difficult when I tried to help her in Adele's absence! We never got anywhere near to having her balanced for more than a very few seconds.

Getting in and out of bed was one of those things that Rita found possible on some occasions, sometimes not. This fell into Adele's court. For two weekly sessions, Adele came to the house instead of us walking to the clinic and she quickly taught Rita a technique that worked for her. So, we had not been in South Africa many weeks before Rita was attending to her own needs during the night. I always woke, but only had to get out of bed when she couldn't find the bathroom light switch.

Adele changed tactics a little and began asking us what activities Rita found difficult or impossible. One was doing up her bra herself. I was amazed at how Adele had an answer for everything, it seemed, and, within a short time, Rita could manage her bras without asking for my help.

A major accomplishment was to get up from a prone position on the floor without assistance, something Rita had not even attempted to do for nearly three years. From lying on her back, flat on the floor, Adele first taught her how turn over and then use furniture to pull herself onto her feet again. Once she could do that – if not easily, at least successfully – the furniture was dispensed with. Now Rita had to lie on the floor, turn over and clamber back onto her feet without help, as though she had fallen in the middle of a field. This took a little longer, but became just as successful. The final technique settled on was rather slow, very inelegant, but always effective!

After a couple of weeks, I talked to Nurse Jenny about ending the daily use of desmopressin. We agreed to change to alternate nights only. The first night led to a wet bed the next morning, the first for several months. Nights 2 and 4, Rita had the regular dose and was up three times during the night, which was normal. On both nights 3 and 5, without desmopressin, she was up five times. I can cope with being disturbed up to three times, but five times was too many. I was losing too much sleep and Rita probably was too. So I stopped the experiment there.

On 18 January, Jenny had arrived to introduce a new carer, Nomvuyo. She spent half an hour with us to ensure that Nomvuyo understood how to help Rita carry out the household chores. As the other carers already knew, Rita should not be put under pressure but work at her own pace. Time was of no importance, even if the household tasks were not finished by the end of the carer's shift. That the jobs might not be completed worried the carers a lot to begin with and they needed reassurance from Jenny, their employer, that there would never be any criticism should jobs be left half-done when it was time to leave, just because Rita was being supervised and helped.

Rita's seventy-second birthday was on 20 January. Adele celebrated it by giving her a brand new list of exercises to learn.

Rita was really into her reading by this time. Towards the end of the first year following her stroke, when she began to show an interest in books once more, she held them upside down as often as not. So I had read to her for some months, then encouraged her to read to me. The next step was to read to herself. This led Rita to pick up my library book as often as her own and read from wherever I had left a bookmark, not realising it was a different story. It took me a while to understand why my bookmark was often in the wrong place! While we had been home over Christmas, she had begun to read well again. The month following our arrival back in Noordhoek, she had read *The Fort* (460 pages), *Fall of Giants* (850 pages) and was starting on *Wolf Hall*. Rita could remember very little of the stories, but was obviously immersed in the book while she was actually reading it.

The week in the middle of February saw our first visitors. Gary, Sheilagh and their three teenage boys arrived to spend the school half-term week with us, which was lovely. There were lots of things they wanted to pack in, so I had pre-booked several activities.

The first day, the boys, Gary and I boarded a small boat at Simon's Town and went deep-sea fishing off the Cape. The Peninsula is dramatic enough from land; from the sea it is even more spectacular and well worth the trip just to see that. The day was quite exceptional in that there was no wind and a flat sea. Barbecued, freshly caught snoek (which looks like barracuda) at home made a tasty meal. There were trips to the Cape of Good Hope, Cape Town, and horse riding on Noordhoek beach for Gary and the boys. We adults booked a minibus and guide for a conducted tour of the winelands around Stellenbosch and Franschhoek, leaving the boys in bed for the day and/or playing on their laptops. The most successful activity for our visitors (excluding Sheilagh) was learning to surf at Muizenberg where it was possible to rent the boards, wetsuits and an instructor. This occupied three half-days.

There was good evidence that Rita's strength was steadily improving. One place we liked to visit was the north end of the three-mile long Noordhoek Beach, where Chapman's Peak rises directly from the sand to around 950 feet. From the car park, a boardwalk descended gently to beach level, followed by a quarter-mile-long walk across the sand to the water's edge. The wheelchair would have been hopeless, the tyres much too narrow to be pushed over the sand when unladen, let alone with anyone sitting in it.

On our earlier visits in October, we sat and watched the sea from the car park. The first attempt to walk across the beach in November 2010 ended halfway when Rita gave up and wanted to sit on the sand, rather uncomfortably, to recover. Later, we did make it as far as the sea – Rita sat on the sand for five minutes every hundred yards or so to recover her strength, but then loved sitting on a rock and watching the huge breakers washing over the sand or breaking on the rocks. On 15 January, Rita walked to the sea's edge without a break for a rest, though the walk back to the car park was tiring, especially the last 200 yards up the boardwalk – that was a struggle. By early March, she was stronger and more confident, but it was not until 6 April, the day before we returned to the UK, that she completed the circuit to the sea and back to the car park with not a single stop for a rest.

An email arrived from our GP on 9 March to say that the manager of the Community Therapy Team, would be carrying out a reassessment on Rita following our return to the UK in early April, but a date had not yet been set. So that was a step forward following the recommendations from Dr Alison of UKRSTC.

Towards the end of March 2011, we were within a month of the third anniversary of Rita's haemorrhage. It seemed a good time to do a summary of Rita's history, beginning with her life-threatening stroke in April 2008, and to review what advances had been made and when and where had they happened. The details of this are in Appendix C.

One table of Appendix C shows aspects of Rita's behaviour as I saw them and how they changed with time. The second table has the 36 months broken down into periods (to the nearest month) when treatment did or did not take place.

By the time we flew back to the UK on 8 April 2011, I was feeling far happier than six months previously. Rita had improved markedly both physically and cognitively. Although she still needed looking after, she was physically much stronger, her balance was better, the incontinence was greatly improved. It was not completely cured but I felt that might happen before too long. Cognitively she was brighter, she could carry on a conversation again and provide useful help with housework and that without much supervision. Somewhere during the past few months, her irrational behaviour had faded away, without me realising it at the time, never to trouble us again – what a blessing that was!

On the downside, her short-to-medium-term memory remained troublesome, her sense of location was particularly poor and, when tired, she still had trouble finding her way around the holiday home, looking for an upstairs that didn't exist. On some occasions she was convinced there were visitors staying with us, usually family, and she had to be firmly dissuaded from laying extra places at the table. But I could live with those relatively minor difficulties.

I have commented several times on how successful the regime in Cape Town was for Rita's rehabilitation and how it was remarkably similar to that defined in the *National Stroke Strategy*, despite the South African therapists never having seen that document. The details of Rita's South African rehabilitation programme are explained in chapter 38, including my thoughts on why it worked so well. However, this programme did display one major difference not suggested in the *National Stroke Strategy*. This was the use of carers to provide therapy. In the UK, carers had never successfully helped Rita's rehabilitation. In South Africa there were two reasons why they could. Because the carers (untrained in any therapy provision) were with us for four hours every morning, they could watch the formal rehabilitation sessions and see the therapists at work. Secondly, the carers were also supervised and helped each week by the therapists. This made it possible for carers to provide useful therapy six days each week. This good idea made such a difference to the speed with which Rita recovered, large quantities of therapy being so necessary to get damaged brains working well once more. And in this way, the costs of providing therapy were reduced substantially, compared with using trained therapists to work with Rita every day.

33

April to October 2011

The Summer of 2011, Back Home in England

Although Rita had improved more during the past six months than in the whole of the previous 30, once we were back home I continued to employ carers to help her shower and dress in the mornings. The time taken for this was much reduced, often having her ready for breakfast in 15 to 20 minutes. She also continued to attend day care four times each week. No therapy was organised, but each day I gave Rita a session of exercises taken from a comprehensive list provided by Adele, before we left South Africa. Most days that the weather permitted, we went for a half-hour walk.

On 19 April, there was a review consultation with the GP. I wanted to discuss what might be done for Rita's quite badly swollen ankles. A change of medicine to control blood pressure was prescribed, changing to ramipril. The doctor was entirely happy with my records of Rita's blood pressure over the preceding two months. A week later, however, it had risen significantly and was typically in the range 165/90 to 195/105, so I emailed the doctor to notify him. He suggested doubling the dose of ramipril.

About this time, our son Duncan, for business reasons, was planning to take his family to live in Kuala Lumpur, Malaysia, for two to three years. He suggested Rita and I should live in their empty house, the thinking being that we could rent our house and so avoid leaving it empty during the winter months. This would also prevent his being left empty for parts of the year. It seemed a good idea. We had got away with leaving our house empty for one winter with nothing going seriously wrong, but it was risky to hope that would continue. So I looked around for a local letting agent who could look after things while we were abroad. We could not sort out any of the inevitable problems that would arise with tenants in an old house from South Africa. I found a competent letting company and set them on the task of finding suitable tenants.

By the middle of May, it was very pleasing to find that Rita was continuing to improve steadily, if rather slowly, despite having no regular physiotherapy or OT, other than the amateur therapy I was able to provide from watching how it had been done by Adele and Estie. Rita was becoming more interested in the routines of life and starting to become bored when she had nothing to do – another good sign. Her incontinence was so improved that we agreed that she should stop wearing continence pads during the day, just retain them for night use. This was a good move and it was 10 June before she had a slight "accident" and then there was not another one for a long time. Then, on 16 July, she stopped using pads during the night. Her incontinence was close to being vanquished. This was achieved, apparently, as a by-product from the six months of daily therapy she had had since the previous October.

The community nurse called in three times during the first ten or eleven weeks, was reasonably happy with Rita's progress, said we must keep a close check on her blood pressure, and took away some packs of spare pads that were now surplus to requirements. After 24 June, we did not see her again.

I received a message that arrangements had been made for Rita to be thoroughly assessed by a senior OT at a cottage hospital about 20 miles from our home. This meant three hour-long out-patient visits during the period 22 June to 7 July. I was very pleased for this to happen; the opportunity to have an authoritative opinion on Rita's status was valuable. I joined the first meeting for ten minutes but was soon banned from the room. Every time the OT asked a question, Rita turned to me for the answer. I was too much of a distraction so had to go. I asked for a copy of the OT's final report on Rita's condition which she was happy to promise, but, as usual, it took a lot of negotiating with the NHS to get hold of this. Then, on 2 August, an OT local to us arrived to start a new six-week programme, one session each week, based on the findings and suggestions from this earlier assessment. So, despite the prognosis a year earlier, it seemed the NHS was now willing to provide some therapy, but it was on a piecemeal basis rather than part of a full programme.

By early July, a young couple had been found to rent our home, terms were agreed and they would move in on 27 August. So we had a timescale for clearing out a huge accumulation of "stuff" and arranging to move into Duncan's and Susan's home. It was a real effort to meet the target date but, with help from the family, we made it.

A new physiotherapist had begun regular work at SAS to help members with their mobility. She was excellent and I employed her privately on several occasions to work with Rita for longer sessions than were possible at the charity's meetings. She made a very good suggestion – that Rita should take a course of Nordic Walking, in the expectation that this would help her balance, strength and mobility considerably. We located a Nordic Walking trainer, Jane, who was based in a village about eight miles from our home. Initially, Jane was wary of taking on Rita as a client. She was worried that she had no training for looking after disabled people and was understandably concerned what might happen if something went wrong. But I persuaded her to give it a try on the basis that any risk was entirely ours and that, if the attempt failed for any reason, there would be no come-back on her.

The experiment didn't fail. It was highly successful and we had eight weekly training sessions when I also learned the technique. The last session was on 5 October 2011, shortly before our return to Cape Town for their summer – South African style! Rita's walking improved noticeably, both in speed and stamina. She never completely mastered the correct technique for using the poles, which are not used as walking sticks, but they gave her a lot of confidence when, later, we were hiking along rough tracks in the mountains of the Cape Peninsula. Some time later, Jane joined the group of therapists working with SAS and gave weekly sessions on Nordic Walking techniques to those members who wanted to improve their mobility.

Having got our house up to the standard required for letting out – with a certificate covering the electrical installation, the oil-fired boiler checked, and a number of other requirements met, we moved to Duncan's house on 11 August. As it was only two months before we planned to go to Cape Town again, we retained the same day-care arrangements. This involved more driving and I cut the number of days to three each week. As Rita was improving steadily and now needed little help in showering and dressing, I decided to provide what help was needed myself and dispensed with carers coming in every morning. What a change from a year before!

We signed on at a surgery local to our new "home". The doctor suggested leaving out the morning oxybutynin pill and, once again, reducing the desmopressin to alternate days, so halving the dose of both medicines to see what happened. We found Rita needed the loo during the night up to four times some nights, notably those when no desmopressin had been taken. She also wet the bed occasionally, but as the Kylie sheets were still being used, the mattress was protected and, this time, we persevered with the reduced medicines.

Rita's progress continued. She was now walking up to two miles, using our newly purchased Nordic poles instead of borrowing Jane's. What was less satisfactory was that she occasionally went off for a walk by herself without telling me first, becoming lost once or twice, though not seriously as I could generally make a good guess at where she had headed off to. She was also playing games like Rummikub, Scrabble and our family card game, Estimation, with little help and winning her share of the games.

Seven and four months, respectively, before Rita had her stroke, I had had both hips replaced with metal-on-metal joints. Some time later, it transpired there was a design fault with this particular model of hip joint, leading to a product recall – somewhat difficult to activate. I needed a small operation on 11 October, under anaesthetic, to remove accumulated liquid from the joints, so Sue kindly came down from Birmingham to look after her mother, then drove us both back to her home for me to recuperate for a few days. Then, on Wednesday 19 October, we flew to Cape Town once more.

34

20 October 2011 to 27 April 2012

Six Months Away, South Africa and Malaysia

This second winter abroad, we planned to spend six months away from home, including Christmas in Fish Hoek with Sue and family joining us, a month in Kuala Lumpur with Duncan and family, followed by another 11or 12 weeks in South Africa. This was made easy by the fact that our home in England was let out and occupied so there was no need to worry about it.

The 6000-mile flight to Cape Town on 20 October was routine. Having given our neighbours strict instructions *not* to do any cleaning before our return, we arrived "home" in Noordhoek to find the house looking dusty, unused and with a good sprinkling of dead insects around the windows and on the floor beneath. But with help from the carers, Doreen and Welekazi, it was clean and tidy again in a couple of days. We dropped straight back into the routine we had left six months before, physiotherapist Adele recommencing therapy on 24 October, commenting on how Rita had continued to improve during the English summer, while Estie began her therapy again in mid November. Rita continued to make steady progress in every respect, even her memory was improving a little.

We began to be more adventurous with our days out, going to the less well-visited shoreline of the Cape Peninsula and to the summit of Table Mountain without support from a carer, on the basis we would be unlikely to run into trouble that we couldn't handle by ourselves. At the beginning of November, we were using the pool again and after a few hot days it had reached 32 °C on the 5th of the month. It was time to pay more attention to Rita's weight. This had reached 73 kg, having been 60 kg at the time of her stroke three-and-a-half years previously. Putting on weight is a common feature of stroke aftermath, a result of sudden lower levels of exercise and more opportunity to eat too much – this having become one of life's small pleasures. With nurse Jenny's help and Rita's disgust, a fairly gentle diet was set up. This eventually brought her weight down by 6 kg, but there it stuck. As, by then, Rita was much fitter and more active, we left it at that.

In the middle of December, Sue, partner Cass and the two girls arrived to spend three weeks with us over Christmas. The girls loved the pool and were in it every day. We took them round all the usual destinations and to our favourite eating establishments, though these were becoming busy as Christmas approached. It was odd to see the shops decorated for Christmas just as in the UK, with reindeers, Christmas trees, robins and snow-covered cards despite it being close to mid-summer. The nearest that most residents of Cape Town get to seeing snow is, occasionally, on the peaks of the mountains 20 miles or more to the north-east and at the opposite end of the year to 25 December. The favourite way to celebrate Christmas Day was a braai (barbecue) on the beach. We barbecued ostrich steaks instead of turkey and cooked them in the garden using our braai with its built-in chimney.

Two days later we were lucky to see a whale with a baby off the beach at Scarborough. They have usually all gone by the end of November, on their journey back to the Antarctic. The mother and baby were swimming slowly north, just out from the rocky shore, so we were able to follow them for 20 minutes along the coast road. Four days later, we found our way to what remained of the wreck of the SS Thomas T Tucker (a second world war Liberty ship which lost her way on her maiden voyage, hitting the rocks off Oliphantsbos Point in a fog in 1942). It involved a mile walking there and back over soft sand. Rita managed this better than I had expected. Another unexpected sight – in Oliphantsbos Bay about six fur seals and several hundred cormorants got together, quite suddenly, and proceeded to drive a shoal of fish onto the beach. Fish the size of sardines were leaping out of the water onto the sand in terror, causing Sue to run back and forth throwing them back into the water. This probably did not help them greatly. There was a feeding frenzy for some ten minutes before everything quietened down.

Our visitors left on 3 January and, four days later, Saturday, again on Scarborough beach, I was bitten on the chest in an entirely unprovoked attack by a large boxer dog, drawing blood and ruining a nice shirt! I rang FHHN to ask advice and the duty nurse was able to tell me the name of the surgery duty doctor at the weekend. Half an hour later I was being treated. The doctor cleaned the wound, pressed a brown paste into it and taped it up. I don't remember ever having a wound heal so quickly.

Soon after, on 11 January, Rita and I left on the long two-plane flight to Kuala Lumpur, capital of Malaysia, to spend four weeks with Duncan and family. We left our home mid-afternoon and arrived at apartment number AA-33A-01 just before midnight the following day, local time – a long journey. This new home of theirs was on the thirty-fourth floor of a tower block, one of a pair. There were amazing views – and it was better not to suffer from vertigo when using the large balcony, with a drop over the waist-high railing vertically down for about 300 feet. Each floor was served by three high-speed lifts, plus a service lift designed for furniture and other heavy goods. The bottom four floors of the complex consisted of service areas, car parks, sports halls and shops. On top of the fourth floor there were gardens, leisure areas for residents, a football pitch and two swimming pools. One pool was 50 metres in length and there wasn't quite room for it, so the end 12 metres or so were cantilevered out from the building, 20 metres or more above the street below. All of it was amazing.

We visited the Genting Highlands leisure centre, mainly for our 11-year-old grandson to try out "sky flying" on top of a fast-moving column of air provided by a vertically mounted jet engine. This allowed anyone willing, and if good enough, to balance on top of the air column and turn somersaults and other acrobatic movements. Callum succeeded in balancing, face down, on top of the column of air and move around by adjusting his arm positions, without losing control too often. There was a day visit to the ancient city of Malacca, which was much too hot and humid for me, but fascinating to see. Plus a weekend to Kuantan on the east coast, where Duncan wanted to begin to learn the rather difficult and potentially dangerous sport of kitesurfing.

Rita and I spent several days in central Kuala Lumpur, visiting the gigantic shopping mall under the Petronas Towers, ascending the Menara Tower, at the time the fourth highest telecom tower in the world. We visited the Orchid Garden, a Muslim museum and spent a lot of time exploring the large Central Market, mainly occupied by Chinese stalls. While we were in Malaysia, the Chinese New Year was approaching so there were lots of fantastic rhythmic drum music, lion dancing and long colourful dragons weaving their way along the streets and calling in on all the shops to bring them luck. Rita was fascinated by all these new experiences and I am sure this helped with her cognitive difficulties.

During the middle of the holiday, we spent a long weekend in Cambodia, making the two-hour flight to the city of Siem Reap at the north end of the 200-mile-long lake near the centre of the country, arriving close to midday. This left time for a tour of Siem Reap by tuk-tuk during the afternoon and an excellent meal at the Sugar Palm restaurant.

Two tuk-tuks were booked for the four days in Siem Reap, chosen for its closeness to many of the temples built close to 1000 years ago, notably Angkor Wat. We visited five, I think (most of the time with me drenched in sweat), all surprisingly different from each other, but Angkor Wat was outstanding and the "must see" one. We set off from the hotel at 9.00 am on the second full day, but by the time we arrived at Angkor Wat there were already thousands of visitors there. What an amazing place! Huge, both in area covered and height, with seemingly miles of beautiful and intricate carvings along the walls, surrounded by a hand-dug rectangular lake, possibly six miles long and 200 yards wide.

On the third day, the others hired a car to drive 60 miles to another temple that involved a lot of scrambling. Rita and I ducked out of that and decided to visit the village-on-stilts, Kompong Phluk, an hour's tuk-tuk ride to the other side of Siem Reap.

This was the "low" season for the water level in the lake and the last seven miles were over a flat plain, steadily becoming wetter, alongside a muddy canal. Eventually things were so wet we could drive no further and boarded a wooden boat that followed others down the canal towards the lake. The boat ahead was much larger than ours and was having difficulty getting through the mud. It suddenly gunned its engines to force a way through and covered the bows of our boat and the boatman – plus the front two passengers – with muddy water. Our boatman was straight onto his cell phone with a lot of shouting and arm waving at the culprit, but all he achieved was to let off a bit of steam.

The visit was again amazing, boating around hundreds of houses supported 10 to 15 feet above the water level on bamboo stilts. There were small, smartly dressed schoolchildren confidently paddling wooden boats that looked far too big for them; and we passed a floating pigsty that looked like any other to be seen on land – except it wasn't. A low dry mound was at the centre of the village, which explained why it was located at that part of the lake. At the highest point of this mound was a Buddhist temple built on top of high foundations of stone. Most of the short streets of sun-baked mud leading from this were largely covered by mats of shrimps drying in the sun, there being no vehicles to demand use of the "roadway". The shrimps were apparently the main export from the village.

Two or three schoolteachers were asking visitors to help the village school by buying pencils and notepads for the children to use. We bought a bundle and immediately a line of small, polite children queued up by Rita. They happily accepted these small gifts from her, the unlucky ones then running off to find the next visitor who might have something for them. Later, lunch was served in a sort of cafeteria on a floating platform.

Our driver gave us lots of information; his English vocabulary was big, but his accent difficult to understand, especially from the back of a tuk-tuk. Anyway, we gathered that he spent most evenings helping at a school for young children, as the education provided by the government was somewhat limited. Would we like to visit the school? Yes, we would. So he picked us up again that evening. There were several classes, for different ages, on open ground around an anonymous building to which a roof, of sorts, was attached to protect the children from rain. The children were active and noisy and had obviously come voluntarily to their second school of the day. I suppose I should have seen it coming, but suddenly I found myself introduced as "The new English teacher for this evening" and given the floor for 40 minutes. I made a pretty poor fist of it, not being a teacher and having done no preparation, but no one complained. The two impressions Rita and I went away with were of happy children who were keen to learn. That evening, our youngest grandchild, then just 3 years and 1 month, demonstrated her ability to count from 1 to 7 in Mandarin, Malay, English and Spanish.

On the fourth full day, Rita and I revisited the remarkable Bayon temple before meeting the others at the Elephant Gate and walking around the temple of the Leper King. Then it was back to the Bayon Gate where Duncan took his children for a ride on an elephant, followed by an evening meal at a restaurant that, during the meal, gave an apparently exciting shadow-puppet show that was completely lost on us, but loudly applauded by locals.

So back to Kuala Lumpur after a truly memorable short visit to, in many ways, a very beautiful country. One of the best outcomes was that Rita had been so excited by all the new experiences. Her incontinence had not been too much trouble – a few accidents, mainly during the night, plus a memorable one during the day when she became stuck on a hole-in-the-floor toilet and had to be rescued. It had been well worthwhile taking the risk of visiting Cambodia.

We had two more weeks in Malaysia which, after Cambodia, seemed quite cool and fresh. Then the two long flights back to Cape Town, arriving on 9 February. Two days later, I went down with a bad head cold, no doubt picked up on one of the planes between Kuala Lumpur and Cape Town. Rita seemed fit enough to avoid it. Apart from that, we were straight back into the usual routine of daily carers, weekly therapists and regular outings, mostly to locations on the Peninsula.

Towards the end of the month, Rita's ankles were swelling more noticeably, so I fixed a doctor's appointment for Monday 27 February. He gave Rita a thorough check-up and wanted to know exactly what medicines she was taking and their strength. He said the problem was probably with the amlodipine. It would be better if Rita took it before going to bed at night rather than in the morning, and put her feet up whenever she was sitting at home. These simple suggestions made things much better.

Following all the exercise we had enjoyed in Malaysia, we became ever more adventurous with our outings, walking further and no longer taking carers with us as an insurance. The Nordic walking poles gave Rita a lot of confidence on the mostly uneven paths that criss-crossed the national park areas of the Peninsula. One day, we climbed a rough path to the plateau below Elsie's Peak, at the south end of Fish Hoek Bay, with views over the beach and town towards Kalk Bay and on to the Cape Flats. One end of the beach that extends the full length of the north end of False Bay, east from Muizenberg, was just visible.

On 17 April, ten days before returning home, we drove to the Silvermine Reservoir where we followed a track that climbed another thousand feet or so, close to Noordhoek Peak, with extensive views over the valley to Kommetjie, about five miles away in the distance. We didn't quite reach the Peak, the last hundred yards were a steep scramble over broken rocks that, together with a gale blowing over the top, defeated us. We made a circular walk of it, continuing north-east and so enjoying dramatic views first over Hout Bay, then a mile further on over the Cape Flats to the Hottentots Holland Mountains, 20 miles to the east, and back to the car, a total of five miles and an amazing achievement for Rita compared with the little she had been capable of 18 months earlier.

At the last session with Adele, she gave us a long list of exercises for Rita to work on during the summer in the UK. We arrived back home again – Duncan's and Susan's home – on 27 April.

35

May 2012 to April 2013 and beyond

A Year and More of Steady Progress

The rehabilitation programme, originally organised by Nurse Jenny in October 2010, changed little for the following three years. This enabled us to get out lives together once more so that chapter 28 to this one represents more a description of how steadily Rita progressed, and less about any changes to her successful treatment regime because there were almost none. Perhaps the main one was a change of occupational therapist in October of 2012, after the summer in England, described later.

It rained throughout the first day back home in England, 28 April. No matter. There was unpacking plus cleaning to be done, and we were pretty tired after a night with little sleep on the plane. Having been away for roughly six months, we had terrible trouble remembering where things were kept or even how the central heating worked. The weather wasn't great and within a week of returning we both had colds. I was stressed by the accumulated paperwork of six months that needed my attention. Rita's routines were upset and she had trouble both cognitively and with occasional continence accidents, but these troubles did not last long.

On the positive side, Rita re-joined the SAS swimming group and Betty quickly had her swimming the breaststroke again, something I had failed to achieve while in South Africa. We enjoyed a weekend with Sue in Birmingham, Rita was ironing clothes to a good standard without supervision and we managed walks of up to three miles.

There was now no need for carers to help Rita shower and dress, she could manage most of her needs herself, getting stuck only occasionally and asking for a little help. I no longer needed time to myself while she was at a day-care centre – nor did she want to go to one – so that previously vital form of help was abandoned. Rita was able to complete, herself, much of the housework and food preparation. We went on days out, visited friends, had friends round for dinner and generally behaved like retired folk with no great demands on our time. Duncan returned from Kuala Lumpur for a couple of weeks at the end of June to spend some time at his factory and was on good form with things going well. He was making progress in his attempts to set up representation in China and Japan, and was beginning to make good sales to Australia.

I was beginning to think about how Rita's and my experiences of recovery from stroke might possibly assist other disabled stroke survivors. Perhaps I should publicise the story of how Rita's recovery had been achieved, even write a book based on the daily journal I had maintained from mid-May 2008? I contacted a few people and received a charming letter from Sir Alan Haselhurst with some helpful suggestions.

Rita was vastly better than she had been just a year earlier, but was still some distance from a full recovery, though I was confident enough to believe this was where we should now be aiming, against all previous expectations! During this summer of 2012, we were effectively marking time until our next winter in Fish Hoek when we would try to push the therapy to its limits. Rita was doing Adele's exercises, if not assiduously, at least from time to time. We were getting plenty of exercise by walking most days. Rita's irrational behaviour had certainly vanished – what a relief – and she still seemed to be making slow progress with the remaining disabilities, rather than regressing, as had happened during the first two years when professional therapy ceased.

On 9 July we drove to a BUPA hospital north of Cambridge for a health check for elderly people. This is something we have done every three years since I was 65. At that time neither of us had needed to see a doctor for anything even marginally worrying for decades, so I thought it might be sensible at that landmark in life for an MOT, so to speak. It was at that health-check that I discovered I had the early stages of malignant prostrate cancer, despite no symptoms being evident. Because it was found early, it has been completely cured so ever since I have considered a regular check-up should be included among my short list of good ideas. After a pretty thorough series of tests this time, I was told I was slightly overweight and had rather high cholesterol (which I have always had). Rita was found to be physically very good with no problems apart from the swollen ankles and a suspicion of a heart murmur. That was later ruled out, after further checks.

In mid-July, we flew to central France to visit Gary and Sheilagh where they were well settled in a house up in the hills of the Auvergne. They are both fluent French speakers and made my feeble attempts at the language appear (as it was) ineffective and embarrassing. Nevertheless, we enjoyed a lovely week in beautiful countryside. This visit we saw a great deal of Sheilagh as she was generous with the use of her car and time. The area is very hilly and walks from the house tended to tire Rita quickly, such that she needed to sit down and rest frequently. On one occasion, she sat on a convenient mound that turned out to be an anthill; that made her hop about for a while.

On 19 July, back home, I rang Rita's bank to enquire whether a cheque she had been expecting had been paid in. Despite my having Power of Attorney over Rita's financial affairs (of which the bank had a record) they would not answer this simple question because I did not have an account with them and because Rita, naturally, could not remember her "memorable date". They suggested the simplest thing would be for me to open an account with them. I said it was simpler to move Rita's account elsewhere.

The rest of July and all of August were spent either quietly at home, or visiting friends for a few days, or having relations visit us. We must have spent much time dodging rain as the night of 30 August was reported, the next day, as having been the coldest August night in some parts of the country since records began, and the summer so far had been the wettest for more than 100 years.

We paid a short and rare visit to our rented-out house to pick up some fruit from the garden. The tenants were looking after the house well, but the garden – most of it still our responsibility and looked after by a gardener – had an untended appearance and the outhouses were in need of considerable work in the "maintenance" category. Also, a vehicle had knocked over part of the front wall a few days previously; our tenant couldn't identify who had been the culprit. We were discovering some of the downsides of renting out our home.

Rita continued to join the weekly swimming sessions with SAS and was doing well – up to six 25-metre lengths without putting her feet down. I had a couple of chats with two of the long standing SAS volunteers on ways in which it might be possible to organise rehabilitation therapy for some of the charity's members. They later emailed me to confirm that, in more than five years, neither had ever met a stroke survivor who had been given what could be described as a formal in-community rehabilitation programme, such as is described by the *National Stroke Strategy*. The, then, chairperson of SAS told me she thought she might be able to find a source of funding to run three-month personal rehabilitation programmes for a number of the members. These would be carefully assessed and recorded to measure quantitatively, so far as possible, any progress made and whether it could be justified financially. This was a great idea and I was fully in agreement, on the basis that Rita was doing so well that a similar regime needed to be given to others as a pilot scheme. I wrote a letter to the Department of Health and drafted a *Guide to Home Rehabilitation*, based on our own experiences, of course. Unfortunately, the idea failed on this occasion. It seemed that the funding was harder to obtain than had been hoped. The chairperson came to the end of her three-year stint, another chairman took over and it needed a new start.

On Wednesday 12 September, a manager from Headway visited us, at my suggestion, to discuss whether carers should be given more help and, if so, how it might be done – and whether Headway could play a part. He said that he, plus all the local Headway management, had agreed with everything I had written to them on this subject, but that there were all sorts of difficulties that he listed for me. That didn't alter the fact that, as a generalisation, carers did need far more help than they were given, in our locality anyway. It was evident to me that the difficulties he listed didn't seem to apply in South Africa! This seemed to be a discussion that needed to continue.

On Thursday 20 September, we left home once more, heading by taxi to Heathrow Terminal 5. There was a huge and slow queue for the security check, but with Rita in her wheelchair and "passenger assistance" activated, we jumped that queue of at least 100 persons in various states of boredom or agitation. We were then subjected to the most thorough going-over with X-rays and "sniffers". The flight was routine. We were, of course, last off the plane as part of a small group of disabled passengers, but again jumped the queue in immigration and were in the arrivals hall at Cape

Town airport by 7.50 am on Friday, where we were met by Adrienne with her taxi. It rained all the way to Noordhoek and for most of the afternoon. This seemed par for the course on our arrivals in the country. At home, we found the hot water switched on, there was a lovely yellow Clivia plant on the table addressed to Rita, and our neighbours Monika and Dickie had, again, clearly been all over the house with a vacuum cleaner, so breaking all the instructions given in advance concerning "no cleaning".

It needed a couple of nights for us both to recover from the journey and we stayed near to home, on the Sunday walking the length of the Longbeach shopping mall and having a coffee at the Mugg & Bean before returning to Pick n Pay for a further stock of food. It was as we exited the shop with bags of provisions that we realised Rita no longer had her handbag over her shoulder. It must have been left, on the floor by the table, at the Mugg & Bean some 45 minutes earlier. Fortunately, it had been found and handed in, so was recovered intact. There had been several adventures with that handbag being forgotten in a variety of locations. Rita's memory wasn't up to thinking about it when we left a restaurant or café and I did try hard, but could never train myself to think "handbag?" when we left anywhere. Nonetheless, it is still with us four years later, after several more misadventures.

Although Rita could get herself up in the mornings with little help, I decided to retain the services of the Fish Hoek Home Nursing carers for four hours each morning, but five days each week instead of seven, beginning the Monday after our return, with Fundiswa arriving at 7.30 am. There were several reasons for retaining the carer support, despite it not being strictly necessary. One was that they were excellent carers. The fact that they were with us for four hours each day gave me time to myself that I did still find to be of value. More importantly, the carers could help Rita with the exercises that Adele would shortly be giving her again, as well as with the household chores once more, meeting the additional benefit of keeping the house very clean. Our membership of FHHN also gave us immediate access to the expertise of the five nurses, should that ever be necessary. Rita was so keen to get herself up that she was already showered and dressed by the time Fundiswa arrived at 7.30 on the Tuesday.

Before we returned to South Africa, I had emailed Estie to ask if she could continue to give Rita the occupational therapy as before. She apologised, but said that her diary was so filled with demands made by disabled children that she was unable to find time for Rita on a regular basis. Once we were back in Noordhoek, I didn't anticipate too much trouble finding another OT to replace Estie's good work, so left it until then.

The Tuesday of the first week, we walked to Adele's clinic where she began by re-assessing Rita's status after the six months back in the UK. Her conclusion was that Rita had made substantial progress, both physically and cognitively. One of the tests involved Adele walking beside Rita and trying gently to push her over. She eventually pushed quite hard but Rita stayed upright without difficulty. Adele was impressed and decided on a revised programme of exercise that included two sessions of hydrotherapy each week. She also promised to speak to a good occupational therapist she knew who might be able to take Rita on as a client.

The following Thursday, we sent Fundiswa home early (they never lost out on the agreed daily wage when we did that) and drove to the Kirstenbosch Gardens. We walked up to the tearoom for lunch. Rita chose a huge Thai calamari salad while I had a beef bobotie. We then walked to the top of the gardens where the proteas were in full bloom and the Ericas had many sunbirds after the nectar, up to six could be seen at a time. Rita walked at a fair speed up the long slopes and short flights of steps. What a difference from our first visit there. We drove home via Chapman's Peak Drive and it began raining steadily as we drove into Noordhoek. This was a pity as we had left washing out.

Despite quite regular rain showers they were, as usual, short-lived. We were soon back to walks along Noordhoek Beach, in the Silvermine Valley and along the Fish Hoek seafront. The swimming pool had already reached 27 °C with help from the solar panels and this was warm enough to start hydrotherapy exercises at home again. Things were looking good for the summer.

On the 27th, just a week after returning to South Africa, we met the new occupational therapist, Shona, at Adele's clinic for a preliminary chat and for Shona to learn something of Rita's background. We got on well and settled on 4 October for a first OT session at Shona's home-based clinic in Fish Hoek, about a mile's drive from our home. This was largely a learning session for Shona to decide on the approach she would take to help Rita. This turned into a routine with some similarities to Estie's system, but many differences too.

The following Sunday, we enjoyed a two-course roast lunch at the pub in Kommetjie, then drove to the surfing centre where there were around 40 heads bobbing in the water, looking for waves. Unusually, a whale began breaching about 400 yards out from the shore. I think it was a humpback. We watched it leap from the water 12 to 15 times before it swam out of the bay. Because rain had been forecast, I had left my camera at home!

Shona was quickly into her stride with Rita's therapy regime. Sessions often began with a huge piece of plain paper taped to the table and Rita was instructed to draw large figures of eight, on their side, with a crayon in her right hand. She was then told to repeat the drawing on top of the first with a different coloured crayon in her left hand. Then she had to hold a third crayon in both hands and draw over the figures already there. Rita hated doing it. "What are we doing this stupid drawing again for?" she demanded to know but, after a few weeks, it was clearly improving her manual dexterity and control. Several new games were introduced, some manual, some cognitive, and Shona loaned us the games between sessions for Rita and the carers to play.

We were introduced to "balance blocks". These were bright blue foamed plastic, very "squidgy", about 16 by 12 inches in size and 3 inches deep. Rita had to stand on one with her shoes off and maintain her balance, which, of course, she was unable to do. I tried it and found I had to concentrate all the time on staying upright as the plastic moved under my feet and needed constant correction to maintain balance; and I still have very good balance, having been a gymnast in my much younger days. So Rita was taught to walk across the block, just placing one foot on the block as she passed across it, which was much easier to do. Shona persevered with this and it wasn't many weeks before Rita was standing on the block without support. Immediately the exercise was made more difficult – Rita now had to stand on the block and play "catch" with a tennis ball. I bought two of the blocks, one to keep in our home in South Africa and one to bring back to the UK. We still use them from time to time.

Another advance arose after I told Shona that, although Rita could do most household chores herself now, they were done very slowly. She always fed herself too, but took 50% longer than I did to finish a meal, whereas before her stroke we used to eat at the same speed. "Do you like table tennis?" Shona asked, which seemed a bit of a non-sequitur to me. Yes, we were both able to play. So, for the next two weeks, we spent part of the OT sessions playing table tennis in Shona's garage, though it was much more like slow ping-pong. Shona explained that, obviously, to play the game well you needed quick reactions. If Rita persevered and played regularly, her reactions would speed up and this would read across to everything else she did. Really – was that so?

Anyway, I believed Shona and we made our way to the Sportsmans Warehouse in Tokai, the other side of the mountains. A helpful assistant demonstrated all the tables they had in stock and we selected a full-size folding model, to be delivered the following week. The two delivery men assembled the table and levelled it, nicely positioned in the empty side of our generously sized double garage. And away we went. None of the carers had played before, but they were keen to learn and were delighted to be paid while playing ping-pong with Rita. I was able to push Rita much harder and we developed to really quite a good standard considering our ages and the fact of Rita's stroke. Just picking the ball from the floor two or three times every minute throughout the game was good exercise too!

It wasn't many weeks before Shona was proved right. Rita was eating at the same speed as I did once again and all her work within the house was completed more quickly. Back home in the UK, table tennis was sometimes played at SAS meetings, where Rita gained the name of "Ruthless Rita" because other members found her so difficult to beat.

As well as allowing us to borrow her games, Shona lent me books about stroke, rehabilitation and the effects of brain damage she thought would interest me. A book by Daniel Amen was largely concerned with exercises for stroke survivors. I noted that out of 20 possible exercises he put table tennis as the best. I thought cycling probably should have been number one, but he ruled that out because of the potential danger of being hit by another vehicle, the benefit gained from cycling being outweighed by this dangerous possibility.

Another book was *My Stroke of Insight* by Jill Bolte Taylor, PhD. She was a brain scientist doing university research, and in her late thirties, when she suffered exactly the same type of stroke as had hit Rita, a subarachnoid haemorrhage. Jill knew precisely what was happening to her and her description of it and the after-effects were fascinating for me to read. Although the type of stroke was the same, the effects caused by the bleeds into their respective brains were in some aspects very different, in others similar. Jill could remember all about the event, Rita could remember nothing for a long time, both before and after. Both suffered a complete loss of motivation to get better. The physical disabilities they each suffered were markedly different. This all emphasised the vital importance of treating every stroke survivor as an individual, assessing their individual

216

mix of disabilities and setting up a programme that was specific to those. To assume that, so far as strokes were concerned, one treatment would fit all could so easily have been the kiss of death, metaphorically speaking, and might be so literally.

The book that, for me, really brought a spotlight onto the subject was *The Brain that Changes Itself* by Norman Doidge. Rita and I had been told by many professionals that parts of her brain had been killed by the stroke and could never be regained. But if that was the whole story, how did some people recover from a severe stroke – because they most certainly did do so and there were plenty of validated examples. This book explained how it happened, to *my* complete satisfaction anyway. I have seen criticisms of Doidge's ideas, but for me what he claimed fitted so perfectly with how Rita made her recovery that I was convinced he was right. The details might be more complicated than he suggests. The brain is such a complex organ, it would be surprising if that were not so. But the idea was simple, plausible, and fitted other observations made on healthy people. The technique was simple to apply (Rita's South African programme was, basically, very straightforward), but a lot of work and commitment was needed. It all fitted together so well that I could not see a serious flaw. This is all discussed in more detail in Part 3 – <u>Why</u> *Rita was able to get better.*

On 25 October, I had a phone conversation with the press office of the Stroke Association, in the UK, concerning their suggestion that Rita and I might be interviewed by *The Times* newspaper concerning the experiences of a "real" couple who had had to cope with the after-effects of a bad stroke, in comparison with how it was depicted in the new film "Amour". We agreed to be available at 3.00 pm, our time, the next day. Right on the dot at 3.00 pm, Eva Simpson from *The Times* called us via Skype. We talked about our experiences and answered a good many questions. The interview lasted 75 minutes. At the end, Eva said she would certainly be using our story. It was later published as a two-page spread, combined with a review of "Amour" in *The Times* of 15 January 2013.

On 20 October, my sister Jen phoned with bad news; her husband Leslie had died that morning, nominally from an infection he couldn't shake off, but really because he had been fighting Alzheimer's for many years and had at last succumbed to that dreadful disease. He and I had been at university together during the late 1950s which was how he and Jen met. He was a delightful man. But we decided not to return to the UK for his funeral. On that day, 29 October, we drove to Kirstenbosch Gardens again and at the time of the funeral, 2.00 pm our time, we sat on a bench above the gardens and flowering trees, looking out over the Cape Flats with the Hottentots Holland Mountains far in the distance, with our own thoughts.

We only just averted a disaster on 7 November. At 10.00 pm, just before going to bed, there was a sudden noise of rushing water from the kitchen. I did a bit of rushing myself, found the kitchen flooded, with water pouring from beneath the dishwasher. Luckily, the isolation valve was sited on the wall above so was quickly turned off. That taught me to close the valve whenever we were not actually using the machine. One end of the hose (that I had never inspected) had obviously pulled off. Despite getting the water turned off less than 30 seconds after the leak began, it took us 40 minutes to dry the kitchen floor. Had it happened while we were out, or in bed, it could easily have flooded the whole of the ground floor. Our handyman, Stanley, fixed it permanently two days later.

On 10 November, Rita made probably her most difficult walk yet. From the Silvermine Reservoir, we climbed the long hill to the north, at the top turning right to follow a contour path around a small amphitheatre to reach the fire look-out post overseeing the whole of the Constantia Valley with a fine view across the Flats to the Hottentots Holland Mountains, and even the full length of False Bay to the Hangklip headland to the southeast. The Elephant's Eye Cave was just above us. I scrambled to it and found it hard going. Rita rested till my return.

I had sent a copy of my *Guide to Home Rehabilitation* to the Stroke Association and there was a reply from the Press Office with an attachment from the Stroke Services Director. She was impressed by what we had achieved, but seemed rather defeatist, I thought (for a Stroke Association Director), in her views on the problems of achieving something similar in the UK.

On Wednesday 14 November, we enjoyed the usual good lunch at the Imhoff Farm "Blue Water Café" then drove the short distance to Klein Slangkop (Small Snake's Head) for a walk down Long Beach. The tide was as high as we had ever seen it, with waves washing at high speed, just a few inches deep, across huge areas of sand to the bottom of the dunes. I found it disconcerting to have water rushing fast past my feet, quite contrary to the fact that I was actually standing still. I was amazed that Rita managed to stay upright throughout this experience. Her sense of balance must have improved hugely. We both thoroughly enjoyed the experience.

Monday 19 November marked an important occasion. We had decided that Rita was fully mobile herself – the wheelchair was now redundant. So, after a little research, we drove round to the entrance of the nearby Masiphumelele township (where most of our carers lived) and donated the chair to the Sinethemba charity that worked with children with special needs.

We were invited for afternoon tea by the couple from whom we had bought our house, to view the excellent job John had done of refurbishing the dilapidated bungalow they had purchased as the "worst house in Fish Hoek". We had met them occasionally at services in the Fish Hoek Methodist church. It was a remarkably good conversion that they were rightly proud of.

Wednesday 21 November was a typical day at home. Thobeka took Rita for a 40-minute walk while I touched up some interior decoration with the white paint universally used for the internal decoration. Rita and Thobeka completed some more of the jigsaw that was on the go on the stoep table, hung out the washing, made coffee, did the scheduled exercises and played table tennis. I planned the menus for the next few days, wrote a shopping list and, when Thobeka left at 11.30, we drove to Rodgers grocers for a few giant avocados and a water melon, then on to Food Lovers Market for more fruit and veg. After lunch (of avocado) we had a swim as it was cloudlessly sunny, then rested. I cooked dinner at 4.30 pm as we had decided to go to Fish Hoek library for a talk by two of South Africa's crime writers, Joanne Hichens and Sarah Lotz. This should have been advertised as 6.00 for 6.30 as there were nibbles and wine first, but the talk and discussion were interesting, something a bit different. We were home by 8.30 pm.

Life continued uneventfully but quite busily for the next three weeks. On 10 December, we packed most of the things we needed in the UK, sorted out all that needed doing to put the house "to bed" and were picked up by Adrienne late in the afternoon on the following day. The flight was full, landed at Heathrow on time – then we had to wait for 50 minutes before a gate became free. The temperature outside was -4 °C and planes were late leaving because their wings had to be de-iced. The drive home was quick, what we saw of it between falling asleep, and all was well at Duncan's home. We soon had it warm again. Duncan had told us they would be returning from Kuala Lumpur sometime during the early summer and could we vacate their cottage by the end of May? The next day I called on our tenants to see how they were fixed. In fact, they said they were ready to move on in the spring and it would suit them to vacate our house by the end of April, so that seemed to work out very smoothly and we gave them the agreed three months' notice.

We had returned home just in time for the SAS biannual fund-raising carol concert, on Thursday 13 December, in the same church as two years before, again with nearly 600 in the congregation. Members from SAS had been invited to read all the lessons. We were escorted to the front row as Rita had been allocated the first lesson (a rather difficult one from Micah that she had been practising). The choir from Clare College, Cambridge, opened the service. Rita then climbed the 15 or so steps to the pulpit and read the lesson loudly and perfectly, without fault. I was so proud of her. Afterwards she received many congratulations that were a big boost to her confidence.

My journal mentions rain almost every day over the Christmas holiday. This restricted our ability to walk, both when and where, without getting unpleasantly wet and/or muddy. On Christmas Eve, we drove to Birmingham to spend a few days with Sue, Cass and the girls and a very pleasant time it was too, much good food and indoor games. Sue settled on a dehumidifier for her present from us as their house was turning out to be suffering from damp during the persistently poor weather. It was a good choice as it removed amazing quantities of water from the air which, Sue said, felt much drier. She was sure it had cut their heating bill too, not having to heat a lot of damp air. We drove down to our friends Ian and Mary near Oxford on the 29th through constant rain, but there was little traffic. We had a happy New Year celebration there and re-acquainted ourselves with most of their family. We returned home on 1 January on dry roads.

Life was returning to normal. Rita enjoyed herself, was not troubled by any of the journeys, didn't miss the wheelchair and was keen to help with any household chores and meal preparation that were being done. It was a remarkable change from only two years before when her chances of recovery from full-time care appeared remote.

In early January, the weather turned colder and the rain to snow or slush, so it was even more difficult to get our regular exercise. I had booked flights back to Cape Town on 20 January, Rita's seventy-fourth birthday. It snowed all day. Luckily, the roads were free of hold-ups going west on the

M25 (not so good in the other direction) and the traffic moved steadily, so the journey took us just 45 minutes longer than usual. The plane was late leaving – de-icing again on the schedule – but made up some time and was just half an hour late into Cape Town where it was 27 °C and sunny. Lovely!

We had an established routine by now, of course, and slotted back into it; with carers from Monday to Friday – not weekends – and weekly sessions held with Adele and Shona. Adele decided to add vibrator exercises to help Rita's blood circulation and nerve response. Rita found it helpful and seemed more lively and active, though she was also finding the sunny days and warm swimming pool (comfortably over 30 °C) much to her liking.

Sunday 3 February was warm but cloudy. After accepting a lift from our neighbours to attend the early service at the Methodist church, we decided to take a walk from the reservoir in the upper Silvermine Valley. Many cars were already parked there. We took the track leading towards Noordhoek Ridge, keeping a good lookout for mountain bikes coming downhill towards us at speeds over loose shingle that would prevent them stopping within about 50 yards unless they adopted the tactic of falling off first. There was an obligatory anticlockwise one-way system for cycling maniacs and we were facing them while they made the most of a high-speed downhill run after a long pull to the top. We had not intended to head for Noordhoek Peak, but Rita wanted to continue beyond the path to the ridge so, after another half-hour uphill walk, we came to the rough but fairly short path to the Peak. This time we got to the top with its marvellous views over Noordhoek Beach, looking down onto Chapman's Peak and over Hout Bay. We continued on along the track to loop round and back to the reservoir on a different track. The five miles took us three-and-a-half hours – a far quicker walk than the first time we completed it, ten months before, when it took all day.

Two days later, we met Adele in the shopping mall and she supervised Rita lightly while she did our shopping from a list we had put together. She had done well apparently, asking staff for assistance when she couldn't find something and dealing with payment at the check-out. Over a coffee afterwards, Adele commented on how amused she had been by Rita deciding she needed to buy a lettuce which was not on the list. "David said not to buy anything not on the shopping list," Adele had reminded her. "We'll soon put that right," said Rita, writing "lettuce" onto the list and throwing one into the trolley.

On Saturday 9 February Gary, Sheilagh and the younger two boys arrived soon after breakfast, to stay with us for a week. After all the good weather we had been having, it rained all morning. The next day we put together a picnic, drove to Oliphantsbos Bay, via Scarborough, and walked to the Thomas T Tucker wreck again. There was nobody else around at all; we had that part of the Atlantic coast to ourselves. Then we went across the Peninsula to a small car park near the Black Rocks for another walk, during which we got dismayingly close to a pair of ostriches who were running around at high speed with wings raised. I wasn't at all sure whether they were being defensive or aggressive.

As usual with our family, physical activities were the big attraction. Further surfing lessons at Muizenberg's Surfers' Corner followed, then a trip from Hout Bay in a large RIB, with around ten others, to go "snorkelling with seals". I went along for the ride, with no intention of going in the water. It took little over 15 minutes at high speed to reach the "seal islands" located below the northern headland framing Hout Bay and home to, allegedly, 4,000 to 5,000 Cape fur seals. What a smell, downwind! Large notices around harbours warned visitors that these were dangerous animals – they were certainly very big when adult – and to keep well away from them. But, attired in wetsuits and snorkels, those who wished to spent about 40 minutes in the water found the seals to be very inquisitive but perfectly peaceful and they really enjoyed swimming among these large creatures. I enjoyed watching the blissful expression on Ben's face as warm water was poured into his wet suit to warm him up afterwards.

The two boys were either active or in bed – levering them out of bed in the mornings was always an effort. One day we left them to it and took Gary and Sheilagh to the Kirstenbosch Gardens for a few hours, which they loved. Then we went on for lunch at the Groot Constantia vineyard on the way back. Our visitors also drove into Cape Town twice to visit the District Six Museum and ascend Table Mountain (very busy). They went horse riding on Noordhoek Beach again, and did more surfing. Not bad for a week. The boys surprised me by both of them claiming that surfing was more fun than skiing. Rita was on form too by winning more than her fair share of games of UNO and Rummikub, played in the evenings. She also beat Gary at table tennis, though no one could beat Ben.

On the 18th, Shona brought an OT from the UK to meet us. She was visiting family in Cape Town but also taking the opportunity to talk to some South African OTs. We chatted for 75 minutes and gave her an outline of Rita's history. She was from Twickenham and claimed that rehabilitation there was much better organised than we had found in our region.

During the rest of the week, Stanley called in several times to repair our garden gate that was rotting along the bottom, repaint the fascias and bargeboards of the house, move two pieces of trellis in the garden to support the bougainvillea plant that was threatening to take over a substantial area of house wall – having existed as a nine-inch stick for the first nine months of its life with us – and to insulate the geyser tank in the roof.

On 21 February we called at the FHHN offices in Fish Hoek to see the managing nurse, Sister Heather Storer. Rita wanted to reduce the days we had carers to just three days each week, Monday, Wednesday and Friday. We also talked about the practicality for stroke survivors flying to Cape Town from the UK and receiving similar treatment to Rita's, modified of course to suit whatever their mix of disabilities happened to be. This was a subject we took up again at a later date and, with Heather's help, developed what I thought to be a good programme in principle (see chapter 40, question 6).

Heather told us that as well as managing FHHN she owned a small care and nursing home at which she provided high quality care, plus whatever therapy was needed. This sounded excellent and I was in no doubt that the care given would be first class; the only negative was that the home was, indeed, small, with fewer than ten bedrooms. That afternoon, Doreen arrived at the door with a friend, for a visit and chat. We knew she had left FHHN and learnt that now she was training to be a missionary with the charity "Living Hope" and expected to be going to Malawi, or Madagascar, or some other African state in a few months' time. She seemed very happy with her new life and we wished her every success.

The following day we set out on what was intended to be quite a long walk on Noordhoek Beach but, after a mile, Rita suddenly had what was, by now, one of her rare continence accidents, so we cleaned up as best we could and returned home for a shower and change of clothing.

At the end of February there was an amusing incident with the local authority. Cape Town was going through a revaluation of all residential properties, revising the figure on which rates payments were based. Needless to say, this was causing much upset and annoyance, if not animosity. The outcome didn't worry me – the rates we paid on the bungalow were so much lower than we would have paid, had it been located in the UK, that whatever the amount went up to I would regard the rates demand as good value. However, I had not received the promised letter advising me of the new valuation and inviting me to object, should I wish to do so. So, I went along to a crowded, temporary valuation office set up in the Fish Hoek Civic Centre and asked for the valuation figure. "Just a minute," I was told. The minute turned into 30 and I could see, eventually, four members of staff poring over a computer terminal at the other end of the room. One returned looking slightly embarrassed. "Your property doesn't exist on our records." I was advised. "In that event," I suggested, "you will not want any further rates payments from me." This feeble attempt at a joke fell completely flat. I won't bore you with the bureaucratic mess that had caused the problem nor how it was resolved. It took several months and eventually involved my attorney to bring some sense to the matter.

One of our favourite walks was to drive two to three miles up Ou Kaapse Weg (the Old Cape Road), turn right down a lane and park on the grass near an environmental centre. We did this on the last day of February and had a lovely walk up the Lower Silvermine Valley, past a century-old, broken-down farmhouse, up a steady climb to a small stream, then back down a different path to the farm. It was a walk that took about an hour and a half to two hours, depending on what we found, or saw and needed to stop and examine. This time we discovered a huge grasshopper, 4–5 cm long, with red-tipped spines all down its long back legs. It was not at all concerned at our presence and allowed me to take several close-up photographs. Perhaps it thought, rightly, it possessed sufficient defence built-in. There was also a large and beautifully patterned angulate tortoise on the path. There must be hundreds of these in the fynbos because the only chance of ever seeing one is if it crosses the path directly ahead of you. It was on a later occasion that we came across a 1.5 metre-long black shiny snake lying across the path near to the farm. It eyed us warily, as we did it as soon as we saw it. We walked round it very carefully, giving it a wide berth. Although I took some photos, they were with the telephoto lens on full extension. A little further on we met three ladies and thoughtfully I warned them of the possibility that the snake was still lying in wait for them.

"What colour is it?" one demanded to know.

"Black," I said.

"Is it shiny black?"

"Yes."

"Oh, you don't bother with those. It's just a mole snake and harmless enough." I felt thoroughly put down.

On 6 March, we travelled to Cape Town by train (still about £1.50 first class return). We walked up Adderley Street, past the parliament buildings and cathedral and had a light lunch in the Company's Garden. Then we went on to the museum at the west end of the gardens, where Rita was enthralled by many of the exhibits. It really is a very good museum. We walked back down Long Street past the many ethnic-style shops and bought a few presents for family birthdays coming up during the next month and so back to Fish Hoek for 5.00 pm.

On 13 March we tried a new path recommended by Shona. When driving to Kommetjie there is a Roman Catholic church signposted to the left. We drove towards it and found a large and totally empty car park nearby. A sandy path wound up the hillside that we followed with some difficulty as we had left our Nordic poles at home, but after 30 minutes or so, it levelled out and ran due west along the top of the ridge with marvellous views north across Noordhoek Bay to Chapman's Peak, Hout Bay and a little of the west end of Table Mountain just visible in the distance, under a cloudless sky. I took a great picture of Rita standing admiring this view and sent it to the Stroke Association because I felt it so epitomised what Rita had succeeded in doing through hard work over nearly 18 months of therapy, and how good the quality of life was that she could now enjoy. Further on there were more views over Kommetjie and down to the lighthouse. There were many flowers, all growing low to the ground as this hill was so exposed to the westerly winter gales. We did find one extraordinary plant we had never seen before, which looked like a variety of amaryllis, but was in the form of a ball of red flowers on a single stalk (no leaves) and about two feet in diameter.

On 5 April we set up a Skype connection to the Stroke Association (SA) and had a half-hour chat with the manager with whom I have been in contact regularly for two years or more, and their press office. The objective was to see how we might go forward as the SA and I had been having a long-running but good-natured disagreement about what was best for stroke survivors and their carers. It seemed apparent that the SA wasn't going to do more, to put it simply, than run campaigns and hand out advice. My view of what was needed by most stroke survivors and carers was practical treatment in the form of therapy. This would help both survivors and carers, as it had Rita and me. We agreed to differ, and sorted out some ideas for working together that seemed promising, but nothing really came of them.

On 11 April we had the last session for this trip with Shona, who was very complimentary about Rita's progress, as was Adele when we saw her the day after. Rita did really well with the exercises and received a big hug from Adele when we left. It was time to go home, autumn was approaching and we were having difficulty getting the pool water temperature above 25 °C! The weather had also deteriorated. With heavy rain and strong winds, the pool was close to overflowing, so I back-washed the filters and put it to bed. Adrienne picked us up in the afternoon of the 18th and we flew back to Heathrow on Virgin Atlantic this time.

We arrived home, Duncan's home, around midday, having picked up the car from one of our small barns. The engine started at the first attempt, so our tenants (away on holiday) had clearly fulfilled their promise to keep the battery charged. Having unpacked, we went out shopping. Soon after our return, a policeman knocked on the door. While we were out, there had been a break-in next door and jewellery had been stolen – not a situation we had ever had to deal with in Cape Town.

Saturday 20 April dawned a beautiful spring morning. We strolled down the country lane to the ancient village church with daffodils, cowslips and violets flowering all around, or so it seemed. It was lovely to be back and to look forward to the summer with no need for carers' daily visits, no therapy needed, no day care and with us both in good physical health. Not only was it a spring morning, but also five years to the day since Rita was smitten by the stroke. It was 30 months since Rita had begun therapy at the start of our first 10-week stay near Fish Hoek, and in that time she had received 18 months of gentle but intensive therapy (if that is not a contradiction). That was a great deal of therapy, but the outcome had made it all fully worthwhile, financially too. Rita had effectively recovered and was able to live a normal life once more.

This has been a long chapter, but I wanted to show how we were moving back to a normal life together, after a dreadful two years, 2008 to 2010, when nothing seemed to go right and Rita's prospects had been viewed in nothing but a negative manner. What a difference a positive attitude and a bit of effort had made. At April 2013, I could see Rita as effectively cured of almost all of her various disabilities. There was rarely an incontinence issue and we had long given up using continence pads and Kylie sheets on the bed. She no longer fell over; her sense of balance was excellent. So were her strength and stamina, with five-mile walks a matter of course. She was once again a self-motivated lady, loved to be busy, could look after the house as she always had and her irrational behaviour had long disappeared – thank goodness. Her good sense of humour was back, she could carry on intelligent conversations, the personality I had always known had returned and, unlike the first two years following the stroke, she no longer suffered from regular bouts of ill health such as urinary infections. The only difficulty was her continuing poor short-term memory that made remembering plans and commitments problematic, but we could cope with that.

For the next three years, to April 2016, we continued to spend five to six months during the UK winter at our home near Fish Hoek. Adele soon told us to stop wasting money on more therapy from her. So far as Adele was concerned Rita was cured – as fit as any lady of her age could reasonably expect to be. However, Rita enjoyed Adele's hydrotherapy group classes every week and continued with those. We also continued sessions with Shona, working on the cognitive and memory difficulties, but after another year or so, she admitted that she was unable to suggest more therapy for Rita that might be useful. However, it was evident that Rita's memory did continue to improve, if slowly. During the summer of 2015 – now that we were in our new English home in a "retirement development" – people who met Rita for the first time rarely picked up that there had ever been anything wrong with her, illustrating how far she had travelled.

It is time now to think about the reasons *why* she had been able to get better, not just the *how* of it.

Part 3

Recovery – and Why it Happened

January 2011 to the Summer of 2015

36

Breaking the Rules to Achieve the Unexpected

How and why did Rita get better against, apparently, all the odds? These are the two questions I have attempted to answer in Parts 2 and 3 of this account. 'How' is the easier of the two. Just listing the events that occurred between Rita needing full-time care in 2010 and being able to look after herself and be completely mobile again in 2013, says how it happened. 'Why' is rather more difficult to answer. How important to Rita's recovery, if at all, were the several events described in Part 2? If they were important, why did they work? Can they be understood in such a way that they can usefully be applied to other disabled stroke victims, given the known wide variation in disabilities that are common among stroke survivors? I believe rational explanations can be found for Rita's recovery from her several disabilities. These are discussed in the nine chapters of this Part.

Before starting, I should reiterate the authority I have to arrive at these explanations, which is little! I have no formal medical training. I have "enjoyed" six years of caring for Rita. During the first three of these, my caring was effectively full-time, after which, over several years, it steadily reduced to near zero. There was ample opportunity to observe how, at first, she did not make progress towards recovery, then how she overcame all but one of her several major disabilities. I do have a scientific degree and several decades of work in industry, firstly on analytical chemistry projects and then on the development of new products. I respectfully suggest there can be advantages in having someone with different training taking a close look at what is happening in another field outside their expertise. I am confident I have identified good reasons why Rita was able to make her unexpected recovery, but I am open to other suggestions and welcome these.

To continue this third Part with a little slightly unscientific and perhaps iconoclastic fun, I will suggest that in recovering so well from disability, Rita broke two "rules". Rule 1 was that nine health and care professionals had decided she could not get better. So she should not have done so! It was most improper that she should have recovered, following this authoritative negative prognosis! It is not too common for professionals in any field to enjoy being exposed as wrong in their assessment of things when they had, as a group, decided otherwise.

Rule 2 concerns the length of time that had passed between her stroke and the beginning of a clear recovery. She and I were told several times, by several people, that it was not possible to make a significant recovery once two years had elapsed following a stroke. For many health and care professionals, this seemed to be a definite Rule. But Rita broke it comprehensively; I think she enjoyed doing so!

The above are, of course, not "rules" in any real sense of the word, but they come over as such to lay people when they are told repeatedly that this is the situation, especially when taking into account the known poor physical and/or cognitive status of the stroke survivor in question and the authority of the people making these statements. Why should what is said by experienced and well-qualified health workers and social service workers be disbelieved?

The first "rule" was introduced during the assessment of Rita's status in June 2010. The conclusion arrived at turned out, to put it simply, to be incorrect. (This apparently unanimous assessment might well have resulted from group polarisation at work, though Rita's status had never been looked at in a positive light, so far as I could see.) The second was a belief, widely held, that once two years have passed, any further progress towards recovery is not possible. This is also incorrect – more of a myth. It is worse than a myth. It is much better described as a self-fulfilling prophesy of the worst sort. Once a few professionals have made that statement about a patient, this is what the outcome will be, almost inevitably (see chapter 41 for an explanation of how this works).

As already pointed out but worth repeating, the frightening aspect of the first "rule" is that, had Rita stayed in the UK and not travelled to South Africa for extended periods, she would not have made a recovery because there was no reason that I can see why she could possibly have got better while continuing to live in the UK from 2010 onwards. Had the poor, predicted, outcome of "no recovery possible" then happened, as was likely, it would both have established the professionals' assessment to be correct and strengthened their belief in Rule 2.

This third part of Rita's story is my attempt to explain *why* she was able to make an almost complete recovery from several major disabilities, so breaking both "rules". I am sure there are rational explanations for Rita's recovery that may be of interest, and of help I hope, to others in a similar unfortunate situation to Rita's and mine.

In an attempt to make my thinking clear, I have examined Rita's recovery from several perspectives. Chapters 37, 39 and 40, for example, represent different ways of looking at her recovery and why it happened as it did.

37

The Reasons for Rita's Recovery

The question is: why did Rita get better, contrary to the negative prognosis given her in the summer of 2010 by UK health and care professionals?

It was not until early in 2013 that I began to think seriously about the reasons why Rita overcame her multiple disabilities. What could they be? Only by that time had it become clear that her physical health and cognitive function were both improving dramatically, and she was holding onto those improvements, not allowing any progress to slip away again as had happened during the first two or three years. It also seemed very likely that this recovery could go a long way yet. Some time prior to 2013 there had not been a recovery to be concerned about in terms of *why*, exactly, it had happened. Now could be the time to think about the possible reasons.

One thing I took to be obvious, it was not due to any African witch doctor or other magical intervention.

Several people commented later, in the UK, that they "saw the hand of God" in Rita's unexpected recovery, commonly described by her friends as "amazing", or that it could be interpreted as a miracle. I was not happy with this as a plausible explanation, not least because it did not assist the understanding of Rita's recovery in a way that might be of use to others. But suppose it was true that God had "broken the rules of physics" and thus, unexpectedly, worked a cure for Rita's troubles? In other words, had performed a miracle? It immediately raised the question as to why God, in his beneficence, should choose Rita, out of the hundreds of thousands of other humans disabled by stroke, to be the recipient of a miracle? The likelihood for this to happen was beyond any law of probability of which I am aware. There was another difficulty. Miracles are usually seen as one-off events. There was only one raising of Lazarus, for example; only one conversion of water into wine, performed by Jesus. It would hardly seem fair that Rita should be the only recipient of such munificence, chosen from among so many others! Taking this argument further, just suppose that God *had* been directly responsible for Rita's recovery, then to help others would mean finding a way to persuade God to do the same again, but with some other disabled person, or better, a lot of other disabled people. How might that be done reliably? I for one don't know the answer to this question. No, that could not do as an explanation for why Rita got better.

There is another way of looking at this suggestion that is no more helpful – that God had *not* been in any way responsible for Rita's recovery, but it was believed by many that he *had* been. This supposition would get seriously in the way of finding the true reason(s) because, if God was not responsible, there had to be other explanations for her recovery. And we needed to find them. But if it was the case that God (wrongly) was believed responsible, the search for the real reason(s) might well be hindered, the supposed, but wrong, involvement of God becoming a distraction.

Invoking God complicated things and made any analysis of possible rational explanations more difficult. That was my view. If practical reasons could be found to explain Rita's recovery, some of these might be applicable to other disabled stroke survivors and could help them. For these reasons, I considered it best to leave God out of the list of possibilities and to look for pragmatic, rational causes for Rita's good luck in finding a road to recovery.

What might these have been? What was different between the UK, when for 30 months Rita hardly made any progress towards recovery, and South Africa, when her recovery quickly got underway and eventually was almost completed during much the same period of time?

My final list came down to six factors, each of which might possibly have helped Rita:

- Climate.
- Attitude.
- Therapy.
- A rehabilitation plan.
- Determination.

- Innate ability to recover.

… what might be the effect of each of these factors?

Climate

Climate was the main reason we went to South Africa originally, though not specifically for its rehabilitative effects. The first winter in the UK following Rita's stroke was terrible. She felt the cold badly, needed wrapping up and putting in a wheelchair almost every time we went out of the house and, in poor weather, we hardly went out at all. She had always been an outdoor sort of person and disliked being restricted to the house most of the time, often all day, even several days in succession and we got on each other's nerves.

The Cape Town weather was infinitely better. Not only was it summer there when it was winter in England, the summer temperatures were typically in the mid twenties and rain was rare (except in spring!). When it did rain, it was almost always short-lived, then the sun came out and everything was quickly dry again. Cape Town is notorious for being a windy place – very windy – much to the distress of most residents who complained about it constantly. But Rita grew up on the Yorkshire moors and wind does not worry her. Based near Cape Town, it was exceptional for us to be constrained to the house for more than one day each month during the South African summer. So we enjoyed two summers each year by flying to Cape Town between September and April, for six years in succession.

While in South Africa, Rita was able to go out every day and visit many interesting and beautiful places within a few miles of home. This helped her recover her interest in life and also assisted greatly with her mobility therapy that was so important.

Attitude

This is an interesting one. As a generalisation, the attitude among health professionals in the UK towards Rita's potential for recovery was universally negative. Only our friend Mo, wife of a Church of England minister, was encouraging and enthusiastic about any small progress that Rita made, and Mo was positive about everything. All the neuropsychologists, consultants, doctors, other health professionals and care workers who met Rita were either negative, or at best neutral, concerning her potential for recovery. *None* of the several reports written following assessments concerning Rita's health and prospects – after summarising her poor status – went on to say something along the lines "But if we tried such and such a treatment we might find she would respond well ..." Everything came to a head during the summer of 2010 when nine health and care professionals all agreed that Rita had no potential for recovery.

Against this UK background, the attitude of the health professionals in South Africa was positive. There were only four of them covering a period of two-and-a-half years: a nurse and three therapists. But none believed the negative prognosis Rita had been given in June 2010 to be valid. They all said she was capable of at least some recovery, though without specifying how much, and they set about proving themselves right with enthusiasm. It had been very discouraging when the UK experts told us, directly or by their attitude, that they hadn't much hope. On the other hand, Rita responded well to the encouragement she was given in South Africa, especially the enthusiasm with which Adele provided physiotherapy.

Therapy

As already described in some detail in Part 1, for 28 months from the time Rita arrived home from hospital, she received little in the way of practical rehabilitation therapy in the UK. There was plenty of contact with other health professionals and care professionals and workers, but not therapists (except during the three months at the rehabilitation clinic). The outcome was that negative prognosis. In Fish Hoek, Rita's rehabilitation programme was organised and managed by a nurse and, in total, three therapists. After an 18-month programme spread over two-and-a-half years (a long time compared with programmes provided routinely by the NHS), all Rita's physical disabilities were effectively cured and she was just left with a poor short-to-medium-term memory. No doctor had any input whatever into the detail of the rehabilitation programme itself, nor was a doctor involved in anything that was done by way of therapy in Fish Hoek. There must be a message here. My view is that the therapy programme was much the most important element for explaining how Rita recovered from her several disabilities, and this was assisted significantly by the clever incorporation of carers into the programme (chapter 38). The good climate and the attitude of those treating her were certainly positive elements.

A rehabilitation plan

In the UK, Rita was treated, for very limited periods, sometimes only two sessions, by around ten different therapists. My view from watching them work was that they knew what they were doing and worked well with Rita, but not one suggested either a long-term nor even a medium-term plan for treatment that might lead towards the correction of Rita's disabilities. They picked out aspects of Rita's status that needed treatment. One worked on posture, one on her inability to get up from chairs or her bed, one put her on a work table and spent the sessions manipulating her joints so that they didn't stiffen. None of them suggested that they might put together a longer-term plan of work, incorporating other therapists, leading to a defined aim.

The therapists in Fish Hoek approached things differently. They assessed Rita, then told us what they intended to do and why. They said that progress would take a significant time because it was so long since her stroke and she had both lost strength and fallen into bad habits, but the aim of the therapy programme was recovery from her several disabilities. They decided where they would begin and would modify the plan depending on how Rita responded. They talked to each other and each knew what the other was doing. This was just sensible project management and helped maintain progress while amending the programme according to Rita's progress.

Determination

By this I include the determination shown by several people (including me!). Rita herself had to show determination, but for a long period she demonstrated no motivation whatever to overcome her disabilities. She was happy just to sit in a chair and let others take care of things. Her disinterested approach to life initially made it more difficult for others to help. But, once a rehabilitation plan was up and running and progress was being made, Rita did, ultimately, show plenty of determination to work on boring and repetitive exercises for as long as the therapists asked her to. That is not to say she did not occasionally become angry. Sometimes, she announced she "Didn't see the point of all these stupid exercises!" But, with a bit of distraction – usually by an immediate change of exercise – she came round to a mood in which she did as she was asked.

The main carer needs a lot of determination because he or she will be the person who works to keep the show on the road, long-term. Just as a small example, it is much easier for the carer – if the patient wants a cup of tea – to make it for them. It seems kinder too. It takes determination to keep saying, "If you want a cup of tea, then *we* will make it!" and then to spend the next 15 to 20 minutes supervising this simple task that the patient struggles to complete.

Lastly, the therapists need determination to maintain enthusiasm and full involvement in what is usually a prolonged task, teaching often boring, simple and repetitive exercises to disabled people who are commonly not really interested in doing them and do not show appreciation for the considerable effort being made on their behalf.

Innate ability to recover, despite all the evidence to the contrary

Regarding "innate ability", it might be asked how this could vary between the UK and South Africa. If Rita had innate ability when in Fish Hoek, she would also have had it while in the UK. It is either there or it is not. What I am getting at here is the *perception* of whether it exists, unnoticed until sought. The health workers in the UK appeared not to believe Rita had a hidden ability to recover; the South Africans were prepared to accept she might until it was proved she had not.

So, how do you know if the ability to recover is there? You don't. The only thing to do is to find out by searching for it. This is what the therapists in Fish Hoek were prepared to do. My suggestion for searching involves working seriously at the job of rehabilitation for a period of, preferably, three months at least. Adele and Estie quickly established that Rita had an ability to recover, provided she was given appropriate therapy. Of the 70 or so health and care professionals who met or came across Rita during the first two years, apparently none noticed she had the hidden ability to get better; but then, none had seemed to look for it in a practical or consistent way.

The big question I am asking in this chapter is *why* Rita was able to recover? The reasons are within these six thoughts. I could not possibly put them in order of importance, even for Rita who I know so well. Even if I could set an order of importance for Rita, owing to the variability of disabilities caused by stroke, it would not be an order that would be likely to have relevance to other stroke survivors and so could be misleading. I will just go so far as to say that, for Rita, *all* the above six were important – at different levels – and had positive effects on her recovery. It seems likely that each could be important to the recovery of any severely disabled patient; none should be dismissed without testing them.

From early 2013, when it was clear Rita was recovering well and her progress between three-month visits to Fish Hoek appeared to be maintained, I put a lot of thought into the reasons for this. My curiosity was definitely aroused – especially in the light of the earlier negative prognosis. My interest was, in fact, sparked off nine months before, as mentioned in chapter 35, when the Stroke Association phoned me. They had been approached by *The Times* newspaper to ask if they could recommend a married couple a journalist could speak to, who had gone through a difficult time with inadequate support after one of the pair had suffered a bad stroke. *The Times* wanted to write a review of the, then, newly released film "Amour" and compare the picture given by the film with the real life experience of one couple. We did agree to be this couple and the article was published on 15 January 2013 in the Body and Soul section of *The Times*.

This bit of publicity for Rita's successful therapy programme encouraged me to write three more articles on rehabilitation that appeared in either *Nursing Times* or *Frontline* (the journal of the Chartered Society of Physiotherapists) towards the end of 2013. They are not reproduced here because what was said is repeated at various places in this book. But one article in *Nursing Times* had an "Expert Comment" editorial attached that was apposite and helpful. It was written by Brian Stone of the Stroke Association:

"Mr and Mrs Guthrie's struggle to gain access to care in the community is sadly not uncommon. We know how much people value rehabilitation services in the UK, but many survivors experience difficulty in accessing them. I work with survivors every day, providing them with information and support, signposting them to appropriate services in the local area and campaigning for better care.

What's resonant in this story is not only the fact that recovery is possible many years after a stroke, but that rehabilitation is the key to recovery. Every stroke is different and stroke affects people in different ways, from one-sided paralysis and communication difficulties through to personality changes and emotional problems.

In an ideal world the transition from hospital to community care would be seamless and every survivor would gain access to the support they need for as long as they need it. In reality, a lack of specialist skills and poor access to proper assessments means that this often fails to happen and many survivors, like Mr and Mrs Guthrie, are left feeling abandoned."

Subsequently, I wrote down a number of ideas as my thoughts developed. Those that related to an explanation for Rita's recovery are the subjects of the next few chapters. Shona, the occupational therapist who took over from Estie in September 2012, helped me a lot, perhaps more than she thought, by lending me a number of books, two of which I found to be particularly illuminating. The first was *My Stroke of Insight* by Jill Bolte Taylor. She was a brain scientist when, aged 39, she experienced the same type of stroke as Rita's. Given the work she was doing, she knew exactly what was happening to her. I found it fascinating to compare Jill's experiences with Rita's. Although both suffered a subarachnoid haemorrhage, pretty well everything else was different, typifying the wide variety of symptoms caused by stroke and the need for accurate assessments of each individual survivor to be sure that appropriate, best treatment is given.

The second, fascinating, book was *The Brain that Changes Itself* by Norman Doidge. He gave me a plausible explanation for something that had perplexed me. I had been told several times that a bad stroke, such as Rita's, results in loss of brain tissue that can never be recovered. It has died. If that was the whole story, recovery would not be possible, but it is. There are enough stories in the media (usually about celebrities, for obvious reasons) who have recovered well from a stroke, usually following "lots of treatment". So it is definitely possible to recover. There was a moving article in *Good Housekeeping,* October 2014, which described Andrew Marr's recovery from stroke (written by Jackie Ashley, his wife). In it, she comments that Andrew had several hours of physiotherapy every day. Lucky man! At the time I wrote this, Jackie Ashley was writing regularly online concerning the effects of stroke on Andrew and herself, and on the population in general.

In my view, Doidge's explanation exactly fitted Rita's history. It explained both why she was able to recover and why it took so much therapy – vastly more than most survivors receive. So, lucky us to find South Africa!

My conclusion regarding Rita's success was that the critical need was to have a rehabilitation plan designed specifically to treat her several disabilities; and that this plan should be allowed to continue as long as it was producing results. The plan should be operated by a team of therapists, each of whom stays with the team for long periods of time and so becomes very knowledgeable of the patient's needs, difficulties and progress. The attitude of the South African therapists was always positive, with no doubt ever being expressed about Rita's eventual recovery. The icing on this cake was the lovely weather of the Cape Peninsula summer that allowed almost daily outings to interesting locations, and so encouraged Rita to work conscientiously on her own recovery, as well as exciting her interest in life once again.

38

Rita's South African Rehabilitation Programme, with a Suggested Amendment for Use in the UK

Overview

This suggested programme is based on the therapy that was so successful for Rita in the small seaside town of Fish Hoek, near Cape Town, between 2010 and 2013, but I have amended it a little for use in the UK. I will describe it this way because conditions between the two countries are different in several aspects, though the programme remains very applicable to the UK. The costs of therapy were somewhat lower in Fish Hoek than back home during the time of Rita's recovery. For paid carers, the hourly rate was far lower, reflecting the high unemployment and availability of labour in that region of South Africa. So, for the suggested UK programme, I have reduced the time spent by carers while still, hopefully, achieving the same results. The basic idea is that the programme could be applied for a period of 12 weeks, assessed for progress and any changes thought necessary applied. Then, if considered justified, another 12-week session would begin. This cycle should continue as long as definite progress is being made.

Not only did this scheme effectively cure Rita's physical disabilities, it made substantial progress in correcting her cognitive dysfunction. For good reasons, the programme includes substantially more therapy time than was routinely offered in our region of the UK during 2008 to 2011, though to reduce costs, carers carry out most of the work under supervision from therapists. This last point is the one major change built into Rita's South African programme, when compared with anything I have seen written on the subject in the UK, including in the *National Stroke Strategy*.

The programme is not concerned with the hyper-acute stage of treatment and the time the patient spends in hospital immediately following a stroke. It begins when the patient is discharged from hospital into community care, by which time the home should have been adapted to meet the patient's needs and medical conditions, such as incontinence, have been assessed, with the correct treatment and products provided. In other words, the survivor is back at home and ready to begin rehabilitation therapy with the aim of recovering as much as possible of their former lifestyle. Importantly, the main carer receives good training in looking after someone with severe disabilities.

For Rita, the therapy treatment lasted far longer than is usual in the UK – around 18 months as already noted, compared with 3 months in the UK (if the patient is lucky). Despite this, the 18 months of therapy was fully justified financially by the large reduction in long-term care costs that would otherwise have been incurred (chapter 42). It should be remembered that Rita only began this therapy two and a half years after her stroke and following a very negative prognosis; it is reasonable to suppose that, had she started the therapy soon after discharge from hospital in line with conventional recommendations, the timescale might have been shortened substantially.

The Rehabilitation Team (that treated Rita, which should be amended to suit individual patients):

- A nurse (experienced in care of the elderly).
- A physiotherapist.
- An occupational therapist (plus other therapists, if needed by the disabilities displayed by the patient).
- Paid carers.
- The main carer (unpaid, "voluntary", probably untrained and inexperienced initially, typically the spouse, partner or close family member – in this case, me).

Responsibilities for each member of the Team:

The nurse. This is very important at the start. She would be the coordinator of the programme and the named contact for the main carer when there are queries or problems to be resolved. The nurse has detailed knowledge of the status of the patient, and good knowledge of the workings of the UK health and care systems. She is the primary support for the main carer and either answers their questions and solves their problems, or knows where to go to get answers. She begins by having regular 1:1 contact with the main carer and patient, but as the programme settles down will withdraw steadily until, probably, she is not seeing the patient more than once or twice each month.

Therapists. They assess the patient according to their expertise, set a programme of therapy to be followed and provide (typically) one 45-minute to 60-minute session each week. They should all stay with the team for the medium-to-long term. They keep in contact with the other therapists and know what approach the others are following. Very importantly, they supervise and help the paid carers to give the patient gentle therapy treatment daily, in between the therapist's sessions. This can be done, simply, by the therapists giving the carers short lists of exercises each week, ensuring they are understood, and asking whether there had been any difficulties at the next weekly meeting. It is very helpful for the paid carers to watch professional therapy sessions so they can see and understand how the therapy is applied.

Paid carers. They are well trained in caring but may not have knowledge on how to give therapy treatment. They work with each patient for, say, 3 hours minimum per day, Monday to Friday, and one hour at weekends (and bank holidays). There should be no more than three different carers for any one patient during any three-month period, to allow good continuity. The paid carers should attend therapy sessions whenever possible to watch how therapy is given, and accept simple instructions from the therapists (as short lists of exercises) that they can help the patient with during weekdays. The work typically done by the paid carers is therefore: every day, get the patient up, dressed, fed and settled. In addition during weekdays: give the exercise sessions prescribed by the therapists, go for a walk (weather permitting), play appropriate games with the patient or keep them otherwise entertained and so allow the main carer a break to do other things. As progress is made, they will help the patient to take up the normal activities of daily living: making drinks, preparing meals, cleaning, etc.

Main carer. Typically, this is the person who has "volunteered" for the job, dropped into it almost overnight, and is unlikely to have any experience of, or training for, looking after someone with serious disabilities. Initially, they are at sea and need a lot of support, especially as they frequently have close emotional ties with the patient as their spouse, partner or close family member. If they are given good support early in the job (as soon as the patient is discharged home from hospital), they will often grow into the work quickly and be able to cope with the new responsibilities. Without adequate support, as happens too often now, they become stressed, suffer ill health, and the patient him or herself may suffer through being treated inappropriately, despite the best of intentions.

Consultants and doctors. Essentially, their work is completed in the hospital. They are not part of the therapy team – though the patient's GP is, of course, kept informed of the patient's status, treatment and progress and can be asked for help whenever needed. They are on call and the nurse can ask for advice at any time, but these specialists are not regularly involved in the therapy plan. The main exception to this is when the patient is also suffering from a medical condition (that may be chronic) needing treatment, but one that is not directly related to stroke disabilities.

The therapy programme

This is set up in stages, each stage lasting 12 weeks (or three calendar months if that makes administration easier). It runs as described above for 12 weeks, though it may be modified as progress does (or does not) occur. It then stops for 4 weeks to give the patient and main carer a break. The paid carers could continue to operate as above, or for just one hour, seven days each week. This is open to negotiation and/or preference. During these 4 weeks, the patient is re-assessed and details of their progress are noted as formal data, including that from multidisciplinary assessment meetings. The nature of further therapy needed, if any, is agreed and a follow-up 12-week programme written. And so on. A severely disabled survivor might need several 12-week sessions to effect a good recovery (Rita made use of six sessions). A much less severely disabled patient may be cured well enough after the first 12-week session.

An important feature is that, to stand a good chance for successful recovery, the survivor and/or main carer *must* be fully committed to the programme. Survivors with severe cognitive dysfunction may have no view on the matter (Rita was totally disinterested in what was proposed, but was willing to do her best when asked to by a therapist, and didn't lose her temper too often!). If the main carer shows no interest in co-operating with the health professionals (and it does need considerable co-operation to be fully successful), it is doubtful that the programme is worth beginning. So my suggestion is that the programme should always be offered, but if either the main carer or patient is not willing to put in the substantial amount of effort required for recovery, their view should be respected and no forced attempt made to go ahead.

The obvious criticism …

of this programme is that, at the time of writing, it is based on a sample of one: Rita. My belief after eight years of being Rita's full-time carer through thick and thin – and meeting many other patient/carer combinations – is that it is highly likely that many badly disabled stroke survivors do retain the ability to make a substantial recovery, but this ability is never realised. Unfortunately, I know of no data concerning how well disabled survivors might recover, if given good quality therapy late in the day, for example, two years after their stroke. Such potential ability has never been assessed by a project, so far as I know. I have toted the idea of a pilot scheme around three Professors of Rehabilitation Medicine in the UK, but have been met with polite disinterest so far.

It is well known that disabled survivors rarely recover once two years have passed since their stroke, but that does not mean they *cannot* recover (see chapter 41). Several observations suggest that it could still be possible for a proportion of disabled survivors to make a reasonable recovery, even though their stroke occurred two or more years previously. For example, there is no reason to suppose Rita was a special case and responded much better than any other stroke survivor might to rehabilitation therapy. Quite the reverse is likely, because she patently showed little evidence of recovery during the first two years when she received little therapy. It was only when the "intensive but gentle" programme was established in 2010 in Fish Hoek that she began to recover well.

There are several well-known celebrities who have made good recoveries after severe stroke or other acquired brain injury (ABI) – and even returned to work. (Patricia Neal, Harry Secombe, Richard Hammond,

Kate Allatt [who has turned herself into a celebrity] and Andrew Marr are examples). The common factor here is that they are all reported to have received a lot of high quality therapy. Maybe it is the quantity and quality of the therapy that is the most important factor, not how long after the stroke it is given? Though there is little doubt that the sooner therapy is provided, the more successful it is likely to be, for two reasons. Muscle strength and stamina are quickly lost if patients fail to exercise regularly. This is because they are in a wheelchair and are not given the incentive to perform daily exercises. Secondly, the brain learns to accept a disability as a "normal condition" after quite a short period of time and rewires itself to make the best of a bad job. A late start with the therapy then requires this re-wiring of the brain to be undone and the brain persuaded to reorganise itself in yet another, more appropriate, way.

The factor that concerns me as much as any is the widespread belief that recovery is impossible after two years (say) have passed. This can so easily become a self-fulfilling prophesy. It is seen as a true fact that almost no stroke survivors recover once two years have gone by. Therefore the assumption is made that they cannot recover. Therefore it is a waste of limited resources to provide therapy after this period of time and consequently there is no chance that they might recover because to do so is dependent on receiving therapy, which they do not get. So how could they recover? They cannot – but that still does not prove they are unable to do so. They might still have the innate ability, but have been misdiagnosed or not given the right treatment for long enough.

Putting this last point more simply and in the way it happens in practice; once two years have gone by, any rehabilitation programme that may have been given is long finished, the patient and their carer have established a routine that changes little day to day. Nothing else changes, so there is no possible reason why the patient should suddenly begin to get better (chapter 41).

Rita was an exception because it was only after two years following her stroke that, suddenly, she did begin an intensive therapy programme in a totally different environment from the one she was used to. Her daily lifestyle changed dramatically and she started on an "amazing" recovery. The difference from most other survivors was that her therapy programme suddenly began after two years. This brought to light her hidden capacity to recover *but only because she received the appropriate treatment!*

I see it as of the greatest importance that other long-term, seriously disabled survivors (that are free of other unrelated illnesses) are tested using the above programme, or something similar, to see how they respond. This would not be a difficult or costly thing to do. It would be inexpensive to set up a well-controlled trial, say in a medium-to-large town so that enough disabled survivors could be recruited within a reasonably small geographical area. This could produce very useful data. (See Appendix E for a suggested programme.)

39

Just Three Facts and Two Observations!

Essentially, three facts and two observations are all that are needed to explain Rita's recovery from her multiple disabilities. And also to explain, despite the complexity of the brain, why quite simple treatment can provide substantial success, why friends and relatives should not be frightened to seek treatment, nor be over-awed by jargon used by medical professionals. Recovery is likely to be hard work, but it is not necessarily difficult to accomplish, given commitment to the task.

This chapter represents another way to describe what happened to Rita, a way to look at her recovery from a different point of view. Why, for example, did her South African rehabilitation work so well. This different perspective might help to make clearer what the remedial treatment is doing and why it works.

You may well ask once again on what authority I can expound on these seemingly complex subjects concerning damage to the brain. The answer to that, as I have said earlier, I have very little authority. I was trained as a research scientist (working in industry, not academia). I have no medical training and, at the time Rita suffered her stroke, knew nothing whatever, either in theory or practice, about caring for anyone with severe disabilities or about rehabilitation from Acquired Brain Injuries. Despite the best of intentions, I made many mistakes. But, as I write this, I have spent nearly six years full-time watching closely how Rita first failed to make progress, then made a dramatic recovery. I now regard myself as an expert on recovery from the disabilities (some of them anyway) caused by stroke and I know, to my own satisfaction, just *how* Rita's recovery came about and *why* it happened. You might even regard it as an advantage not to have medical training, so that I can apply fresh eyes and a different training to the subject! I once worked for a company which, when advertising for a small number of young scientists, stipulated that knowledge of the company's field of work was not necessary, even a disadvantage, but applicants did need to have an iconoclastic approach to their work.

Anyway, as you might imagine, there is a lot of detail to be summarised and I have reduced it to the title above – **Just three facts and two observations!**

The first fact is self-evident. Stroke is an injury, not an illness. A stroke represents physical damage to the brain and should not be grouped with degenerative illnesses such as dementia, Alzheimer's or Parkinson's disease. The human body is good at getting over physical injury, especially when given help. Giving help to overcome physical damage to the brain sounds to be a tricky exercise – for Rita it was relatively straightforward despite the severe stroke she suffered – but our experiences showed how essential it was that she received *professional* rehabilitative help, or her recovery from such a bad stroke was unlikely to happen.

A way to appreciate what treatment is needed is to use an analogy. Whenever a serious physical injury happens, recovery is in two parts. The first stage is to stabilise the patient, treat the shock that usually occurs, avoid possible infection and repair any damage that could be life-threatening. Once the patient is stabilised, such that their life is no longer in immediate danger, recovery (rehabilitation) treatment can and should be provided. This is the second important part of the whole process.

For a stroke patient, speed is of the essence during the acute phase (the first few hours following the stroke) to minimise, as far as possible, consequential brain damage and so also minimise the physical and cognitive disabilities caused by that damage. An operation may be needed to seal a leaking blood vessel, or clot-busting drugs may have to be administered, with extra treatment to overcome side effects that may result from operations within the skull and the trauma of a stroke. Once the patient is stabilised – the end of the first stage of recovery – the period of rehabilitation can, and should, begin.

Unfortunately, this second part of the treatment for stroke is often ignored, or can be, at best, inadequate. Once stabilised, it is common for the stroke survivor to be discharged home with only very limited rehabilitation therapy arranged. This happened to Rita and for two years she made little progress towards recovery. A rehabilitation programme, especially important for life-threatening strokes, is as much part of the overall treatment as the emergency scenario. The purpose of rehabilitation is to get round, in some way, the damage that was caused to the brain. If this is successful, the survivor can return to a near normal life in many cases. The fact that rehabilitation from brain injury often takes longer than recovery from a bodily injury is just one of those things that is rarely adequately recognised.

So I will briefly return to the analogy I began earlier: *Not to provide rehabilitation to a stroke patient is equivalent to not resetting a broken leg.* It is as if the patient with the broken leg is stabilised, immediate injuries repaired, then sent home without first setting the leg, in effect saying that it might mend itself, but if not, there are lots of people who will help the patient and their carer get used to the idea of life in a wheelchair from then on. Not to reset a broken leg is unthinkable. Equally, not to provide a rehabilitation programme to a stroke survivor should be unthinkable; it is a vital part of the whole stroke recovery process.

There are thousands of survivors of serious strokes who never recover their former physical and cognitive ability to more than a limited level. But recovery can be achieved, as shown by the well-known celebrities who not only recovered from stroke or other severe brain injury, but recovered sufficiently well to hold down demanding jobs once again. People such as Andrew Marr and Richard Hammond are good examples, as already mentioned. Possibly they, or their carers, were able to organise full rehabilitation programmes and, if so, they have demonstrated just how much is achievable with the right treatment. Injuries to the brain can be more complex than physical injuries when it is easier to see where the physical problem lies. It may happen that some brain injuries occur in a region of the brain that precludes recovery. It is also evident that those who do suffer a serious stroke need to work hard and for many hours to recover, but no one should forget that a stroke is an *injury* and, therefore, is often amenable to treatment.

The second fact is rather less evident. I will describe it by reference to what happened to Rita. Some hours following her stroke, she was transferred from a general hospital to a neurosurgical unit about 30 miles away, where my written agreement was sought to conduct an operation, the statistics of which suggested there was a 30% probability of non-survival. The alternative was not to operate. I was told this would have resulted in Rita's certain death. Rita did survive the highly technical operation performed by expert surgeons. She spent the next two weeks in an intensive care ward, where she lay immobile and attached to a dozen or more instruments with 1:1 nursing 24 hours a day. The important point I am working up to is that, despite all appearances to the contrary, the only injury was to her brain – her body, from the neck down, was exactly the same as it had been immediately before the stroke and was without physical injury. The same claim (with one qualification) could have been made nine weeks after her stroke when she was discharged home from hospital to an uncertain future. At that time, she suffered from multiple disabilities, both physical and cognitive. But the same claim was still valid, which represents the **second fact** that, despite all the physical disabilities she displayed, her body from the neck down remained uninjured in itself, free from physical damage.

The one qualification mentioned above was that, because of her almost complete lack of mobility through those nine weeks, she had lost significant muscle strength and muscle tone due solely to lack of exercise. This is where therapy, especially physiotherapy, becomes so vital. Not only has work to be done on the disabilities caused by stroke, but attempts must be made to recover lost muscle strength resulting from no exercise, or the objective of recovery from those disabilities becomes steadily more and more difficult to achieve.

It took me several years really to understand this second fact as no one pointed it out to me. A stroke is an injury within the brain. The body is not immediately affected, it just appears so because, so often, damage within the brain manifests itself as a variety of bodily disabilities. But these physical failings are caused by damage to those parts of the brain that control the body, not weakness or failure of the body itself.

Here is another analogy. Modern cars are fitted with primitive "brains". These are the ECUs, the electronic control units that control the operation of the engine and several other parts of the car's function. What happens if an ECU suffers a "stroke" and fails to work as it should? Possibly the car will refuse to start. If it does start, it may run roughly, without power. Other functions of the car may not work, such as the ABS or the suspension control. If this happens, no one takes the engine apart to look for the fault. It is quickly obvious that the engine itself is undamaged and contains no fault whatever. What is needed is a replacement ECU and, once fitted, off the car goes as good as ever.

What we cannot yet do is take out the old damaged brain from someone who has suffered a stroke and fit a new, undamaged, brain. Perhaps as well really, there's no knowing who you might get! But it does mean that it is not immediately obvious how to repair the damaged – though stabilised – brain and it is a task that cannot be done by operating directly on the brain. The only way to overcome the neurological damage is indirectly, through the body itself – and this is the process we call "rehabilitation".

With hindsight, and bearing this second fact in mind, I found some of the tests Rita underwent difficult to understand. During the first year following the stroke, she was called back to hospital every three months or so for a range of tests aimed at treating her urinary incontinence that was such a nuisance. And at that time, I had wanted these tests to be done. They took a variety of forms and some were quite technical. At the end, the conclusion was that there was no physical reason for her incontinence and her condition was untreatable by surgery.

Well, of course there was no physical reason for the incontinence! Rita wasn't incontinent before the stroke and her body itself was not damaged by the stroke. It was only her brain that suffered physical damage and it was this that caused the incontinence. Maybe the messages from the body indicating that a toilet was needed were not reaching the brain; maybe the brain was no longer controlling this part of her body. Whatever was the cause, it appears Rita's body just reverted to the behaviour of an untrained toddler and it urinated or defecated when it felt the need. As a toddler can be toilet trained, so could Rita. With the training she later received in South Africa, her incontinence was corrected. Now she is 100% continent – and what a bonus that is! It is a fact to be remembered – that in the short term, the body itself is *not* damaged by the stroke.

This story leads directly into the **third fact** which is the least obvious of the three, but is the one that best explains Rita's almost complete physical recovery from her status in 2010 of – to put it bluntly – an NHS reject.

The third fact is much less well recognised. It is that the brain is plastic – meaning that different parts of it can be trained to do different things, given time and effort, motivation and practice. This is usually described as "neuroplasticity". Marcus Chown says, "Neuroplasticity is the brain's great secret". This statement, I think, refers back to the view current through much of the twentieth century that specific areas of the brain controlled specific actions and that, once one part of the brain was lost, so was the action it controlled – forever. It is now known that the brain can rewire itself. More than that, it is recognised that human brains are rewiring themselves constantly, it is a necessary part of living and exercising the brain is as important as exercising the body. Norman Doidge describes the development of the understanding of neuroplasticity and provides many examples of its strength in his books *The Brain that Changes Itself* and its sequel, *The Brain's Way of Healing*.

During the first two years following Rita's stroke, I was told by several health professionals that parts of her brain had died and could never recover, the implication being that she was unlikely ever to recover from the loss of those particular brain functions. Death of parts of the brain may well happen – I did not dispute that – but if that was all there was to it, how then *did* people recover from a stroke? As I have mentioned already, several well-known people have made remarkable recoveries. Their recoveries may have taken a long time to achieve, but they did happen. Were these successes due to a rehabilitation programme that took advantage of the concept of neuroplasticity? I don't know what treatment these celebrities received, but suspect that taking advantage of neuroplasticity was an important part of it.

Having watched Rita recover under therapy treatment in South Africa, I am sure that neuroplasticity provided the perfect explanation for Rita's almost complete physical recovery that did not even begin until two-and-a-half years after her stroke. Her recovery may have taken many months of work to achieve, but it did happen – once she was given the right therapy by trained professionals. And that is a critical feature of recovery from stroke, obtaining the right professional therapy to address the specific disabilities displayed by any individual survivor.

Two statements follow from the above. (1) Obtaining the right therapy can be difficult (as it was in our region of the UK. A statistic reported in the Summer 2016 edition of *Stroke News* from the Stroke Association was that: *Stroke survivors in England told them: More than 45% felt abandoned when they left hospital: 47% were not contacted by a healthcare professional when they left hospital: More than a third didn't receive a six-month assessment of their health and social care needs*). (2) The therapy itself is straightforward, as was shown in South Africa. The big difficulty arises from the fact that it takes time to invoke neuroplasticity – actually, to train the brain to do something new can take months of persistent work. Unless you were quite exceptional when young, it probably took you a considerable time to potty train, to learn to read and write, to learn road sense, to ride a bicycle, to learn to drive. For those who want to become real experts in their field, such as leading sportsmen or ballet dancers, it can take years of determined effort both to build up the body *and* to train the brain (via neuroplasticity) to have the fine control over the muscles that is needed.

Unfortunately, it is not common for sufficient time to be given to stroke survivors' rehabilitation. It was only when Rita was given a time-unlimited programme (and shown what to do, professionally) that she began the road to real recovery. And the time needed can be substantial, partly because an adult brain does not learn as quickly as a young one and partly because a stroke survivor also has to contend with the trauma that follows a stroke.

These comments lead on to the two observations referred to in the chapter title.

The First Observation is that, once they are discharged from hospital, it can be very difficult to get good rehabilitation started for a patient that is still badly affected following a severe stroke that has caused multiple disabilities, both physical and cognitive. This is especially so when only the "early" part of ESD (Early Supported Discharge) is invoked and the "supported" bit is ignored to all intents and purposes. If the patients are as disabled as Rita was at this stage, then they need 24-hour care. The need to get this care set up and running is urgent; anything else comes second. And what comes second includes the rehabilitation programme which is so necessary for eventual recovery. The patient can live without rehabilitation for a while; a rehabilitation programme can be put on hold while the urgency of providing full-time care is dealt with.

So, what then happens once the care requirement becomes, if not routine, at least under control on a daily basis? Who remembers to set up rehabilitation, or is responsible for doing so? For Rita, the answer in 2008, in the region of the country in which we lived, was "No one was prepared to accept responsibility for this, nor did it appear to be anyone's job to do so".

That begs the question, who are the people who might have taken on the responsibility for ensuring Rita received the therapy she badly needed, and that proved so effective once in place? Who were the likely candidates?

First, the stroke survivor. But Rita suffered from severe cognitive disability. She could not understand what was needed, let alone have any motivation to get better. She was happy to sit in a chair, hour after hour, inspecting her fingernails. In her book, *My Stroke of Insight*, Dr Jill Bolte Taylor has quite a lot to say about the lack of motivation typically shown by stroke survivors, based on her own personal experience. For Rita to manage her own rehabilitation was a non-starter.

Second, the NHS. These are the people one might expect to have the knowledge, experience and responsibility for setting up and running a recovery programme. For Rita, in 2008 and in the region where we lived, there was no therapy programme of any sort provided that included trained therapists at the time she was discharged from hospital. The best that happened was, six months after discharge from hospital, Rita was given a six-week OT course during which progress was made, then lost again once it stopped. In mid-2009 our, then, Member of Parliament, Sir Alan Haselhurst, persuaded the (then) Primary Care Trust (PCT) to fund a 12-week residential rehabilitation course at a clinic some distance away. Again, Rita made progress during this course, but once more regressed when it ended as there was no follow-up therapy provided. From that time (September 2009) until her major negative assessment in June 2010 – a period of nine months – Rita received no therapy from the NHS and, after that negative prognosis, there was never likely to be any.

Third, the main carer. That was me, Rita's husband. The main carer is frequently a spouse or other close relative of the stroke survivor. I had the determination to do all that I could to help Rita's recovery, but despite meeting, phoning or writing to more than 70 different employees of the NHS, Social Services, Local Authority Services and several charities over two years, my attempts to find appropriate treatment failed miserably, as measured by the fact that Rita was little better in June 2010 than she had been two years earlier. We received plenty of sympathy, but found no one willing or able to provide practical treatment. The fact that, at that time, I didn't really know what I was looking for did not help this enterprise.

My difficulties were probably similar to those of many carers of seriously disabled stroke survivors, who have been "volunteered" for the job almost overnight. I had no knowledge of stroke and its effects on survivors, nor any experience of, or training for, looking after disability. I had to take on all the responsibilities Rita had held in our marriage (cooking, household budget, and so on) and I was looking after Rita 24 hours a day, seven days a week. This left little time for sorting out rehabilitation treatment and I had no real understanding of what exactly was involved in treating disability. With hindsight, my failure to achieve anything was not at all surprising. Without any doubt whatever, the best decision I made was to follow Mo's recommendation and take Rita to Cape Town.

Fourth, the Social Services. The Social Services are responsible for ensuring the disabled are properly cared for, not for providing expert rehabilitation treatment. They are the one professional group with a valid excuse for not providing a recovery programme. Despite this, all that was laid on for Rita when she was discharged from hospital was a "re-enablement" programme (lasting six weeks maximum) which was managed by the Social Services. This comprised carers coming in several times a day for 10 to 15 minutes at a time. The programme included the word "rehabilitation" in its description even though no qualified therapists were involved. I could see that for someone who had suffered a mild stroke, this programme could be helpful, but for someone with Rita's combination of disabilities it was hopelessly inadequate. It was also a standardised programme, the same for everyone. This was another failing. I hope I have made it clear that stroke survivors suffer a wide range of different disabilities at different levels. Each patient needs to be assessed independently to identify their individual needs, not just be handed a standard programme.

Fifth, charities. There are thousands of dedicated people across the country, paid and unpaid, who work hard to help those who have suffered a stroke. They do good and valuable work, but it seems more weighted towards helping with care and, perhaps, teaching survivors how to live with disability rather than working towards recovery. Over more than six years, I have had close association with four charities, national and local, but none of these provided significant rehabilitation therapy or other practical help directly and purposefully aimed towards correcting disability. I was told by two of them that the provision of therapy was not within their remit (even though, in my experience, practical therapy is the one thing most needed by stroke survivors).

As an illustration of this problem, I drew a circle on the map, radius 15 miles and centred on our house. This covered an area of approximately 700 square miles in a quite heavily populated region of East Anglia. I chose 15 miles because it was the longest distance I would want to travel regularly when taking Rita to a rehabilitation clinic or centre (should one be available). Within this area, I knew of no charity that provided practical courses of rehabilitation therapy for stroke survivors. Some distance outside this area, I knew of one. When I applied for Rita to be accepted as a patient there, she was rejected for two technical reasons (she was too old and did not live in the right county).

As long as all the above limitations continue to apply, the conclusion has to be that it is very difficult to set up an effective rehabilitation programme, in our region of the country anyway. The necessary services are just not available in anything like the quantity needed. Yet in South Africa it was easy and inexpensive to find exactly what was required.

The Second Observation. In the light of all I have said above, the second observation is both surprising and encouraging. When, during the first two years, Rita was given programmes of treatment (six weeks of occupational therapy (OT) then later, 12 weeks in a rehabilitation clinic) she did show good signs of recovery. It was disappointing that, once the treatments ended, Rita lost any gains that had been made quite quickly. Perhaps treatment should have continued longer; perhaps it was not intensive enough (or too intensive), perhaps the lack of follow-up was the cause of her regression.

Whatever it was, Rita made little progress during the first two years following her stroke. However, from the start of the South African programme in early October 2010 the outcome was different. The first programme there lasted for two visits to Cape Town of 10 and 12 weeks respectively, between October 2010 and April 2011. A total of 22 weeks is a long time (compared with what is commonly available in the UK) and the therapy ran seven days a week throughout these periods of roughly five months. When we returned to the UK for the summer of 2011, I did not attempt to set up any therapy between May and September. Rita had made substantial progress towards recovery and, despite there being no therapy provision in the UK, *this* time she did not lose what had been gained. In fact she continue to improve steadily, if slowly, on her own.

It seemed that she had got "over the hill". By April 2011, her disabilities had improved to such an extent that she had gained her own motivation, actually wanting to get better, and was prepared and able to put in much effort on her own. This effect was repeated, only more so, during the summers of 2012 and 2013.

The summary of Rita's experience is that it is possible to recover from the disabilities caused by stroke, even when severe. What is needed is the recognition that stroke is an injury only, that the body itself (despite appearances to the contrary) is not directly damaged in the short term and, given help, the brain can be taught to rewire itself to get round the damage caused by the stroke. But getting the rehabilitation treatment started can be very difficult – even though the actual treatment is straightforward – and needs someone with the necessary knowledge who has been given the responsibility to put it together. Furthermore, it is necessary that the survivor – or more likely the main carer – must have the determination and motivation to ensure that the patient works on the prescribed therapy *regularly,* preferably every day of the week and for several hours each day. The difficulty is compounded by the fact that the disabilities displayed by stroke survivors vary widely. This is because the extent of any individual's disability is determined by what part of the brain has been damaged and how badly. As a result, of course, there is no standard therapy programme that can be applied automatically and successfully to all survivors. Each needs their own individual programme that addresses their particular mix of disabilities.

My claim above – that the body itself is unaffected by a stroke in the short term – requires a "But". This "But" is that it soon *will be* affected if nothing is done to correct the apparent physical disabilities caused by the stroke. Doidge points this out and calls the effect "learned non-use". For example, if the survivor is affected by poor posture or a bad limp as a result of the stroke, something must be done about correcting these physical disabilities. Otherwise neuroplasticity again comes into effect and, in time, these disabilities will become permanent. The way this happens could be that the brain notes that the right leg is strong but the left is weak. It will accept this as fact, even "normal", and will rewire itself to make the best of this bad job. Correcting this physical disability thus becomes steadily more difficult the longer it is left untreated and it may eventually become a permanent part of the patient's constitution. This is a very plausible explanation why long-term disabled stroke survivors are often regarded as incapable of recovery. That is because they *are* incapable of recovery. Their physical disability has become built-in, by neuroplasticity, as a permanent feature because it has been left untreated. The good news is that this effect can take a long time to become permanent. Rita was still able to recover even though her full rehabilitation programme did not begin until 30 months after her stroke.

This discussion has explained the points in the title of this note – three facts and two observations, plus some additional comments. Having observed closely, over more than six years, how Rita has responded to treatment (or lack of it) these three facts and two observations have provided, for me, a very plausible explanation for why Rita was able to recover from her several serious disabilities. What she needed was the right treatment (straightforward therapy) but a lot of it – the length of teatment being at least partly explained by it starting more than two years late.

Since first writing this chapter I have had more ideas. Two more relevant points have become apparent. These are not directly related to Rita's practical recovery so do not affect the comments already made, but whose outcomes have been the opposite of what might have been expected. These also are worth a comment. To begin with, take a different look at the *first* 30 months following Rita's stroke (April 2008 to September 2010), compared with what happened during the *second* period of 30 months (October 2010 to March 2013).

During the first 30 months, Rita received the piecemeal therapy described in Part 1; there having been no rehabilitation plan specifically designed for her. Outside this piecemeal treatment, she received little more than a few privately arranged physiotherapy sessions. However, she did have regular appointments with doctors for one problem or another. During the winter of 2009/10, she had three emergency admissions to hospital for events that I could not handle. She saw several consultants during the 30 months and, in addition, was assessed by three different neuropsychologists who all wrote reports with recommendations for action. The end result, in June 2010, was the assessment that she had no capacity for recovery. Following that, a social worker with the title of Senior Practitioner told me it would be in Rita's best interests if she was placed in a care home. Further, in September 2010, I was told by a stroke consultant, following another 40-minute assessment of Rita's status, that I should expect a steady deterioration in her condition from that time on. Sadly, I am confident that the consultant would have been proved correct in this prediction, had we stayed in the UK.

The second 30 months began in October 2010 in Fish Hoek, with the rehabilitation programme designed to address the specific disabilities from which Rita was suffering. This programme (chapter 38) was put together and managed by a "community" nurse, a physiotherapist and an occupational therapist. No doctor had any input into what was happening, and certainly no consultant had any say in the design of the therapy. As described in Part 2, during the 30 months following October 2010, Rita spent 18 of them near Cape Town, during which the programme was active seven days a week. The outcome at the end of the 30 months was an almost complete recovery from all her physical disabilities. The only remaining severe disability was Rita's continuing lack of a short-term memory.

These two approaches could be summarised concisely as: first period – little therapy and all doctors; second period – all therapy and no doctors. Maybe the different outcomes resulting from the two approaches were cause and effect; maybe they were coincidental. Make of them what you will. Possibly the doctors will be miffed by the implied criticism that their efforts had little or no positive impact on Rita's well-being. But they should not be, because the outcomes bore little relation to what doctors do or do not do once the survivor is in the recovery phase and given there are no underlying medical conditions, independent of the effects of stroke, that need treatment. The doctors' work was largely completed in the initial acute phase of stroke treatment, when Rita was in hospital. What this comparison *does do* is demonstrate the overriding importance of a practical therapy programme of stroke rehabilitation – needed to ensure that the concept of neuroplasticity has enough time to find a way round the damage caused by the stroke. So this is really all there is to it – in my opinion – *given also* that the patient and/or their main carer are totally committed to completing conscientiously everything required by the programme. This last requirement is not a minor consideration and some people may find difficulty in meeting it.

The sad observation is that the one treatment best able to help disabled stroke survivors to recover a better lifestyle was the one that was almost unobtainable in our region of the UK! That treatment was long-term practical therapy, applied daily. What organisation in the UK do you know that is able and prepared to give stroke survivors a time-unlimited programme of therapy along the lines described in chapter 38? Yet such a system was the one immediately activated when Rita and I arrived in the developing country of South Africa. And it was cheap, relative to any other course of action that had been proposed or used – far and away less expensive than the residential course in 2009.

That leads into my very last point for this chapter, which concerns the financial justification for funding a programme that may continue on a daily basis for as long as 18 months. Or, for Rita, 18 months of therapy applied within a total time period of two-and-a-half years, some six times more therapy than any commonly available as a formal programme in the UK, so far as I am aware. This is an important enough subject to be discussed in its own right. See chapter 42.

40

Eight Questions Answered

Several questions are posed by Rita's recovery which followed the totally negative prognosis she received in the summer of 2010. After some thought, I came up with eight questions that should be answered. There may well be more that are relevant, but these are my answers to the questions that occurred to me.

1. Why was Rita able to recover from all those disabilities?

I believe it was because she must always have had the ability to do so, but this ability required activation by the right treatment. As has already been explained, it took many months to obtain access to the treatment Rita needed. A major reason why stroke survivors should respond well to treatment is because stroke is an injury, not a disease. The big problem is that stroke is an injury to the brain – regarded (possibly for good reason) as much harder to understand and treat than a physical injury to the body.

Treatment for Rita's life-threatening stroke was in two parts. First, the remarkably effective emergency treatment to stabilise her and treat resulting side-effects, such as hydrocephalus, followed by a stay in hospital for a few weeks until she was returned home under the Early Supported Discharge (ESD) system. Unfortunately the "support" element was of poor quality, with much too short a timescale. Compared with the therapy given three years later in Fish Hoek, the rehabilitation prescribed for Rita after discharge from hospital could be seen as inappropriate for the disabilities with which she had been left. In effect, it was useless.

This ESD rehabilitation therapy can be compared with that provided for a severe physical injury. To reprise my earlier analogy, suppose someone suffers a road traffic accident and is rushed to hospital with life-threatening multiple breaks in their legs. The emergency treatment stabilises the patient and any side effects are treated. When the injuries are no longer life-threatening, the bones are set, the patient returns home and then spends weeks, possibly months, undergoing physiotherapy to help them walk again. Now, consider a hypothetical alternative regime for this same injury. What if the bones were not re-set but the patient is sent home, being told that their legs might recover spontaneously, but it had been a very serious injury. Unfortunately, the physiotherapy services were limited to a few weeks and the patient might well just have to learn to live with their disability and spend their life in a wheelchair? That action would be unthinkable, but is analogous to how many seriously disabled stroke survivors are treated. Their health is stabilised, but the necessary rehabilitation programme is neither designed nor activated.

The difference between this unthinkable hypothetical example and Rita's stroke is that the first concerned a physical injury to the body, the second a physical injury to the brain. In the second case, the need for suitable treatment seems to be inadequately understood, despite being well documented in the UK. I suspect that health workers can become frightened by a brain injury – a "What do I do now?" "Is it worth doing?" "Are there the resources?" syndrome – whereas the actual treatment needed can be straightforward. It is much easier to see what action to take for a physical injury; much less easy when a brain has been damaged and recovery can (for good reasons) take longer, but can still be achieved. Rita was treated very expertly in the UK in the first emergency phase, but received no effective treatment for the second rehabilitation phase when it was most needed. This left her in a wheelchair for more than two years despite the fact she had the latent ability to recover, as shown by what happened when the South African therapists began to work with her.

One difficulty is that brain injuries following stroke may not be widely understood, largely because the trained resources needed to treat those injuries are just not available in some regions. But that does not prevent quite simple therapy being very effective for at least a range of ABI patients, including those experiencing strokes.

Supporting evidence for the efficacy of therapy to cure brain injury is in the number of recorded instances when celebrities (usually) have received much high quality and appropriate therapy, resulting in excellent recoveries. Also, and ironically, the treatment Rita was given in South

Africa was a close match for that recommended by the *National Stroke Strategy*, adding weight to the view that the NSS document knows what it is talking about, as did those who wrote it! Regrettably, Rita was refused the recommended NSS treatment by the powers that decided these things in our region of the NHS at the time we needed them. The fact that she did retain the innate ability to recover, given correct treatment, was either not seen, or ignored for reasons of expediency.

2. Could others, similarly afflicted, also be capable of recovery?

It is almost certain that many could recover to a significant extent, though there are, so far as I know, no relevant statistics on the ability of disabled stroke survivors to get better once two years have passed without suitable treatment. There is no reason to believe Rita was a special case and was able to respond better than most to rehabilitation treatment once it was given. Quite the reverse could be concluded because she made no significant progress for more than two years after being discharged home. As a result, it would be easy to assume she had little capacity to get better – and this was the conclusion arrived at by nine health and care professionals in the summer of 2010.

My assessment, after eight years, is that many disabled stroke survivors almost certainly have a latent ability to recover, but this needs activating by rehabilitation, both of good quality and in high quantity. There are qualifications to this claim. An important one concerns the willingness of both the survivor and the main carer to put in the time and effort to overcome the disabilities displayed. For severe, multiple disabilities, there is no doubt that a great deal of time must be applied to working on exercises that are always, necessarily, just a little bit too difficult to be done comfortably. Week after week after week of them, and many of the exercises are boring, too. During this time, the carer needs to provide the support and encouragement and cheerfulness to keep going. Recovering is not an easy task, but the effort is well worthwhile once a better quality of life has been achieved.

Other factors to be considered are:

- Some survivors may have damage to parts of their brain that cannot be treated and so, regrettably, recovery may not be possible.
- For each individual survivor, someone has to organise (and possibly pay for) this large amount of therapy. I completely failed

this organisational task in the UK. One difficulty is that, when they first take on the job, few carers, and probably no survivors, have much idea of what is involved, nor of the extent of the task ahead of them. I was certainly in that position.

- Many seriously disabled survivors are left with no motivation to get better; they are just not interested. This puts even more of a burden on the main carer. The book My Stroke of Insight has quite a lot to say on this subject.

I suspect it is only by signing on for a full rehabilitation course that the "recoverability" for any individual survivor can be ascertained. To try it and see is the only practical way to find the answer to this question.

3. Why is the "story" that recovery is impossible after two years have passed believed by so many health and care workers?

It is believed for the good reason that it happens that way. Two years after their stroke, survivors are rarely, if ever, seen to get better and this fact is well known (Rita being an unusual exception). But, just because survivors do not recover does not mean they cannot recover. I suggest that many retain the ability to do so, but this remains a latent ability because, after two years, it never seems worthwhile to start giving therapy, especially when doctors and other health workers claim recovery is now impossible. It is also true that, as time passes, it does become more difficult to achieve recovery. The reasons for this increasing difficulty have been explained earlier.

This third question is a good one that is discussed in some detail in chapter 41. Interestingly, I was told the same thing in South Africa by a doctor responsible for organising a weekend workshop at Stellenbosch University, which had the objective of discussing how to set up new stroke units in several hospitals across South Africa. Our telephone discussion got onto the subject of rehabilitation which, the doctor said, was not well implemented in SA. (Same as in the UK, I guess – good therapists combined with dodgy management. As usual, management wins.) She added that, "Of course, once two years have passed since the stroke, they won't get better anyway." It was this comment from another country that persuaded me to put my thoughts together, in chapter 41, on the ridiculousness of this belief.

Of course, it is true that a proportion of stroke survivors will never recover for a variety of reasons, few of which have anything to do with the elapsed time. But I am confident that it is also true that another proportion has the latent ability to recover despite the lengthy time interval since their stroke, but they don't get better because they are never given the chance to do so. There are pressures on health workers and their managers that encourage the misdiagnosis of survivors, such that innate ability to recover from disability is either not seen or ignored. See Appendix E.

4. Is it possible to set up a project to discover how widely a hidden capacity to recover exists among survivors, two years or more following their stroke?

Of course it is. The biggest difficulty in setting up a project such as this is funding it. It is an idea I took to three professors of rehabilitation medicine located across the country, but I was met with polite disinterest. There were at least three difficulties with the idea. One was that I am a layman so far as medical theory and knowledge is concerned, having no medical qualification. So I have no authority and "don't know anything". Another difficulty was that Rita's story was described, correctly, as anecdotal. So it was viewed as effectively valueless. A third reason was that the professors were running a number of research projects on stroke already and regarded these as taking precedence over my proposal. They were all very polite about it.

In the book This Idea Must Die, edited by John Brockman, Nicholas G Carr contributes a chapter on the dangers resulting from ignoring anecdotal evidence. To quote, "The danger in scorning the anecdotal is that science gets too far removed from the actual experience of life, losing sight of the fact that mathematical averages and other such measures are always abstractions".

My minor contribution to the debate is that many important discoveries of science were made by accident, to the extent that the scientist involved was actually working on an entirely different project when they made an observation – or saw something that looked wrong – or got a strange result that was odd enough for them to stop what they were doing and investigate. Such discoveries often makes nice anecdotal stories. This is often described as "serendipity" when it leads to something new. One anecdote that everyone knows concerns Alexander Fleming's observation of an unexpected result on just one of his experimental Petri dishes. If he had required funding to investigate his observation (as a double-blind, statistically large, carefully designed project) before anyone was prepared to listen, the discovery of penicillin would possibly have been delayed by a few years.

One professor I spoke with, who happened to be a leading Stroke Director at the time, suggested that, if the South African therapists wanted to prove they had something new, they should run a double-blind test on a large enough sample of severely disabled stroke survivors to be sure the results could be shown to be statistically significant. That was a suggestion that, for at least two reasons, was not going to happen.

Firstly, the therapists who treated Rita had nothing to prove. They were well trained. They assessed Rita and decided what her problems were. They gave her the treatment they decided (correctly) that she needed. Rita got better. End of story. The therapists moved on to the next patient. They had no interest in proving to anyone they knew what they were doing, and there was no funding to pay them to take this on as a research project anyway.

Secondly, and despite some criticism, it is generally accepted that a double-blind arrangement is the gold standard for running this type of statistical investigation because, if properly designed, set up and analysed, it should give unequivocal results. It means that the patients do not know whether or not they are being given the treatment under test (usually a medicine), and the researchers who analyse the results do not know which of the patients received the treatment and which received a placebo. But there are obvious difficulties in applying this test to rehabilitation therapy because the object under test is not a small pill, but a long course of exercises. How is the control cohort established? How is who-had-what kept secret from the analysts, and so on? I am not about to solve these difficulties definitively, though I make a suggestion on how it might be done in Appendix E.

I would like to see the results of applying Rita's regime of therapy, described in chapter 38, to a number of severely disabled survivors who, with their carers, are keen to try it. It would begin to build up data to establish whether or not we have something that works. But it still needs a fair amount of funding and organisation.

5. What is the reason for the apparent difference in attitude towards rehabilitation between health workers in our region of the UK and in Fish Hoek, South Africa?

I suspect that a difference in culture between the two countries, combined with different systems of paying for health services, explains much of the difference in attitudes. Darwin's theory of evolution by natural selection has convincingly explained how life has, over time, developed into the wide range of creatures we see today and are known to have existed in the past. Cultures evolve too, though I am unsure to what extent natural selection might play a part in this. There is plenty of evidence that, over time, groups of people living in geographically separated parts of the world have evolved dramatically different cultures. It is not uncommon to hear the complaint that uncontrolled immigration into the UK will "destroy British culture". The long history of multiculturalism in England is criticised for much the same reason. Different cultures exist and compete with one another.

Subcultures also exist and it is differences between subcultures evolved by medical workers in the two countries that interest me here. In South Africa, there is no equivalent to the NHS "free for all at the point of use" medical service. Better-off residents either have medical insurance or pay for treatment privately. Many doctors and therapists are, effectively, paid by their clients and not by the government. They are in competition with each other to provide a service. In the long run, how well they provide that service will determine how much work they get. They need to keep their clients, those ill people who arrive at their surgery doors, happy. Rita and I paid for all the rehabilitation given to her in Fish Hoek and we were highly delighted by the quality of the therapy and the manner in which it was provided.

When the NHS was established, it was designed to be free – no resident of the UK would have to pay for any medical treatment to which it was assessed they were entitled. This sounds wonderful, and it is. What the designers of the NHS in 1948 may not have taken into account adequately was that everyone dies of something, eventually. The average physical health of the British has improved over 60 years; longevity has certainly increased. New and expensive treatments have been developed. Many people have been cured of diseases that would have killed them during the first half of the twentieth century. Some may have been cured of different diseases three or four times before they eventually die. I am now 79 (this book has taken a long time to write!) and have been cured twice of illnesses that might have been fatal without modern medical intervention. Rita's life was saved at great expense by the NHS using techniques for stroke treatment that were certainly not available in 1948.

The obvious result is that the cost of health care has risen rapidly in Britain and threatens to reach unsustainable levels. Budgets are imposed, targets are set, rules are made to limit costs. NICE is established to control the range of illnesses for which the NHS is required to provide a treatment. NHS employees are not paid directly by the patients but indirectly through taxes, with the government as their direct employer. Is it possible that, as a result, service to patients may come second to complying with rules set by the health workers' employers, the government? All NHS health workers must follow the rules and there are lots of managers to ensure they do. I know this is a generalisation, but there is truth in it.

The NHS is great when in emergency mode. When it comes to treating chronic conditions it can be another matter, where the so-called postcode lottery may come into play. Treating chronic conditions, of which stroke disability is only one example, is often seen as long term and therefore expensive; resources are tied up and boxes cannot be ticked to indicate targets are being met. To take a cynical view, perhaps if somebody's stroke disability can be defined as "untreatable", the patient can be transferred into care and so becomes the responsibility of Social Services, not the NHS. And funding for care is means-tested in the UK, reducing the cost to the government. The way that Rita and I were treated made me believe that the resources needed for rehabilitation treatment did not exist in our region, though no health professional we met ever admitted this to me. What happened when I asked for the treatment, as defined by the National Stroke Strategy, was that it was refused, or just never happened. I got cross and battle lines were drawn up. The net result, from our point of view, was that a very negative attitude appeared to prevail in the NHS, specifically regarding Rita's rehabilitation. This was so different from the attitude we found in South Africa.

There is another thought I had about the way the NHS is established and operates which is not directly relevant to rehabilitation treatment, but, nonetheless, this seems an appropriate place to mention it.

One of the frequently extolled virtues of the British health service is, as has already been said, that it is "free at the point of use". Unfortunately, if the desired treatment is inaccessible or not available, the fact that it would be free, if it were available, becomes irrelevant! This is a bit of a shame, when it is patently needed.

This implies that a good subject for discussion could be: "Which health care philosophy is in the better interests of the British public? (1) All authorised treatment will be free, even though some treatments that have not been deemed "official NHS treatments" may not be available, or (2) All treatments will be available, though some must be paid for, in whole or in part."

The NHS is clearly positioned in option (1). If it was not, there would be no need for the National Institute for Heath and Care Excellence (NICE) as presently established. One purpose of NICE, as I understand it, is to assess potential new treatments – to be offered by the NHS – and to adjudicate on whether the expected outcomes justify the costs of providing the treatments. In recent years, some have been accepted and some have not. I have no disagreement with that idea in principle. It seems a sensible approach. The discussion concerning the future status of new treatments is usually open (so far as I know) and any interested parties can have their say.

But what if some decisions concerning treatment have been taken covertly? There may have been no open discussion about them. I have no evidence whatever that this has happened, but it *could* happen. There are lots of pressures on the health service: limited budgets; targets to be met; an aging population and so on. Something has to give and targets and budgets are, rightly, important. But are they more important than patients' treatments? Maybe it would be better if all treatments (that are known to be effective) should be available, but the new terms of reference for NICE were amended to judge whether individual treatments should be "free at the point of use" or have to be paid for (in full or by part payment) by anyone who decides they would like that particular treatment? This approach might solve – or at least reduce – some of the funding problems apparently experienced by the NHS. It's just an idea. However, I suspect it wouldn't be difficult for many people to find arguments against it.

Of course, the change briefly described above is never going to happen. We are stuck with what we have, but this does result in important implications on how stroke survivors are treated. So, to narrow this discussion to the treatment of stroke disabilities only, consider the following short list of statements. They are all supported by evidence and I believe each to be true. Note that in putting forward these statements, I am applying them primarily to the survivors of severe strokes that may have been life-threatening, such that survivors (patients) are sent home from hospital with multiple disabilities (for brevity, I will use the word "patient" as a synonym for "survivor of a severe stroke").

- There is good evidence that, in the UK, the means of providing the best treatment for stroke recovery is well understood and documented.

- When stroke patients are discharged from hospital, they have just two options. One is to work towards making a recovery from their disabilities, the other is to learn to live with the disabilities. The latter is the default option because, if recovery is not achieved, living with the disabilities is what has to happen.

- To recover from severe disabilities needs professional treatment and guidance over an extended period (much longer than six weeks, or even three months!).

- The wide range of disabilities exhibited by stroke patients means that not all may be capable of recovery but, until a serious attempt at recovery is made, the capabilities of any individual patient may be uncertain, if not unknown. Consequently, this means that patients should be treated as individuals and assessed accordingly, not forced into some standardised treatment which may be (and is even likely to be) inappropriate.

- If, as now, the majority of patients are not given a full recovery programme as an automatic part of their early treatment, many of those capable of recovery will be missed.

- There are obvious and major benefits that result from recovery from disability. These are not available to those whose only option is to live with their disabilities.

- If patients are not given the treatment needed for recovery, then they automatically fall into the default option, which is the situation for most UK patients, where they do no more than learn to make the best of their limitations.

- There are no data on the proportion of seriously disabled survivors who might be capable of recovery. This is because too few are given sufficient rehabilitation for these data to be determined. (Taking Rita's examples. She was given little treatment after being discharged from hospital and, two years later, she was assessed as having no capacity for recovery. She was effectively written off. Yet, once the right therapy was given, she did recover almost completely.) Clearly, she had the innate ability to recover all along, but it needed to be identified. It is possible that a significant proportion of patients who do not recover from disability might be capable of doing so in a similar manner, had the best treatment been given to them as an in-community rehabilitation programme.

I have commented in the past on the subject of neuroplasticity of the brain. Recently I found another reference to it. This is in a book, *Max Your Memory* by Dr Pascale Michelon (a DK publication). On page 22, the author discusses plastic changes that can follow a brain injury. He claims that stroke survivors can recover the use of apparently paralysed limbs, thanks to reorganisation within their brains; this I have described earlier using the layman's term "rewiring". He qualifies this claim by saying that access to proper rehabilitation is essential. In my opinion, this is absolutely right. It is my contention that the majority of seriously disabled stroke survivors (in our region of the country anyway) do not have access to proper rehabilitation. They therefore end up in the "default" option, where they are helped to make the best of the situation by the care industry – and are required to pay for this privilege in many cases. (As things stand at present, were they to be treated by the NHS, there would be no cost to them. Is there a conclusion to be drawn from this?)

I would very much like to see all survivors of moderate-to-severe strokes being offered a course of "proper rehabilitation" automatically when discharged from hospital. This may happen in some regions already, but as a generalisation I am far from convinced that Early Supported Discharge leads to "proper rehabilitation" in any meaningful way for many patients. Why it is not already offered is a question that needs an answer.

Once Rita had clearly made a good recovery from her disabilities, we made another discovery about "attitude" in the UK that was both astonishing and sad. Remember that in the summer of 2010 eight health and care professionals (and two months later, a stroke consultant) arrived at the unanimous conclusion that she had no capacity for recovery. It is not that decision that concerns me here, but what happened once it was clear that Rita, against all their expectations, did establish an ability to recover. Regrettably, nothing happened. Not one of the above nine people showed any interest in exactly how Rita had been treated to reach this unexpected outcome, and neither did any of the quite large number of other professionals from the health, care and local authorities, who had known Rita between 2008 and 2010, show any interest whatsoever in how her recovery had come about.

It took two e-mails to our GP to elicit the response that he was "truly pleased that Rita had recovered", but nothing more. Having chaired the meeting that had decided Rita could never recover, was he interested to learn why he had been wrong? Apparently not.

The hospital stroke consultant had assessed Rita several times up to September 2010. I wrote to him to suggest it might be interesting to assess her now she had recovered, to see what had changed compared with the earlier data on her status. There was no reply to this suggestion.

Dr Peter was the neuropsychologist, who had first met Rita in November 2008, then again six months later as the senior consultant during the time she was a resident at the rehabilitation clinic. According to the notes I had of the professionals' meeting in June 2010, his opinion had been requested prior to that meeting. I wrote to him by e-mail to tell him of her successful rehabilitation in South Africa. There was no reply. I did know by now he was a colleague of the expert who, on behalf of the PCT, had assessed the appropriateness of the arrangements for Rita's discharge from hospital. Coincidentally I had, unknowingly at the time, attempted to contact the Professor of Rehabilitation Medicine in whose department they both worked. Again not receiving a reply, I e-mailed the professor once more. Immediately a very polite message arrived saying she had asked Dr Peter to write to me, since he knew Rita. "Hadn't I heard from him?"

Don't these people want to know about occasions when their opinions have been shown to be wrong? Are they not interested in finding out why?

When I was working on R&D in industry and the result of some work was completely contrary to expectations, the immediate reaction was to try to discover why. It would have been irresponsible to ignore such a result. Usually it was found that equipment had been set up incorrectly, or the wrong reagent bottle had been picked from the shelf. However, sometimes it produced new and important knowledge about what was going on. It is well understood that, often, the best time to find out exactly how something works is when it goes wrong!

This might have been an opportunity lost to discover something about rehabilitation that would help other sufferers from disability. The experts in the field were best placed to assess this possibility but seemed disinterested. I found this very sad.

6. Could other badly disabled survivors find help by spending time in South Africa?

Almost certainly they could, and they would probably enjoy the experience very much if they chose to stay somewhere on the Cape Peninsula. After all the tribulations we had in the UK, it was a delight to find the medical services so readily available in Fish Hoek. In early 2015, I mentioned this possibility to the managing nurse of Fish Hoek Home Nursing, Sister Heather Storer, and found she was interested in the idea. We had a few chats about it and put together a tentative programme designed to provide a good rehabilitation programme for stroke survivors from the UK. We came up with two lists and an estimate of costs.

The first list concerned the medical status and available back-up any potential patient from the UK should meet to have a realistic chance that the therapy would be successful. The second covered the ways in which FHHN could help by providing management services, advice and support. We were both of the opinion that, to arrive at a fair assessment of how well a patient might recover on this programme, the first visit should last 12 weeks, or something close to that.

List 1: Suggested attributes needed for a stroke survivor to be well suited to a 12-week trial rehabilitation programme in Fish Hoek

It is assumed that the stroke survivor has been discharged from any community therapy programme in the UK, but still exhibits significant physical and/or cognitive disability. Ideally, they should meet the following requirements:

- They must have access to sufficient funds, including payment for further visits to South Africa if the first visit demonstrates a good potential for recovery.

- They must be free to travel abroad for a period up to 12 weeks without any foreseeable difficulties, ie, with no dependent children or family, and with the approval of close family.
- They must be accompanied by a close family member who is competent to act as carer and also as companion or chaperone. This companion needs to be fully in favour of the enterprise and support the therapy proactively.
- The survivor and/or the companion need strong motivation for recovery and must be prepared to work hard at the prescribed therapy. *(It is common for stroke survivors to lack motivation for recovery, as did Rita. This must then come from the companion.)*
- It is best if neither the survivor nor the companion have any significant illness or chronic condition that is not stroke related and that would need treatment in addition to the rehabilitation therapy.
- Prior to flying, medical advice should be sought concerning the fitness of the stroke survivor to undertake long-haul flights.
- The stroke survivor needs to understand and accept that there is no promise or guarantee that his/her recovery can happen, but that they are trying out an opportunity for recovery that has been successful previously. Also, it is believed that success will, to a considerable extent, take advantage of the neuroplasticity of the human brain. Success will also depend on the patient's willingness to work daily throughout the 12 weeks at what might well be boring and repetitive exercises.

At worst, the stroke survivor should enjoy a long holiday in a good climate and beautiful surroundings, and will have been well looked after!

List 2: The (provisional) services that FHHN might provide

- Trained carers for whatever hours are required, seven days a week.
- Back-up nursing services, 24 hours per day, seven days a week.
- Assessment of potential accommodation as being appropriate for disabled visitors.
- Help negotiating favourable rates for stays of 12 weeks or so.

- Organise the necessary therapists and ensure they worked with the carers.
- Register clients with a local doctor's surgery and with a pharmacy during their stay.
- Register clients with Cape Medical Response (a private company that provides emergency paramedics and ambulance services throughout the South Peninsula) to cover possible emergencies.
- Arrange introductions to local churches for pretty well any denomination desired.
- Arrange taxi services for local trips and visits. (Taxis can be hard to find in the Cape Town district!)
- If several clients were at Fish Hoek together, arrange day visits to places of interest around the South Peninsula, of which there are many. Make it a real holiday too.

My own comments on the above

Rita and I found our own way around this part of the Western Cape. We found our own accommodation, discovered the local culture and how things worked for ourselves and, when we first came to Cape Town, we had no idea that rehabilitation therapy would be available. Had the above lists of help been available to us, all of it would have been so much easier – not that it was especially difficult anyway!

- There is no doubt that competent and high-quality representation to support clients while in South Africa will be an important part of the programme.
- The FHHN quickly became an integral part of Rita's successful rehabilitation treatment between October 2010 and April 2013. We found the Trust to be highly competent, always putting the interests of patients as top priority.
- FHHN is a non-profit organisation. Their website is www. fhhomenursing.com
- It seems sensible to take advantage of the competence of the FHHN and their extensive local knowledge. It must be less costly and more efficient to use their facilities and manpower than attempt to do things on one's own.

Estimated Costs, as at March 2015

We estimated costs for two people to spend 12 weeks in the Fish Hoek district, including air fares (economy), accommodation, travel insurance (very much a guess) and therapy for one, at a total roughly in the range £12,000 to £15,000 at 2015 costs. The difference between the two figures is mainly owing to assumptions on the standard of accommodation required, for example, either self-catering or a guest house. These estimates should be recognised for what they are: only approximate figures to use as a guide. They will change with time. For example, inflation in South Africa was running at about 6% per annum while we were there. To more than offset this, during the past two to three years, the pound sterling had strengthened against the Rand from about R14 to the £1 to R20 to the £1 in 2015. What will happen in the future is anyone's guess.

To these estimates should be added a contribution to FHHN overheads, relating to management costs, for what is, effectively, provision of a local representative to provide support and problem-resolution services. Spending money, that might include car rental, theatre, visits to places of interest, purchase of any personal items and gifts, also needs to be included.

It is worth noting that, of the total cost of a 12-week programme, the three most expensive elements will almost certainly be the air fares, travel insurance and accommodation/living expenses. The therapy and care costs are likely to represent quite a small proportion of the total.

I have spoken with a small number of relatives of disabled stroke survivors who have written to me and suggested this as a way to determine the potential for recovery of their disabled relative. A lot of interest was shown but no one has yet tried it. An impression I have is that many carers and families believe that their disabled relative has been poorly served in respect of rehabilitation treatment, but they seem to expect the therapy to come to them. There appears to be a general unwillingness to go out and find it for themselves. So, at the time of writing, there exists a potential scheme for providing stroke therapy in Fish Hoek, but currently no patients are taking advantage of it! How long this potential service may remain available it is impossible to say. Anyone interested will need to enquire about the current status of the service at that time.

7. Was all the time and expense of Rita's years of therapy justified from a financial point of view?

Yes, it was, by a big margin. This is an important consideration and is given quite a thorough discussion in chapter 42.

8. Can recovery be guaranteed?

The human brain is a highly complex organ and, despite the fact that the understanding of its functions is developing rapidly, it has to be said there must be types of damage caused by stroke that preclude the chance of recovery. In addition, for an adult to recover from loss of part(s) of their brain needs professional guidance, much time and effort put into boring and repetitive exercises, and a determination to keep going in the medium-to-long term. Because it is common for survivors of severe strokes to lack motivation to get better, much of the necessary determination has to come from the main carer who, in all conscience, is unlikely, initially, to be well equipped for this task.

During my time as a carer, I have met a considerable number of stroke survivors who I am fairly sure would be capable of a significant level of recovery, were they given the opportunity. Regrettably, in the region of the country in which we have lived, they have not been given that opportunity, other than in rare instances.

What has been apparent has been the lack of understanding or appreciation of two vital pieces of knowledge. The first is that stroke is an injury, not a disease. Once it is seen as an injury, the necessary treatment becomes more obvious and easier to implement.

Secondly, there seems to be an astonishing lack of understanding that stroke is an injury to the brain alone, the body itself is – in the short term – unaffected. It just looks as though it is affected, by exhibiting partial paralysis, poor posture, loss of balance, difficulty with normal bodily functions such as speaking, swallowing or incontinence, and so on. Putting it another way, immediately after a bad stroke the body itself, from the neck down, is actually not affected in any real way. It just appears to be damaged by the stroke, but it is not. Rehabilitation is not a process of overcoming bodily faults resulting from stroke. It is a process of retraining the brain, through the brain's plasticity, by exercising the body and so persuading working parts of the brain to take over functions that have been lost. This needs considerable effort, as can be seen by comparison with learning to drive a car:

To drive a car automatically (I'm not talking about a car with automatic gears) without thinking about each movement needed and in what order, needs much practice over a long period – much longer than the time needed just to pass a driving test. How many of us, deep in thought while driving, have suddenly realised we remember little of the last few miles, having driven the car more-or-less in automatic mode while thinking of other things? Once one can do this, the car is being driven in the same way as you run, ride a bicycle, play tennis at a high standard, and so on, though in no way am I recommending this mode for safe driving. We have now trained our brains to regard the car as an extension to our own body. What rehabilitation from stroke is (or should be) attempting to do is retrain the brain to get round disabilities caused by stroke damage. It can be done, but it is even harder for stroke survivors because their brains also have to cope with the trauma caused by the stroke itself.

Recovery from stroke cannot be guaranteed. But there is, I am sure, considerable scope for many stroke survivors to improve their quality of life substantially, given that they are prepared to put in the effort required and they receive guidance from professional therapists over the long time period that is probably needed to recover from a severe stroke.

41

Loss of Ability to Recover

Statement: "Disabled stroke survivors lose, permanently, the ability to recover after a period of time, often seen as two years."

Is this claim True or False?

If False, does belief in this claim do harm?

This chapter is an analysis of the above statement, with particular reference to the two questions, based on Rita's and my experiences of treating disability over eight years in the UK and South Africa. Only the cohort of seriously disabled stroke survivors, suffering from multiple disabilities, is considered here because they are the ones who suffer most if the statement is believed, and therefore acted upon, but is in fact wrong.

Background

During Rita's first year following her stroke, we were told several times that there was a time limit on any ability she might have to recover. The limit was put at 6, 12 or 24 months, depending on which health or care professional was talking to us. It was never longer than 24 months. We have heard it stated on radio programmes about stroke. One rather distraught lady claimed she was given a precise date, to the day, when her ability to recover would end. Other stroke survivors and their carers, whom I have asked, have told me that they have been informed of the same "fact".

Is it true that patients do not recover once 24 months have passed?

Of course it is. It happens all the time! After two years it is uncommon to see a severely disabled survivor make an unexpected recovery. Rita is the only example I know where almost complete recovery has occurred after such a long delay in starting therapy. As readers will now be aware, her successful therapy only began once 30 months had already gone by. The information I suggest is *not* known is how many stroke survivors *may* still have the capacity to recover after two years, but their potential is never realised.

Why does late recovery not usually happen?

It doesn't happen because there is no reason why it should. Consider the status of stroke survivors after two years. Any rehabilitation programme they might have been given is long in the past. They have learned to live with their remaining disabilities. They and their carers have slipped into what is (hopefully) a comfortable routine. There is no reason for anything to change. If they are then to recover, major changes must be effected in terms of new treatment, but why should this happen? It doesn't.

Should we expect recovery still to be possible?

Yes, indeed so, and why not? Although there are at least two reasons why recovery becomes more difficult as time passes, there is no reason, in principle, why significant recovery should not still be achievable – *if* the survivor is sufficiently determined to get better, receives the right treatment for their disabilities after this long delay and has not suffered an injury that precludes the possibility of recovery.

How many survivors might recover, once therapy has been delayed for two years?

I cannot answer this question. So far as I know, no one has run a controlled trial to determine it. In any cohort of two-year stroke survivors there will be some who will never recover, some who might make an excellent recovery with the right treatment, and a good many who could make a slight to reasonable recovery. I am an optimist – I would not be surprised if up to 50% made a significant to good recovery, given that several important provisos are met. These are: that the survivors are given the best treatment specific to their individual disabilities; that the treatment continues for months rather than weeks ("as long as they need it", as the *National Stroke Strategy* puts it); *and* they are prepared to work hard at recovery, every day. These three factors are not trivial matters.

Is belief in the statement (about a time limit on recovery) dangerous?

It certainly is, because it can cause survivors who are capable of recovery to be written off, without their potential for a possible recovery ever being investigated. I suspect this may be common.

This is how it happens:

A medical or care professional (who believes in the truth of the statement, and there are many of these) tells a patient they must recover before x months have passed because, after that point, they can make no further progress. The patient believes this, very reasonably, because a professional medic stated it. It then becomes a self-fulfilling prophesy. After the x months have passed, the patient doesn't expect to get better and their doctor doesn't expect them to. By then, no therapy is being given, so why should anything change? Because, after two years, it is observed that patients do not get better, it is assumed they cannot get better. Because it is assumed they cannot get better, it is obviously a waste of scarce resources to give them any further rehabilitation therapy. Without that, there is no chance they ever will recover – and so on! This is a cyclical argument that is not going to be broken easily.

Are there any examples of it being broken?

Rita is the only example I know. A haemorrhagic, life-threatening stroke left her with multiple disabilities, physical and cognitive, and needing full-time care. For two years she received little by way of rehabilitation therapy (as described in Part 1) and she made little progress. After 26 months, a committee of eight health & care professionals assessed her, resulting in a negative prognosis of "no capacity for further recovery". *It seems that the error here was due to the assumption that, because Rita had made no progress to speak of during two years, she was incapable of progress. The correct conclusion (with the benefit of hindsight) would have been that she had not recovered because she had not been given the appropriate therapy*. I am certain that, had Rita stayed in the UK following this negative assessment, she would never have overcome her disabilities. In September 2010, three months following that committee meeting, a ninth professional, a stroke consultant, tested Rita for 40 minutes and confirmed the negative prognosis (chapter 27).

Two weeks after seeing this consultant (a total of 29 months after her stroke), the cycle was broken by flying Rita to South Africa, 6,000 miles from London, and into a totally different environment where therapists did not believe the negative prognosis she had been given. Three weeks after arrival, she began gentle but intensive rehabilitation designed to address her specific disabilities. Within weeks she was showing clear progress. Eventually, this rehabilitation course lasted a total of 18 months, spread over the next two-and-a-half years. By then, all Rita's physical disabilities were effectively cured. She was left with just one cognitive disability – a poor short-to-medium-term memory.

Eighteen months represents a lot of therapy and a long time, much longer than any rehabilitation course I am aware of being made available to patients in the UK. But there are reasons for this long therapy course being necessary, as explained below.

Could all long-term disabled survivors be cured?

One has to say "No". There may be brain damage that is irrecoverable. There are also reasons why delaying rehabilitation makes recovery steadily more difficult – see below. Also, the survivor must be strongly motivated to recover and many are not (Rita wasn't, for a long time). Recovery then depends on the determination of the main carer, and/or therapists, because it demands a lot of hard work over an extended period, as I keep emphasising.

What are the reasons why recovery becomes more difficult with time?

I know of two:

One – A result of severe stroke is that the patient immediately becomes much less active than in their former life. They may be in bed for several weeks, they may then be confined to a wheelchair. The result is that the body's muscles quickly lose strength and muscle tone is lost. Partial paralysis makes exercise difficult – so more strength is lost. Anyone who has spent a week in bed knows about this effect and how weak they can feel when they first get onto their feet again. So, if rehabilitation is delayed for several months, the physiotherapist has not only to overcome the problems caused by the stroke, but also work on strengthening the body once more. To do this effectively can mean a lot of relatively hard exercises, every day.

Two – In my experience, this does not seem to be commonly understood. It is based on the neuroplasticity of the human brain. See the book by Norman Doidge, *The Brain that Changes Itself*, for a much better explanation than I can give. My layman's understanding of what happens is that the brain is constantly rewiring itself and the more we exercise our brains, the more this happens (which is a Good Thing to do, like exercising the body). When a serious stroke occurs, part or parts of the brain are lost (die). This means that the part of the body formerly controlled by the "lost" part of the brain no longer functions properly, if at all. If this was the whole story, recovery would be impossible, but recovery clearly does happen for some survivors. This is down to the brain's neuroplasticity, meaning that other parts of the brain can be persuaded (trained) to take over the duties formerly performed by the "lost" parts. This training is not difficult to do (perhaps surprisingly) but it takes a long time and needs qualified therapists who understand what they are doing. This also explains why the activity of just caring for a patient, however lovingly, will not help with the process of recovery. *Professional* rehabilitation therapy is required, mere loving care is not enough. I am convinced that Rita's good recovery was effected by a combination of excellent physiotherapy and occupational therapy. Using these means, the South African therapists were able to reprogramme parts of her brain. There is lots of evidence that this in fact happened.

The sooner that therapy begins the better it is, because it must be expected that the process of reprogramming (via neuroplasticity) is more difficult the longer the delay before rehabilitation begins. For example, if a partially paralysed hand is exercised regularly and hard, it is likely to improve markedly. If it is left untreated, the parts of the brain that might have been available to retrain for this function will be transferred to other duties! In effect, the brain accepts that a poorly working hand is now "normality" and rewires itself to accept that situation, thus making recovery of the use of that hand much more difficult. (This is a simplistic but plausible explanation and probably true, in principle.)

Three – I know I only mentioned two reasons, but there is another one which has nothing to do with the subject under discussion (the reasons that recovery becomes more difficult with time) but I see it as so important that I will mention it here for completeness.

Let's go back a stage. When stroke survivors are discharged home from hospital, they have just two options – they either recover (to a greater or lesser extent) or learn to live with their disabilities. There is no other option. Recovery needs trained therapy. If only care is provided, spontaneous recovery is unlikely. However competent the carers may be at caring, they do little more than help survivors make the best of their disabilities.

When a severely disabled patient arrives home, the first need is to set up an adequate care system. This is the essential first task. If the patient does not recover to any extent, the caring will then continue indefinitely. At the time of hospital discharge, rehabilitation treatment is not the essential first activity, it can be put on the back-burner for a while. But once the caring has settled down, who then is responsible for setting up an appropriate therapy programme and ensuring that it happens?

In the UK, therapy is the responsibility of the NHS and is "free at the point of use". Care is paid for by the patient (under a means-tested arrangement). The care industry is huge, if all unpaid family and charity workers are included, as they should be. What is the ratio of carers to trained therapists in the UK? I have no data on this but would not be surprised at a ratio of 25:1 or more. And, however loving and attentive the caring is, it will not replace the need for professional rehabilitation treatment. The lack of trained therapists obviously leaves scope for survivors *who are capable of recovery* to be overlooked. To take a very cynical viewpoint, the State (which pays for all the therapy) has a financial interest in providing minimal therapy and pushing survivors into the care industry as soon as possible – maybe with too little regard to their recovery potential – so that the cost is no longer a charge on the NHS budget. This is a big enough subject for a deeper analysis! (Who might be responsible for providing the necessary rehabilitation programme is discussed in more detail in chapter 39, under "The First Observation".)

Summary – Belief in the claim, that there is a time limit to how long stroke survivors retain the ability to recover is widespread.

This is possibly because it is observed that, two years after their stroke, badly disabled patients almost never recover. But the claim is, in principle, false.

The danger arises when both medics and their patients believe the claim to be true. It then becomes a self-fulfilling prophesy that is difficult to avoid.

If a stroke survivor has the potential to recover, he/she will retain that potential almost indefinitely (assuming nothing else goes wrong). Except that …

… The longer the delay between the stroke and the beginning of therapy, the more difficult it becomes to fulfill that potential. This is due to loss of muscle strength, which then needs to be recovered, and the brain accepting disability as "normality" and rewiring itself to do what it can to get round that fact, rather than correcting it.

Rita was disabled to the extent she needed full-time care for more than two years. She was professionally assessed as a "no-hoper". This changed after 30 months when Rita began, for the first time, an in-community rehabilitation programme designed to address her specific disabilities. This plan was our salvation and gave us back our lives. So it is understandable that we regard it as a wonderful programme. For me, Rita's plan had three main attributes: (1) A high level of success (100% for a sample of one!). (2) It was straightforward and easy to organise and control. (3) It was inexpensive. It is now important to trial this programme on other long-term stroke survivors. To date, I have had no success in encouraging anyone else to take up this challenge.

Rita's rehabilitation took a long time, needing 18 months of therapy, far longer than is usually available in the UK for a therapy programme (despite the fact that the *National Stroke Strategy* states such programmes should continue as long as is necessary). This long time requirement was largely due to the fact that recovery from severe disability is a protracted process, and partly due to the reasons given under One and Two above. It is arguable that, had Rita's plan started within a few months of hospital discharge, her recovery could have been achieved in less than 18 months.

How many other badly disabled stroke survivors may have been misdiagnosed, as Rita was, and so consigned to a life of being cared for? I would be delighted to hear comments on the suggestions made in this chapter.

42

Justification for the Financial Cost of Rehabilitation Therapy

Rita was severely disabled by the life-threatening subarachnoid haemorrhage she suffered. Two years after this stroke she was assessed as having no capacity for recovery. Her main therapy programme did not begin until 30 months after the event, by which time it is often considered too late for rehabilitation to be effective. Together, these three factors made it unsurprising that her recovery took such a long time – 18 months of therapy, starting at one to two hours every day, working up to three or more hours. The big surprise was that she did fully recover all but one of her lost abilities.

The question for this chapter is: *How can one possibly justify the cost of 18 months of rehabilitation treatment that is applied every day throughout that time?* The short answer to this question is "Easily"! What seems always to be considered first in the UK is the cost of any proposed medical programme. What should also be taken into account is the cost of <u>not</u> providing that treatment. Rita's history is a good example of this lack of comparison. (Einstein might have included it as his "Third Law of Relativity").

So far as Rita was concerned, the alternative to providing the rehabilitation therapy was *not* to provide it and, instead, place her in a care home, as I was advised to do. The theoretical third alternative – for me to continue looking after her full-time at home, which I had been doing for two and a half years – could not have continued for much longer because I would not have survived the stress. In the opinion of Social Services, the care home was the preferred option. I have forgotten the exact words used by the senior social worker in July 2010, but they were along the lines "Rita's interests will be best met by a care home environment". Once in a care home, a resident with Rita's disabled status would never leave it. However loving and attentive the care in that home might be, it is *care* that is provided, not rehabilitation therapy at the intensity needed for recovery.

So the point to be resolved here is to compare the cost of Rita's long period of rehabilitation with the cost of her living in a care home. A good residential care home in 2010 might reasonably have been expected to cost perhaps £25,000 to £30,000 per annum. Plus a similar cost for each year for the rest of Rita's life (ignoring inflation). That could soon add up to a lot of investment – around half a million pounds if she lived to the same advanced age that her mother achieved!

I paid for the 18 months of therapy and care that Rita received in South Africa so I know what it cost. The combined fees of the therapists, nurse and all the carers over this time came to a total of about £9,500 at the, then, current exchange rates between the Rand and pound sterling. That was the cost for 18 months of therapy and care through the period September 2010 to April 2013.

Not included in this figure are the costs of living in South Africa. These are omitted because we had to live somewhere. In fact, our cost of living in Fish Hoek was significantly lower than when we were home in England. Nor have I included the cost of purchasing the second home in Noordhoek, just outside Fish Hoek; it was a holiday home and the cost was unrelated to Rita's recovery from stroke (even though that was why I bought it). Anyway, most of the costs of purchase could be recovered by selling it, as we did in 2016. Neither have I included the costs of flights between Heathrow and Cape Town, on the basis that we should not have needed to go to South Africa to find a decent level of rehabilitative treatment. It should (and, from a technical point of view, easily could) have been available in the UK. There is no doubt that the techniques for rehabilitation are perfectly well documented and understood in the UK.

This figure of £9,500 solely for treatment was low owing to a number of factors. Effectively, I was paying only for the direct costs of Rita's therapy and care, with only small managerial charges and little in the way of overheads included. It is partly explained by the lower cost of these services in South Africa, especially the provision of carers. Another factor is that I did not have to pay for doctors, consultants or health service managers, as these people were not involved at all in Rita's South African treatment. This clearly kept the overall costs down to a remarkably low total.

Knowing the number of therapist sessions, plus the numbers of hours worked by Rita's carers over those 18 months, it was perfectly possible to estimate the costs for a similar rehabilitation programme in the UK. A quick calculation showed that similar treatment here, for the same period of time and including only therapists and carers, would amount to a total in the order of £18,000 to £20,000. This remains a significantly lower cost than just one year in a UK care home.

It is my firm opinion that the cost of Rita's therapy was fully justified by the successful outcome achieved. It came within the scope described by that awkward Americanism, a "no-brainer". If it could be shown to be successful for a large proportion of seriously disabled UK stroke survivors, it is such a sensible thing to do that *all* should be offered this programme, or one very like it, given they are willing to take on the commitment of hard work needed to ensure the best chance of success. Not all survivors may be able to match Rita's success, but it will cost much less to identify, quite early on, those who will be able to recover and those who cannot. There are also the non-financial benefits that are almost too obvious to mention, but they are so important I will mention them nonetheless. Firstly, Rita now enjoys a quality of life that would never have been possible in a care home, however well managed. Now (2016) she can look after all her own needs, she requires zero therapy or professional care and she is probably physically fitter than most ladies of her age after all that physiotherapy! She is capable of and enjoys five-mile hikes across country, as she always used to. She lives in, and takes good care of, her own home. As for me, I have my wife back, and my own life, now with no full-time caring responsibilities.

A second reason is "the elephant in the room", a purely administrative failing of government policy. The simple picture of this justification is that, by spending a one-off £20,000 (estimated total UK equivalent costs for Rita's cure) on rehabilitation, ongoing costs of approximately £30,000 per annum on care home fees were avoided. The problem here should be obvious: the charge of £20,000 for therapy would come from the NHS budget and the NHS is already strapped for cash. The saving of £30,000 per annum would benefit the Social Services budget, which is within local authority budgets as I understand things (except when the care home fees are paid privately, as they are until the survivor's savings virtually run out).

It is clear that both the charges for treatment, and the savings resulting from that treatment, should all be reflected in a single budget, and this is something that parliament should have resolved years ago!

This financial justification for a prolonged period of therapy is a most important point. So I will illustrate it another way. Despite the fact that Rita and I paid for all the return flights from London to Cape Town, for us both over six years, plus all the therapy costs incurred by Rita's treatment abroad, plus the costs of maintaining two houses, our savings remain in far better shape than they would have been by now, had I accepted the advice given me in 2010 and placed Rita in a care home. However good that care home might have been, Rita would not have made the recovery that she has because it is not the function of care homes to provide intensive and professional rehabilitation therapy. So, we would have been stuck with a substantial ongoing annual cost to us for her care that now does not exist.

Because, in 2016, Rita can look after herself, there is no requirement for carers, physiotherapy or for OT. Thus the current costs relating to her stroke are close to zero, little more than helping with her missing short-term memory. And while we continue to live together these are effectively zero. I am confident there are many stroke survivors similar to Rita who could benefit from this straightforward but necessarily prolonged treatment. If this treatment was applied widely, I suggest there should be a substantial overall reduction in the total costs for taking care of this class of, often elderly, stroke survivors.

Because it is so important, I will mention once again that this financial justification takes no account of the subsequent huge improvement in quality of life enjoyed by both the stroke survivor *and* their main carer! This has to be a major consideration in any civilised country.

43

The Pointlessness of Anecdote?

Anecdotal stories – such as "interesting" histories of one-patient experiences – are commonplace, especially in medicine. They cannot all be, or deserve to be, investigated. It is probable that this view was taken into account when, unsuccessfully, I tried to interest several Professors in Rehabilitation Medicine in exploring Rita's story to investigate whether it holds something valuable that could benefit other patients.

Plenty of scientific discoveries have been made as a result of following up observations of one-off events or results. Alexander Fleming, as I keep pointing out ad nauseam, followed up why one of his Petri dishes, unlike all the others, showed areas of bacteria to be dead. In astronomy, pulsars were discovered as a result of one astronomer examining an unusual signal from billions of light years away.

In the book, *This Idea Must Die*, edited by John Brockman, Nicholas Carr contributes a short chapter entitled "Anti-anecdotalism". In it he says

> *"'Anecdotal' has become something of a curse word, at least when applied to research and other explorations of the real. A personal story, in this view, is a distraction or a distortion, something that gets in the way of a broader, statistically rigorous analysis of a large set of observations or a big pile of data. ... The danger in scorning the anecdotal is that science gets too far removed from the actual experiences of life, losing sight of the fact that mathematical averages and other such measures are always abstractions."*

Out of the hundreds of thousands of individual stories experienced in the UK by stroke survivors over the past ten years, Rita's was different from the great majority in that, contrary to expectations (and also contrary to prognoses by professionals) she did, eventually, make an almost complete recovery from severe disability. This suggests her history might be interesting to anyone who may be curious as to why it happened. It is a fact that her anecdotal story is by no means unique. Other, not dissimilar histories have been published in the media, describing how ABI (Acquired Brain Injury) victims have made recoveries from serious disability sufficiently successfully to return to their former careers. Perhaps unsurprisingly, most of these stories refer to celebrities – people well known to the general public. Perhaps also unsurprisingly, an inference to be drawn from the detail in these reports is that the celebrities appear to have received far more rehabilitation therapy than is available to the average stroke victim.

There were three main factual differences between Rita's life-after-stroke history and those commonly experienced by most other disabled stroke survivors that we have met and talked to:

- It is rare for a stroke survivor to make a substantial recovery, having shown little or no sign of this possibility for as long as two years following their stroke. Rita showed little sign of recovery for more than two years yet, beginning 30 months after her stroke, steadily began to get better, eventually making an almost complete recovery. How did *that* come about?

- Two years after a stroke, most survivors are settled into a comfortable routine of care that does not include significant amounts of rehabilitative therapy, if any. There are few changes in the routine of their lives or those of their carers. Conversely, after two-and-a-half years, Rita's lifestyle and environment changed suddenly and dramatically when she was transferred 6,000 miles to South Africa, avoiding six UK winters, and instead enjoying the Cape Town summers.

- As a generalisation, no stroke survivors in the UK – two years or more after their stroke – receive unexpectedly substantial and intensive rehabilitation for a long period of time (such as a year or more). Compared with this normality, 30 months after her stroke, Rita began a gentle but intensive therapy programme, seven days a week, one to two hours each day, soon rising to three or more hours per day, for a total of 18 months within an overall period of 30 months. At the end of this time, she was well enough to need no further paid care or therapy of any sort and could live a normal life at home.

This outcome has resulted in two obvious and major benefits for Rita:

1. She enjoys a huge improvement in her quality of life compared with being disabled. She is in control of her life once more. This release from a life of disability and dependence also releases me, as main carer, from my caring role that I was never any good at and had no aptitude for. To a lesser extent, all her close family have been released from a worry. Rita's general health has improved substantially, with no more urinary infections or other minor ailments that occurred regularly during 2008 and 2009, and her state of fitness in 2016 is excellent for her age.

2. The costs of maintaining full-time care for a person with multiple disabilities, especially if the services of a care home are needed, are well known in the UK. My experience of paying for all Rita's therapy and care over 18 months in South Africa was that the total cost came to well below the cost of keeping her in a care home for just one year, let alone the rest of her life. While acknowledging that costs of rehabilitation therapy near Cape Town are significantly below those charged in the UK for similar treatment, Rita's actual therapy costs can be adjusted to UK levels and they still, by my calculation, come comfortably below those typical for a year in a UK care home. Accepting these figures as reality, achieving recovery from disability allows a substantial saving in potential costs of long-term caring.

During the period 2008 to 2010, there was much speculation concerning Rita's treatment and condition, but a shortage of hard facts and data. As has already been described in some detail, there were major disagreements between health professionals and me concerning Rita's ability to recover, what treatment she should receive, how much she had been given and how much she was entitled to. There was lots of talk and very little practical action. It is my view now that Rita always did have the innate potential to recover, despite the negative prognosis in 2010. This view was eventually proved correct by the fact that she did lose all but one of her several disabilities! It is also my view that it was the excellent therapy programme provided by the Fish Hoek therapists and carers that was the major factor in enabling that recovery. But that is speculation again, by me this time.

Given these arguments, is it right that Rita's history should be regarded as just anecdotal, of no value to any other stroke survivor and hence pointless? The follow-up question then is: *"Was Rita's recovery a one-off anecdotal story of one lucky person; or could it be used to show that many badly disabled stroke survivors may still have a similar potential to recover if given the appropriate treatment?"* If they do retain that innate potential, how many might benefit substantially as Rita has done? The answer to that last question is unknown (so far as I am aware) and will only become available as a result of some properly conducted experiments. And that, so far, is where I have failed to interest any senior rehabilitation experts in evaluating this potential.

Rita's two benefits resulting from her recovery are so major that I suggest they justify investigation to determine whether other badly disabled ABI patients could be helped by the straightforward regime that Rita was given. The Stroke Association, on their website, claims that approximately 1.2 million residents in the UK are living with the after-effects resulting from a stroke, plus 100,000 new people experiencing strokes each year. It does not need a high proportion of these to respond positively to treatment to have a substantial, beneficial effect on a great many lives. At present, I am not aware that anyone can provide good quality data to suggest what that proportion might be.

Appendix E outlines my suggestion for a small investigative programme that, quite quickly and at relatively small cost, would provide sufficient data to indicate the extent to which Rita's therapy programme might help other stroke-disabled people. If the outcome from this small investigation indicated sufficiently positive results, more extensive work would be justified.

It would be unfair to disabled people and ethically unacceptable to ignore this possibility for recovery, given the large number of people who might, potentially, benefit.

44

Pushing the Boundaries!

This book relates the story of my wife's recovery from multiple disabilities caused by her severe stroke. Inevitably it is anecdotal, being the history of one person only. Even so, several indisputable facts are evident that may have wider relevance to, for example, other survivors of strokes who are struggling with their disabilities.

Fact 1: The surgeon described the stroke as life-threatening. It was only his skill and that of his team during a complex operation, followed by two weeks in intensive care, that saved Rita's life. But because there had been a period of around 11 hours between the stroke and the operation, Rita's brain had been quite badly damaged. She was left with severe disabilities.

Fact 2: Little progress was made towards overcoming Rita's multiple disabilities, both physical and cognitive, during the next two years.

Fact 3: At the end of two years, nine health and care professionals concluded that Rita had no capacity for recovery; the implication from this assessment, that no further rehabilitation treatment was justified, was confirmed in a letter.

Fact 4: During the second half of year three, Rita began an in-community therapy programme in South Africa that, after 18 months of daily therapy, cured her effectively of all disabilities except one, and that was much improved.

There is little doubt that the prognosis by the neurosurgeon was correct. Rita did not die as a result of the stroke, but without his medical intervention it was as certain as can be that she would have done so.

Fact 2 is an interesting one. There is no disagreement over the fact that after two years Rita remained badly disabled and needed full-time care. What was in dispute, between a director of the, then, PCT and me, was whether appropriate treatment had been provided. The director's view was that it had been, though, because I was never given access to the supporting records, I cannot comment on the validity of that view. My contention was based on the recommendations of the *National Stroke Strategy* and the *National Clinical Guideline for Stroke* concerning how much practical therapy represented best practice. In my view, what Rita had received fell well short of what should have been available. My daily journal recorded how much physiotherapy and occupational therapy there had been. I knew the dates, how long the sessions had lasted and the names of the therapists. Outside the residential course in 2009, I have to say there were very few sessions recorded. But irrespective of which of us was right, it was obvious Rita had not made a significant recovery during those two years.

Fact 3, that, to put it bluntly, Rita was assessed as a "no-hoper", was recorded in minutes of meetings and subsequent letters. Later events in South Africa showed this assessment was a mistake. Rita *was* still capable of a good recovery, presumably dependent on being given the appropriate treatment. So it raises the question as to how the erroneous decision of Fact 3 was arrived at by senior managers, consultants and therapists. I could think of three possibilities. One was that these professionals were all certain that Rita had been given sufficient and appropriate treatment and was just too badly disabled to recover. A second was that I had been so much of a bloody nuisance over two years that, by saying that recovery was impossible, Social Services would have to take full responsibility for care and the health authorities would then get rid of Rita (and me) from their books. A third was that the PCT did not have, and never had had, the resources to give Rita the therapy recommended by the above two documents. This was a distinct possibility and, I suspect, the right one. This is all speculation on my part and maybe the real reason was something I haven't thought of with my now rather cynical outlook on things.

Fact 4 happened just as described in Part 2. Eighteen months of rehabilitation in Fish Hoek were needed for Rita to reach the stage where no further therapy or support from carers were called for, but it was clear within a few weeks of starting this programme that good progress was being made.

This last fact raised several questions. Was Rita a "one-off" in that she responded to therapy far better than other stroke survivors? (This was unlikely. Why should she be highly amenable to treatment? In any event, she had gone two years showing almost no recovery potential despite the good therapy the PCT claimed to have provided.) Why *did* she begin to get better only after two years – and more – had passed since her stroke? This almost never happened in practice to other survivors, as was well known (see chapter 41). What was special about South Africa? Just moving to a better climate than that of the UK winter hardly seemed sufficient justification for an almost complete recovery. Perhaps Rita retained an innate ability to recover and this was missed during the first two years and more following her stroke? Maybe this ability would only come to light when the "right" treatment was applied?

This last suggestion seems to hold merit. Rita did overcome, eventually, the worst of her disabilities and so must always have held the ability to do so. This ability must have been well hidden because none of the 70+ health and care staff who had dealings with her during the first two years in the UK noticed it. But, once she was in Fish Hoek, her ability to progress was quickly discovered. So what was different about life in Fish Hoek that could cause this welcome advance? This is discussed in chapter 37. My view was that perhaps half a dozen factors helped, but by far the most important was the quality of her South African rehabilitation programme – a view strengthened by the fact that the programme bore a strong resemblance to that recommended by the *National Stroke Strategy* as best practice, even though the therapists in Fish Hoek had never heard of that document. (An interesting observation!)

The three therapists who were based in Fish Hoek and helped Rita were all Afrikaans ladies and were all graduates of the University of Cape Town (UCT). They all followed the same general policy – to keep "pushing the boundaries", though it was only Adele who verbalised this admonition. She regularly ordered us to keep pushing the boundaries because not to do so could result in a halt to Rita's progress – and she followed this policy herself. As soon as Rita managed to do a new exercise correctly,

Adele immediately gave her a slightly more difficult one, ensuring that Rita was always pushed from her current limit of ability to do better and more. She was always being given work or exercises she was not quite able to manage. Estie and Shona followed the same practice, though without explaining it as explicitly. Adele instructed me to "push" Rita in the same way in the other "activities of daily living" as they had been called in the UK. Once she could sweep the wood floor in our home, she should next relearn how to wash it. Once she could walk a mile with me through the hills of the Cape Peninsula, we should aim for two miles. Once she could walk a half-mile across soft sand to the sea's edge, we should paddle through the shallow, fast-moving water from breaking waves to help Rita's sense of balance. Once she could stand on a balance block without falling off, things should be made more difficult by playing catch with her while she stood on it.

Adele pointed out that once Rita stopped "pushing the boundaries" she would stop progressing. I remonstrated with her once or twice on the basis that, if Rita kept trying to do things she couldn't quite manage, she was liable to have an accident. Adele retorted that everyone, fit or disabled, was likely to have an accident at any time and that the accidents Rita would have while "pushing her boundaries" would be less serious than those that would happen if she stopped trying. When I thought about this and the many small accidents Rita had suffered, Adele was absolutely right!

All this led on to yet another question. Why was Rita the only stroke survivor we knew who had managed to recover well, two years after her stroke, having shown no signs of this ability earlier? At no time had I read of anyone doing this, though I suppose it must have happened from time to time. Could it be that other seriously disabled stroke survivors still retained an innate ability to get better but it had not been recognised, as Rita's had not? (see also chapter 41). Rita had obviously had this ability and it seemed far more probable that others would have it too than that she was the only survivor in the country with a hidden ability to recover. And if this ability was not recognised in a survivor, nothing would be done about it and the ability would effectively be wasted, that person probably spending the rest of their life in a state of dependence. The above discussion provides a neat explanation why loving care does little or nothing to promote recovery. Loving care does not "push boundaries".

It did not take much thought to come up with several ways in which a real but hidden ability to recover might be missed.

Start with three assumptions. One: we are dealing with survivors who are severely disabled, much as Rita was, and need good quality rehabilitation to have any real chance for recovery. Two: they have an innate ability to recover, but to identify this ability needs "best practice" therapy provided over the medium-to-long term (as recommended by the *National Stroke Strategy*). Three: Care and Rehabilitation are two different ways of supporting disabled people. Care means helping patients make the best of their troubles, so that they can be as comfortable as possible while living a life of dependency. Rehabilitation is the treatment process aimed at ensuring survivors' recovery from their disabilities (so far as is possible). This can be an uncomfortable process and requires much effort and hard work from the survivor (and others) over a long period. However loving and expert Care may be, it is unlikely to lead to recovery from disability.

Given the above, it is possible to see how survivors having a real ability to get better are processed through standard rehabilitative programmes that are never going to find this ability.

Here is a non-exhaustive list covering some of the ways we came across that would fail to identify an ability to recover:

- The six-week re-enablement programme given to Rita following her discharge from hospital was totally inadequate. It could never correct the level of disability she had at that time.

- See Appendix B, the consultant's review of the quality of Rita's discharge from the stroke unit in our local hospital. At the end of his review he comments, "*Sadly for Mr and Mrs Guthrie, their experience only serves to underline the fact that, if there is to be rapid discharge from hospital there must be adequate support in the community to assist patients and their families to manage patients with complex needs.*"

The Stroke Association, in the summer 2016 issue of its magazine *Stroke News* quotes the following statistics:

Lives and recoveries are being put at risk. Stroke survivors in England told us:

More than 45% felt abandoned when they left hospital.

47% were not contacted by a healthcare professional when they left hospital. More than a third didn't receive a six-month assessment of their health and social care needs.

- Throughout the eight years, Rita and I have never met a survivor/carer combination who claimed to have received a rehabilitation programme that fully reflected the best practice recommended by the *National Stroke Strategy.*

- In parts of the country, the recommendation for follow-up rehabilitation, when Early Supported Discharge from hospital is invoked, includes a 45-minute session every day of the week by all the therapists needed by the patient. This is likely to include physiotherapy and occupational therapy. It could also include speech therapy and, maybe, others. Even allowing for the fact that this level of treatment may not continue for long (enough!), there are not the numbers of therapists in the country available to support this level of treatment. Again a statistic from the Stroke Association website. It records that the number of survivors in this country suffering from the after-effects of a stroke is around 1.2 million, and that there are approximately 100,000 new strokes every year. (Note that the Fish Hoek therapists used their own services efficiently, while also reducing the costs of treatment. Their system enabled a more economical use of therapists' time than in this country as is explained in chapter 38).

We all know, in mid 2016, how short of cash the NHS is said to be, with the need for savings to be made wherever possible. Patients with long-term chronic problems are about the last thing the NHS wants to see, but there are so many of these: cancer, diabetes, kidney and other problems with organs, progressive mental disorders and, of course, stroke. Stroke patients differ from many other chronic disorders in that stroke is an injury, not a progressive disease. Most progressive diseases need continuing medical intervention; stroke is, I believe, different. Once stroke survivors are stabilised and have been given a rehabilitation course of variable quality, they reach a plateau of greater or lesser disability. At that point, their primary need is seen to be care and support, most often supplied by family members with help from charities and the Social Services.

I may be maligning the NHS here, but the impression I got, as far as Rita was concerned, was that, because she was known to be seriously disabled, any therapy, if it was to be successful, would be long-term and expensive and the probability for success was thought to be poor. The cost of any therapy provided would come from the NHS budget. The cost of care would be paid either by the patient or Social Services (local authority). If Rita was assessed as untreatable (as she had been in June 2010), there would be no further NHS costs attributable to her treatment. Social Services would take over and had already voiced a preference for Rita to live in a care home.

I have no evidence whatever that this was the thinking behind the negative prognosis given to Rita in June 2010, but I can understand the pressure to keep medical costs as low as possible and to avoid spending money on patients who could not benefit from such treatment. I can also understand the pressure to move patients with reasonably stable long-term chronic conditions from the close-to overwhelmed medical services into the huge care industry. But I can also see how stroke survivors having an innate ability to recover – if it existed – might be overlooked in these transfer operations. Once within the care industry, the likelihood of finding their hidden ability to get better would be close to zero. I am certain Rita would never have recovered as she did if she had stayed in the UK, following the outcome of that meeting in the summer of 2010.

* * *

My concern in this long-winded argument is that a significant proportion of severely disabled stroke survivors may still retain an innate ability to recover well, but their ability is never identified. Rita must have held on to that ability for more than two years before the major change to her environment and start of an intensive in-community programme brought it to light. And as I have pointed out several times, there are several well-known instances of celebrities suffering severe strokes, and then recovering well from resultant severe disabilities. Yet some of the issues raised in chapter 41 show that, within the general population, it is almost unknown for stroke survivors to live a life of dependency for more than two years, then begin a successful and almost complete recovery.

So I believe what is unknown is, firstly: do *many* disabled stroke survivors have the hidden ability for recovery but it needs a particular form of rehabilitation programme to identify and take advantage of it? Or, secondly, does this hidden ability only exist in a *small minority* of stroke survivors?

My eight years of experience with stroke rehabilitation leads me to suspect that the correct answer lies in the former question – an ability to recover is quite common unless there is some other over-riding factor that precludes it, such as an illness additional to the effects of stroke. But I have no hard evidence to support this hypothesis.

There are two strong factors that make it really important to know whether that innate ability to get better exists, or whether it doesn't. If it does exist and can be activated, a seriously disabled survivor might (as Rita did) move from a life of dependence to a near normal quality of life again. Not only is their life vastly improved, but so is the life of volunteer family or friends who spent so much time looking after them. The second is that the costs of caring might be reduced to near zero; and if a care home was the alternative to recovery, the reduction in future care costs might be tens of thousands of pounds per annum.

These two factors are so important that, if there is a reasonable possibility for badly disabled survivors to recover, this possibility must be explored before they are consigned to a life of care and dependency.

The next step needed is to measure the proportion of severely disabled survivors who may still possess the hidden ability to recover. Appendix E describes a fairly simple and practical project that should give a good idea of this proportion. If the number is found to be significant, the next step is already known: implement fully the *National Stroke Strategy*, though, for obvious reasons, I favour the amended version used by the therapists in Fish Hoek (chapter 38).

Whatever is done for stroke survivors, all concerned need to keep "Pushing the Boundaries".

Appendix A: Letter to the PCT, November 2009

The PCT requested a report from the hospital that treated Rita. This report was to explain the circumstances of Rita's discharge from hospital. The request was replied to by the hospital CEO. I wrote the letter below, addressed to the PCT, to give my comments on the CEO's report.

26 November 2009

Director, PCT

Dear Madam,

Report from the CEO, [our local] Hospital

Thank you for sending a copy of the report from [the CEO]. While not disputing any of the facts as stated, there are two sides to this situation. One side is the statement from the hospital that your expert now has. The other side is the patient's view – were her needs met? For your external expert to make an informed assessment concerning my complaint, I suggest that he/she needs both views. For this reason I would be grateful if you would forward a copy of this letter to the expert.

I have always found the staff at the Stroke Unit pleasant, helpful and competent, and I have no doubt that what was done to cover Rita's discharge in June 2008 was done with the best of intentions. Regrettably, from the patient's point of view, and as a generalisation, it completely failed to meet her needs. I could write several pages explaining why this was so (and will do so if requested) but it is beyond the scope of what I want to say here. But I would like to give some support to this conclusion:

1. There was no written discharge plan that had the agreement of all concerned and specified who would do what, when and for how long, and there was no "case manager" to resolve difficulties. When things fell apart, as they did, there was no one but me to find a solution.

2. I received no training whatever from anyone on how to care for a severely disabled person. Just picked it up as I went along.

3. "Rehabilitation" is mentioned several times in the report. During the first eight months following discharge, Rita received two sessions of physiotherapy treatment. A short OT programme in December 2008 was useful and effective, but was not restarted following the Christmas break. It took me seven months to negotiate a residential rehab programme for Rita, and that only happened following intervention from our Member of Parliament. The *National Stroke Strategy* document (see below) sees immediate and prolonged rehabilitation as vitally important.

4. There was no follow-up from the Stroke Unit to ensure things were okay. The re-enablement programme was so far from what Rita needed that the manager of the team agreed that it should be cancelled after one week, as not meeting Rita's needs. I then received no help from the NHS or Social Services in resolving the care problem and employed a live-in carer myself. The continence nurse only appeared eight days after discharge. The continence pads she provided were totally inadequate. It took seven months to persuade them to provide pads appropriate to Rita's needs and for several months I bought them over the Internet to try to minimise the frequency of wet and soiled beds and clothing. We did have a review with [the Nurse Consultant at the hospital] on 12 August 2008 that highlighted several needs. For various administrative reasons no practical help was provided in dealing with any of these. I had the strong impression that they had plenty to occupy themselves with and regarded Rita as no longer being their responsibility. We did not have the six-monthly and annual reviews that the NSS says are important.

5. Only during the last seven/eight months have I discovered two relevant documents, the *National Clinical Guideline for Stroke*, and the *National Stroke Strategy* (NSS) from the Dept of Health, which claims this Strategy is being implemented. Both these documents define what treatment should be provided for stroke patients during recovery, summarised in a series of Quality Markers. The ones that are particularly relevant for Rita are QM3, QM10, QM12 and QM14. I doubt whether Rita, in the first year of her recovery, received 10% of what these documents suggest should

be provided. The many actions in [the CEO's] report really did not comply at all with NSS recommendations.

To summarise; stroke patients vary greatly in their recovery needs. It doesn't require me to point out that for each patient his/her needs should be identified and a plan prepared to meet them. It is only basic good management to ensure that this plan, once in place, is checked regularly for effectiveness and modified if or when necessary. The NSS lays it all out perfectly clearly. It seems to me the NHS has got very badly out of balance: brilliant neurosurgical teams, followed by seriously deficient aftercare. If the aftercare cannot match the surgery, then what is the point of expensive neurological surgical units keeping bodies alive and causing huge problems of care, often to people totally untrained to carry it out? I never expected to say this, but the last 18 months have almost destroyed me. Our family has always been close, but the last months have caused a serious rift between our children (all in their 40s) concerning what is to be done with their mother. I have had to lay down the law and make it clear that any decision on that is mine alone, but it is another battle I could do without and is caused primarily by the huge difficulties we have.

Finally, I cannot believe Rita is a special case, there are probably many others like her. [The CEO of the hospital] says he seeks to improve the standard of services and is keen to learn about patients' views. I would be only too happy to help in any way I can to provide better aftercare for stroke patients should my experience be useful. The offer is there.

Yours sincerely,

David Guthrie

cc [CEO, Local Hospital]

Appendix B: A Summary of the Independent Consultant's Report on the Circumstances Surrounding Rita's Discharge from Hospital in June 2008

The report was four pages long, dated 17 May 2010 and I received a copy on 29 June. It was written by a Consultant Physician in Rehabilitation Medicine, based at a Rehabilitation Unit in London. The author had been assisted by the Professor of Rehabilitative Medicine and by Dr Peter. It was addressed to Mrs Matthews, at the county NHS Trust. The report was divided into headings. Summarised are the main points made, with comments by me in italics.

Diagnosis: Severe traumatic brain injury.

Impairments: Significant cognitive/communication and physical problems. *Listed were the various documents he examined including my letter to the PCT Director specifying my areas of concern [Appendix A], the* National Stroke Strategy, *records from the hospital and correspondence between me and professionals. He doesn't say whether he met or interviewed anyone else involved. I still find it odd that he did not find it necessary to talk to me.*

In **Background information** he summarised the history of Rita's illness pretty accurately, but says that Rita was continent while at the rehabilitation clinic, though this aspect of her condition was not commented on in the final report from the therapists there. [*She was frequently not continent when Sue and I visited her there, as described in chapter 13*].

The **Medical discharge summary** section records that, according to our local hospital, Mrs Guthrie suffered from extensive subarachnoid haemorrhage, but there was no description of her current functional status ... and ... simply records her to be "well with no symptoms" (*which was clearly incorrect, see paragraph below*). In addition, there was very little information on the record of her progress through the neurological hospital and then at the local one, which is often very helpful for the community teams *(which were never set up for Rita)*.

The section **Occupational therapy report** records that an OT report was prepared for Rita's discharge from hospital in June 2008, but was undated so may not have been the final version. This report does clearly identify her cognitive difficulties, including very poor memory, difficulty with executive skills and frequent disorientation in the hospital. A number of difficulties on discharge were identified by this hospital report, requiring structural changes, but he was unable to find any record of how these were going to be implemented prior to discharge. In neither report could he find any record of what information was given to the patient and her family *(there was none)*. Although her care requirements were identified there was no clear indication of what care had been set up for her at home, other than the re-enablement programme, subsequently cancelled. A multidisciplinary team discharge meeting did take place in which Mr Guthrie was informed *(misinformed, would be more accurate)* about his wife's problems. However, as Mr Guthrie says, there is no evidence of any specific training or advice offered to him to help him cope with these problems.

Oddly, there was no comment concerning physiotherapy. Effectively none had been provided on an in-community basis, though Rita had received some physiotherapy prior to discharge and at the rehabilitation clinic.

Findings and recommendations. The author said that "Firstly, it should be recognised that Mrs Guthrie had an unusual presentation with a subarachnoid haemorrhage complicated by hydrocephalus and traumatic brain injury. This type of diffuse brain injury often leads to cognitive and behavioural difficulties … and it is not altogether surprising that the hospital Stroke Service struggled to meet her needs." (*If these hospital staff, working full-time looking after stroke survivors, had difficulties in meeting Rita's needs, it was hardly surprising that I had major problems in trying to cope on my own without any guidance or training.*)

"Ideally, in my opinion, she should have been referred to a specialist rehabilitation unit … more used to identifying and managing the problems of acute brain injury … to manage a graded discharge and prepare the family properly to support the ongoing care needs. … However, as it was, she was managed in a local stroke service and one has to accept that this type of service is unlikely to have either the resources or stroke skills to support the complex discharge planning arrangements that this type of patient requires." (*Is this intended as an excuse for the unsatisfactory arrangements? It seems to me to make a referral to a graded home discharge even more necessary.*)

"Discharge summaries should contain complete and consistent information to facilitate ongoing care by the community teams. In this case there do appear to have been some important inconsistencies … as well as incomplete information."

"All reports should be dated and should contain details of (a) ongoing care arrangements, and (b) information and training provided to the patients and their families." (*This information was missing, probably because none of the described services and guidance had been provided. The consultant regularly talks about "care". What about "rehabilitation" which is essential for recovery?*)

"Finally, I note from Mr Guthrie's complaint that there was no input from a case manager and inadequate support from the community rehabilitation team. Unfortunately, in our experience, this is not unusual. … The [region in which Mr and Mrs Guthrie live] is by no means unique in having inadequate community services to manage patients with complex needs." (*This does not explain why there was so much prolonged resistance by the PCT to my requests for the treatment that Rita should have been given.*)

"Sadly for Mr and Mrs Guthrie, their experience only serves to underline the fact that, if there is to be rapid discharge from hospital there must be adequate support in the community to assist patients and their families to manage patients with complex needs."

[name]

Consultant Physician in Rehabilitation Medicine

Rehabilitation Unit.

These are, in my view, the main points of this report which is politely critical of the lack of services provided for Rita and me. The author indicates our experience is not uncommon and that the hospital staff, in some respects, did the best they could with the inadequate resources that were available to them. But, if medically trained staff, in what they proudly claimed was a good specialist stroke unit, are unable to provide adequate care arrangements for seriously disabled patients, how on earth can lay people with no training or experience be expected to cope with the situation?

The author makes no comment on the reason, repeatedly given by the nurse consultant, for not providing Rita with rehabilitative treatment, which was that we lived in one PCT area whereas the hospital was located in an adjacent PCT region. Thus the hospital that treated Rita had, she claimed, no further responsibility to provide after-treatment following discharge. Discussion of this fact was at least one good reason why he and I should have met.

Was there an outcome resulting from this report? There may have been changes made to the discharge plans and procedures within the Stroke Unit of the hospital, to assist later patients and their carers and families, but I have no information on whether this happened or not.

I had optimistically, and naively, expected that if the consultant's report was critical then the PCT would be morally bound to make some attempt to replace the treatment and support that was missing during the first year that Rita spent at home, at the very minimum. There I was sadly mistaken. I cannot identify any practical benefit whatever that accrued to Rita following the submission of this report in May 2010. This was disappointing. Mrs Matthews (PCT) had, after all, written to Sir Alan Haselhurst on 19 March in terms that could only be inferred to represent a strong commitment to helping Rita in the future. Then she wrote again to me on 15 April to advise me that she placed a high level of importance on the *National Stroke Strategy* document. Despite all this, Rita received no further rehabilitation treatment whatever from this PCT since that report was submitted. I consider this to be disgraceful.

The only action Mrs Matthews mentioned following the recommendations from the independent assessor, was to provide the Commissioning Manager for the hospital with a copy of the report and to say that she would be meeting with her in due course to discuss how the PCT would take these recommendations forward, to improve care for stroke patients in the future. I hope this happened.

Appendix C: Summary of Rita's History and Progress, April 2008 to March 2011, the First Three Years

Listed below is a summary of Rita's rehabilitation treatment over a period of 36 months. Taking April 2008, the month of her subarachnoid haemorrhage, as month 1, the length of each period is shown to the nearest month. She spent the first nine weeks recovering in two hospitals, successively, during the later part of which she received some occupational therapy and physiotherapy. She was discharged home at the end of Month 3, so Month 4 (July 2008) was effectively the first month she was back in my care.

Months 4 to 6	no occupational therapy whatever; three sessions of physiotherapy.
Months 8/9	a six-week programme of occupational therapy at home.
Months 10 to 14	no NHS rehabilitation treatment.
Months 14 to 16	three months of rehabilitation in a residential clinic.
Months 17 to 30	no NHS rehabilitation treatment
Months 31 to 36	included 20 weeks of programmed therapy in South Africa by a physiotherapist and an occupational therapist, plus additional supervised therapy by carers, increasing from one to three hours each day every day.
Months 4 to 30	No named health professional in overall charge of Rita's treatment for stroke recovery.
Months 1 to 30	No formal advice or training provided for the main carer, other than that organised by local charities.

| Months 31 to 36 | Rita's treatment overseen by a nurse, experienced in care for the elderly, who also provided advice for the main carer while we were in South Africa. |

The following table shows Rita's capacity to carry out a number of activities at three dates during those 36 months, plus her general health status at those times. There were occasions when she was given quantitative tests – insofar as any tests of severely disabled patients can be quantitative – especially during the three months of residential treatment. I was not given all the results (which anyway would have been largely meaningless to me) and Rita was not tested in a planned programme over this whole period, so there is no record of how the results progressed over the timescale. Consequently, I have used my amateur observations and records to indicate her status at these dates and progress between them.

The first date I chose was the end of August 2008 (Column A) when she had been home approximately two months and caring for her was very difficult. Column B was two years later, August 2010, two months following the negative prognosis. Column C was February 2011, when Rita had received about five months of therapy in South Africa in two sessions, before and after Christmas 2010.

Measurement or Observation	Column A	Column B	Column C
	Month 5	Month 29	Month 35
Number of months following hospital discharge	2	26	32
Average No. of falls each month	5	2	0.7
No. of continence pads used daily, averaged over a month	4.05	2.30* (1.3)	1.15* (0.15)
No. of continence "accidents" each month	18	3.5	0.7

*This looks like a halving of daily pad usage over six months from 2.3 to 1.15, but that is misleading. This is because pads were changed after being worn for 24 hours whatever their state. So the reduction in pads per day *that were wetted or soiled* would more accurately be shown by the figures in brackets.

Time to walk 60 yards in garden, seconds	115	69	50
Ability to:			
get up from a chair without assistance	No	Not with me in the room	Yes
make cup of tea	No	With considerable prompting	Yes
peel vegetables	Poorly	With prompting	Well
wash up	No	With supervision	Well
dust furniture	Only with close supervision	When supervised	Yes
hang out washing	Not safely	When supervised	Yes
complete six-piece jigsaw	No	With prompting	Yes
complete 100-piece jigsaw	No	With help and prompting	Slowly, a little help
play dominoes	No	With prompting	Yes
solve concise crossword clues	Yes	Yes	Yes
fill in crossword grid	No	No	With errors
read to herself for extended period	No	No	Yes
initiate conversations	No	No	Yes
drink normally	No, just sips	No, very slowly	Yes
eat meals at normal speed	No, very slowly	Slower than normal	Rather slowly
go to toilet at home without assistance	No	No	Yes

go to strange toilet, (café etc) without assistance	No	No	Yes
in and out of bed without assistance	No	Often needs help	Yes
use toilet at night without assistance	No	No	75% of time
watch TV with interest	No	Rarely	Yes
get into car and fasten belt without assistance and help	No	With prompting	Yes
put on own footwear	No	No	Yes
get dressed without help	No	No	Mostly, some help needed
know what day it is	No	No	Rarely
know what year it is	No	No	Usually
find her way around the house without prompting	No	No	Often makes mistakes
find her way to a different location in town, on own	No	No	No
know where in kitchen plates, etc, are kept	No	No	Occasionally gets it right
irrational behaviour	Frequent	Quite common	None

Several conclusions can be drawn from the above:

Rita made slow progress overcoming some disabilities during the first two-and-a-half years, but the only time it accelerated markedly was during the first five months in South Africa, when rehabilitation was provided regularly by trained, professional therapists. The attempts to provide rehabilitative treatment that were made by Social Services, friends and family were pretty much a waste of time. Spouses are particularly inappropriate for this task as the relationship is too close. (I am sure that untrained helpers and carers – such as I was – could help positively, provided they were properly advised and supervised.)

Rita did make some significant, if slow, recovery during the 29 months to August 2010, though severe limitations remained. A large part of this improvement occurred during the period of residential rehabilitation during months 14 to 16.

Once a consistent regular rehabilitation programme was established, in South Africa, from month 31 onwards, using trained professionals and watched over by a senior nurse who understood Rita's disabilities, substantial progress was made in a relatively short period of time and these advances were maintained.

The improvement in Rita's condition during the six months, 31–36, greatly exceeded what had been achieved during the preceding 24 months. She reached a stage where her full-time care became straightforward, not the chore that it had been. This was largely due to the huge improvements in her incontinence, her motivation, her balance and stamina, and the loss of the irrational behaviour somewhere along the line after month 30. Irrational behaviour is an awful thing and losing it was a huge benefit to me.

The period of fastest, and greatest, improvement occurred *after* 30 months had passed following the haemorrhage – good evidence that the often-repeated mantra that "significant improvement after two years is not possible", is untrue (chapter 41). This period of fast recovery also followed the assessment by nine UK health and care professionals that Rita was actually incapable of further recovery.

Both periods of sustained recovery were during times when trained professionals treated Rita regularly in accordance with a planned programme, the first being the 12 weeks at the rehabilitation clinic.

Authoritative books and documents (including the *National Stroke Strategy*) on the treatment of stroke victims say that the best time to apply rehabilitation is during the first six months following the stroke. In hospital, Rita was apparently making good progress, certainly in mobility, and was receiving regular physiotherapy and OT, so I was told. Once she was back home, all treatment stopped abruptly (the Social Services "re-enablement programme" cannot be regarded as rehabilitation when applied to severe disability) and Rita's serious problems surfaced. One has to wonder how much she would have advanced, and how much more quickly, if those four months immediately following discharge from hospital had not been wasted.

It is clear (with hindsight) that Rita always had innate potential for recovery, notwithstanding various judgements to the contrary. It was by great good fortune that we eventually stumbled on a regime in South Africa that provided the treatment that was needed, and Rita blossomed. Why are the recommendations for rehabilitation treatment, clearly given in the *National Stroke Strategy*, not applied to all badly disabled survivors? It is an official document published by the Department of Health and, presumably, was intended to be followed. Just suppose in September 2010 we had *not* gone to South Africa but had remained in the UK for the long cold winter with, obviously, no NHS rehabilitative treatment of any sort being provided. What would have happened? Rita would not have recovered because there would have been no reason why she should. She may even have regressed under those conditions, as was predicted by the stroke consultant. That could well have "proved" the assessment of the nine professionals – that Rita could make no further progress – to be correct!

Now that *is* a scary thought!!

Appendix D: Thoughts, Ideas, Comments and Suggestions

This is a random list of items of information – or of knowledge – that I would have liked to have known during the early weeks and months of my role as a full-time carer. Some may strike a chord with you, or even be helpful with a bit of luck. There is no considered order in which they appear. For brevity, when I use the word "patient" below it is used as a synonym for the phrase "disabled survivor of a severe stroke". The list is in the order I thought of them, which was random.

- It can be difficult for carers to understand the range of disabilities that their patients suffer from and exhibit, especially cognitive problems that can be quite subtle and often hidden. It can be so helpful if you can find someone "skilled in the art" and knowledgeable about stroke disability who is able to advise and help you.

- When the virtues of Early Supported Discharge (ESD) are extolled, be very careful about being talked into having your patient home too early, much as you would like to have them under your care. "Early" favours the hospital as it frees a bed. "Supported" favours the carer but is organised by the hospital and/or Social Services. It is difficult for a new carer to appreciate what they are letting themselves in for. Be as sure as you can that all you need will be in place *before* you accept your patient home. If uncertain, ask – and keep asking until you are completely happy about everything. Make sure, if you can, that everything recommended by the *National Stroke Strategy* document is in place.

- My understanding of *Care* and *Rehabilitation* saw them as two different things in more ways than one. Rehabilitation is paid for by the NHS. The prime aim of Rehabilitation is recovery from disabilities. Care is paid for by the patient (when they have the funds) or, perhaps more likely, a spouse or close family member takes on the role of carer, having been "volunteered". This role may well be full-time, which does <u>not</u> mean a thirty-seven-and-a-half hour week – it could be 80 hours or more. You may be helped by having paid carers calling in several times each day; this practice does not always work as well as you might hope, for several reasons commented on in the main text. The main aim of Care is to help the patient make the best they can of their disabilities – to have as comfortable a life as possible.

- When the patient arrives home, establishing an adequate level of care is the first priority; rehabilitation can be set on one side for a while, and often is. But who then has the responsibility at some later date for establishing a rehabilitation programme designed to meet the patient's needs and desires, and makes sure it happens? This should be established very early on, preferably before the patient is discharged from hospital. This subject is discussed in greater detail in chapter 39 under "*The First Observation*".

- The care industry is enormous. Anyone can be a volunteer carer, especially close family members who can be talked into the job, or feel it is their responsibility, and so effectively become carers who are: voluntary, unpaid, untrained and inexperienced in what needs to be done. In other words – you and me! Of course, you do the best you can, and with the best of intentions. Do you make mistakes? You bet you do!

- Quite early on you should feel the need to decide whether you want your patient to recover as many of their lost abilities as they can; in other words, return to their old selves as the ideal. The alternative to this is the default position, that is, to build up a routine of carer + dependent which is a long-term condition that does no more than make the best of a bad job and will hardly change with time. Of course you want recovery, it goes without saying. But there are hurdles to be jumped to achieve this.

- Assuming you are keen to work with your patient with the objective of them recovering, so far as is possible, their former life, these are the documents that were the most useful to me. They all took a long time for me to find, not knowing they even existed when I began my caring career:

Rita's Discharge Assessment written by the hospital social worker and describing her status and what support needed to be in place before she was sent home. Clearly, I should have had a copy before Rita left hospital but, not knowing of its existence, I did not acquire one until 12 months later.

National Clinical Guideline for Stroke, Third Edition July 2008, [the fifth edition was published in October 2016] Royal College of Physicians, incorporating recommendations from the National Institute for Health and Care Excellence. I was emailed a copy nine months after Rita's hospital discharge.

"Cerebrovascular Event Rehabilitation" a 'PatientPlus' article found online, after nine months.

National Stroke Strategy, Department of Health, 2008, Document No. 284536. Told about by a Stroke Association manager, 11 months after Rita's stroke.

Stroke Rehabilitation in Adults, NICE Clinical Guideline [CG162], published June 2013. Obviously, this was published too late to be helpful to me, though it would have been!

Rehabilitation After Brain Injury, a leaflet published by Headway UK in 2007 and available online. I have no record of when I got hold of this.

There must be other sources of good information and the Stroke Association website is an obvious place to look.

- *Care*, however loving and attentive, is not rehabilitation. It is little more than ensuring that the patient is as comfortable as possible. Patients who have suffered mild strokes may recover quite well spontaneously, but in this book I am discussing the after-effects of a severe stroke. Spontaneous recovery is improbable when only care is available, especially if both cognitive and physical disabilities are displayed.

- *Rehabilitation* needs input from professional therapists for success. These are people such as physiotherapists, occupational therapists and speech therapists who have skills that required a long training to build up. Having watched first-class therapists work with Rita over several years, I am in no doubt that good therapists are essential for the best chance of recovery.

- Compared with the number of carers in the UK, qualified therapists are a rare breed. There are just not the numbers to provide as much therapy as most badly disabled patients need to take their recovery as far as is possible. The number of moderately-to-seriously injured stroke survivors in the UK in 2016 is said to be in the region of one million. That, plus the many other demands on therapists' time from other sources make the possibility that rehabilitation could continue "as long as it is needed", as recommended in the *National Stroke Strategy*, impractical. This is why the use of "supervised therapy by carers", such as Rita received in Fish Hoek, seemed such a good idea (see chapter 38).

- So, just organising sufficient therapy is a practical problem that can be of major proportions. What do you do about it? We went to South Africa and found there the therapists Rita needed – though I must admit we did not know they were there before we arrived in Fish Hoek. Of course, it really should *not* be necessary to fly to South Africa to access appropriate therapy.

- Frequently, cognitively disabled patients have no motivation to get better. They are happy to spend the day sitting in a chair. The determination must then come from someone else, typically the main carer who is likely to be a close family member. Some help to understand and implement this extra task is highly desirable. Often, stroke charities can provide help, as can membership of a stroke group.

- To recover from disability is hard work, and especially so when there is no guarantee it can be achieved. The patient must work at boring and repetitive exercises, preferably building up to several hours every day. It is easy to give up. The carer needs to be strong enough to provide the considerable support and encouragement to keep going.

- As progress is made, the exercises continue to get harder, just a little bit each time. Otherwise a plateau is reached. It is not surprising if some patients decide a life of dependency is the easier option. But this may not be the easy option for the carer, of course, or what he or she wants.

- As Adele (the physiotherapist working in Fish Hoek) told Rita and me regularly, we have to keep "pushing the boundaries". Rita had to keep trying to do things that were just beyond her capability. Luckily, she did have the determination to keep struggling with more difficult exercises, helped enormously by Adele's positive attitude, encouragement and expectation that Rita could recover.

- There is a hill to surmount. First, everything seems difficult, but with perseverance it may be possible to "get over the hill". Once at the top, the way becomes easier, progress more rapid and it all becomes worthwhile on the downward path.

- A level of scepticism is healthy. Be prepared to disbelieve things you are told. Professionals from whom you want help may be overworked, or restricted by rules or budgets they don't tell you about. There is also the postcode lottery. You may be lucky where you live and good therapy programmes may be available; or the opposite may happen. You won't know until the situation arises, when you can then only respond to whatever the situation is. If in doubt, ask questions until you get an answer you can believe.

- Many professionals assume they are being helpful by handing out reams of leaflets, brochures and other documents describing stroke disabilities. We found this action applied especially to local authority employees. It may well make them feel helpful, but they are not being so because most such leaflets are too general. It is not helpful because the variety of stroke disability is so wide. A carer is not interested in the disabilities their patient does *not* suffer from, just the ones they do. That is quite enough to occupy them and the time available. What are needed are face-to-face meetings with someone with experience who can assess your patient's actual disabilities and explain them to you. If such a person can be found, treasure them!

- Become as expert as you can about "stroke". That is hard because carers have plenty else to do besides extensive research, so maybe there is a friend or family member who would be good at doing research for you, for example online? There are lots of helpful statistics and good advice on the Stroke Association website, for example. Become familiar with documents such as the *National Stroke Strategy*, the *NICE Clinical Guideline 162* and the *National Clinical Guideline for Stroke*. There are several more documents that can be downloaded from the Internet. Highlight the parts that are especially relevant to your patient – what treatment should be provided and maybe isn't being – and go and argue about it.

- Join a local stroke club, more than one if possible. It is so helpful to discover other people have, or have seen, the same problems you are experiencing. You are not alone. You may find someone has a good answer to some difficulty you are struggling with, having already met it. Carers are always keen to pass on any helpful information they may have come across.

- It is often said, and is true, that rehabilitation programmes should begin as soon as possible. There are at least two good reasons. One is that a patient who sits in a chair all day quickly loses muscle tone and strength. Once that has happened the therapist has to work to recover that lost strength as well as overcome the problems caused by the stroke. The second is more subtle. It is true that brains are continually rewiring themselves, especially when pressurised to do so, and it is largely this that allows recovery from stroke when parts of the brain have died. The downside is that when a physical disability, like partial paralysis, is left untreated, the brain comes to believe that this is "normality" and, over time, rewires itself to make the best of a bad job. Later, this rewiring then has to be undone to permit recovery, and if the rewiring has gone too far, any paralysis or other disability might possibly become permanent.

- Conversely, it is *not* true that there is necessarily a time limit on a patient's ability to recover, it just may become more difficult as time passes, for the above reasons. It is certainly true that patients rarely do recover once two years have passed, but it is my contention this lack of progress is more to do with the fact that the essential rehabilitation therapy is never given after this period and not because the patient has lost all ability to recover.

- This one is important for administrative reasons. Rita and I were lucky that, a few years before Rita's stroke, we had organised Enduring Powers of Attorney (PoA) for each other. Without that, it would have been significantly more difficult to look after Rita because I would have had no control of her financial assets or affairs, and she certainly was not able to manage them herself. So then, what do you do? The laws in this country are now so complex concerning the "rights" of the individual, personal confidentiality and suchlike that my responsibilities would have been raised to another level of complexity. The Enduring PoA has now been broadened and become a Lasting Power of Attorney, but the outcome is much the same, though rather better. It is very sensible to have Powers of Attorney arranged with your loved one(s) while it is possible – before a disaster happens such as a severe stroke involving cognitive disabilities, when it may become impossible to arrange.

Appendix E: How Many Severely Disabled Stroke Survivors Might be Able to Recover?

Given the arguments outlined in chapter 43, is it right that Rita's history should be regarded as just anecdotal, of no value to any other stroke survivor, and thus ignored? Alternatively: *"Was Rita's recovery a one-off anecdotal story of one lucky person; or could it be used to show that many badly disabled stroke survivors still have a similar potential to recover, if given the appropriate treatment?"* If survivors do retain that innate potential, how many might benefit substantially, as Rita has done? The answer to that last question is unknown (so far as I am aware) and will only become available as a result of some properly conducted experiments. And, so far, that is where I have failed to interest any senior rehabilitation experts in evaluating this potential.

The two major benefits of recovery – getting one's life back and saving substantial sums in long-term care costs – are so important that they justify some investigation to determine whether other badly disabled ABI patients could be helped by the straightforward regime that Rita was given in Fish Hoek and described in chapter 38. If a reasonable proportion of severely disabled stroke victims actually recovered, it would represent a substantial saving in care costs. Plus – and, perhaps, more importantly – a better quality of life would be achieved for all concerned, especially the stroke survivor.

To me, as a non-expert in setting up controlled experiments to test hypotheses in the field of rehabilitative therapy, it does not seem difficult or expensive to run a small well-controlled test. If a small programme indicates significant promise, then this can be followed up with a bigger test and, if that confirms the first results, decide where to go from there.

From a purely practical point of view, it seems not to be possible to run a full double-blind project. This is because we are proposing to test a course of intensive therapy, not the effect of a new medicine. In testing a new medicine, it is reasonably straightforward to give one group of volunteers a pill containing the medicine under test and the control group a look-alike, but placebo, pill. No volunteer patient, or doctor, or member of the assessment staff, knows who has received which. Whereas, when it comes to testing a rehabilitation therapy that continues for some weeks, it is clearly not possible to hide from the volunteers or doctors or therapists who has had the programme under investigation and who hasn't. So I suggest the following procedure.

Outline of the first programme for testing

- Select a fairly small group of stroke survivors, all suffering multiple disabilities. I am open to advice on the number, but, because I am looking for a large difference between those who are given treatment and those who are not, any change as a result of treatment needs to be substantial for the therapy to be regarded as successful. (I would regard an improvement of, say, 10% as failure, so we do not need a lot of people for the result to be mathematically significant.) The group could also be selected for certain other attributes, discussed in chapter 40, question 6. In particular, the survivor should show willingness to put in the daily effort required over 12 weeks. The main carer should also be strongly in favour and be prepared to give necessary support and enthusiasm. The survivor should not suffer from any non-stroke related illness that needs additional treatment separate from the rehabilitation therapy. All volunteers should be assessed as strong enough to undergo the full treatment. The time that has passed between the stroke and this test is immaterial. It may be thought that in stipulating these requirements I am "cherry-picking" the volunteers to be used. This is not so, as is discussed later.

- Divide the whole group on a random basis into two equal parts, A and B.

- Both groups will already have been told, during the selection procedure, that they will be used to test a rehabilitation treatment aimed at overcoming their disabilities. This is a programme that has shown success before on a small scale. There is no guarantee of its success with every individual, but the expectation is there and this test programme is to try and get a measure of that success rate.

- One group, say B, will be given the full rehabilitation therapy over a period of 12 weeks. Just before starting, Group A will be told that they *will* receive the therapy, but due to limitations on the availability of therapists (a small white lie, perhaps) their programme will be delayed for three months.

- All members of both groups will be assessed regularly (say every four weeks) in as quantitative a way as is practical for any changes in their status. At the end of 12 weeks, all results will be assessed for both groups and any differences compared statistically. Have Group B members made progress towards recovery, compared with Group A, or not? I would hope to see Group B make a significant advance, certainly with a 98% confidence level (using Standard Deviation analysis, this would be termed a 3-sigma confidence level), but the answer will be in the results. (It would not be surprising to see Group A advance a little, just because they would probably respond positively to having an interest being taken in their welfare.)

- Group A will then be given the same therapy routine that Group B had already received. Both groups will be assessed quantitatively every four weeks once again, to determine their status regarding any recovery. This should show (1) whether Group A repeated the progress (if any) shown by Group B, and (2) whether Group B held onto the progress that might have been achieved, once therapy ceased.

The results, and observations and comments from volunteers and the assessors, should be used to decide what further assessment of the programme might be justified.

The reason for selecting the whole group of volunteers with defined attributes (as described in the first point), is to use stroke survivors who have the best likelihood of success. What we are then measuring is *not* the proportion of survivors who might be capable of a good recovery, given the prescribed therapy. We want to find the proportion who are capable of recovery, within a group who are considered to have the best chance. I suggest this because, if these specially selected volunteers show no significant progress after 12 weeks of therapy, the whole idea can be written off.

It can safely be assumed that not all survivors will be able to recover well, for all sorts of unfortunate reasons. What we are interested in is how many might recover, selected from those who are thought to have the best potential. If this little experiment proves successful, it could be extended in several ways to learn more about the process. If it is unsuccessful – write it off!

If successful, it might encourage some of those survivors who said they were not willing to put in the amount of effort needed, to change their minds!

Epilogue

This is a chapter about me. For more than six years following Rita's stroke, I did not take a single day off from full-time caring as a result of any illness of my own. Then, in 2015, I fell quite ill myself. So how did Rita face up to this change in circumstances? Would it put more pressure on her boundaries than she could cope with?

On 21 January 2015, we left Heathrow, destination Cape Town once again. About a week earlier, I had gone down with the worst head cold I had had in many years, certainly nothing like it since Rita had been ill. It was just past the worst after four days and I decided to fly, but it hung around for several weeks once we were back in the South African summer and despite the warm dry weather.

During the week beginning 9 March, I developed a dry cough. Nothing particular to worry about, I thought, just an irritation. I bought a bottle of cough mixture that did no good whatever. Early the next week, I still had the cough and had begun to feel unwell. It was still nothing specific; just a feeling of general lassitude, plus loss of energy and appetite. If it remains like this after the next weekend, I told myself, I will see the doctor. I should not have put it off, it was obvious I was not my usual self.

I rang the surgery at 9.00 am on Monday. The phone was answered immediately. "Could I please see my doctor today?" "When would you like to come?" the secretary asked. "There is an appointment at 10.45 or several during the afternoon." I chose 10.45. The doctor listened to what I had to report and picked up his stethoscope. "You have a 'crackling' at the base of your right lung," he reported. He took a sample of blood to be tested and told me to go to the radiological unit in Fish Hoek for a chest X-ray that afternoon. Then I must see him again the next morning when he could confirm what was causing the trouble.

The next day, at 10.15 am, my X-ray was displayed on his monitor and he had the analysis of the blood sample. "What you have," he told me, "Is a minor atypical pneumonia infection of the right lung. What it isn't, in case you were wondering, is tuberculosis. Nor anything else. Just pneumonia. We should be able to clear it up in a week with antibiotics." He prescribed me a course of antibiotics which were dispensed from the surgery's pharmacy.

A week later, I was not better; in fact rather worse. That called for a different antibiotic. I went back for a fourth appointment at 9.00 am on Thursday 2 April, which happened to be Maundy Thursday. By this time, I was clearly worse still and the doctor became concerned. "Right," he said. "I want you to go immediately to the blood analysis laboratory in Fish Hoek; here is the address. They will take about four samples and will have the results back to me within two hours. I will telephone you this afternoon and say what we are going to do with you."

The call came about 3.00 pm. "I have arranged for you to be admitted to hospital," he told me and named a hospital about 30 minutes' drive away in south-east Cape Town. "The sooner you get there the better; they are expecting you."

"Do you mean today?" I asked, really for want of something to say. "Yes, definitely, if you can make it," was the reply.

The next two hours were occupied in organising Rita, who had not spent a night alone for seven years, since before her stroke. Monika and Dickie kindly said they would "look in" several times a day. I organised a nurse from FHHN to call every day I was in hospital. If Rita was in any difficulty, they would know what to do and they had my authority to take whatever action they deemed necessary. I gave Rita about Rand 1000 and written instructions on how to operate the rather quirky house alarm system (with my fingers firmly crossed). She wasn't in the least concerned about looking after herself for what might be two or three days, but turned out to be five.

I drove over the mountains and found the hospital without difficulty, arriving there about 6.00 pm. As it was outside visiting hours, there were plenty of free parking spaces within 50 m of the main entrance. They were, indeed, expecting me, including the respiratory specialist (consultant) to determine just what was the trouble and to decide what should be done. That all took two hours, by which time I was installed in a four-bedded

330

ward with a canula inserted in my hand (feeding me with antibiotics, I think), a pile of pills taken, more blood samples, an oxygen feed up my nose and a nebuliser by the bed that I had to use regularly. My blood pressure was taken every half-hour or so (always low, as mine is) and oxygen saturation which was sometimes below 80%. There was also an evening meal saved for me. This had suffered somewhat by being reheated twice before I was allowed time to eat it, but it was a kind thought.

The next morning I felt a little better. Things continued that day as they had begun the previous evening, plus a physiotherapist pummeled my chest twice a day as if it were a drum. Despite it being the Easter weekend, the specialist came in every day to check my condition. By Easter Monday I felt almost normal, just a little weak, and I suggested I returned home. The specialist agreed I could leave on Tuesday, provided I survived what he called "the physio's walk". This consisted of a brisk 10-minute walk around hospital corridors, part of the grounds and up and down two or three flights of stairs. I was a bit puffed by the end, but I kept up with her. So, discharge papers were put together and I drove home on Tuesday morning with no instructions and no follow-up medicine to take. In fact, the specialist suggested I would be fit enough for a hip revision operation that was scheduled for the end of April in the UK. He was wrong about that.

Rita had managed well, living by herself. She had been shopping. Luckily Longbeach Mall was only a ten-minute walk away and no roads had to be crossed between the Mall and our house. The only upset was that she managed to set off the house alarm three times, and so activated the "Armed Response" that is threatened on the signs nailed to the outside of our fence. The armed response consisted of a black man with a gun arriving within five minutes of the alarm going off! I knew it had happened because I received automatic notification of the alarm on my cell phone. But Rita was able to convince him each time, without much difficulty, that she was not an intruder and had just "pressed the wrong button".

We returned home to the UK on 18 April. I felt much, but not entirely, better. The orthopaedic surgeon had already said there was no way he would operate on my hip within a month of me being in hospital with pneumonia. Another reason to put off the operation also developed. During the first few days of May, all my symptoms suddenly returned, plus an acute shortness of breath. For two days I had my usual morning shower, then sat on the edge of the bed for up to ten minutes, panting for breath as though I had completed a 400 m sprint. This is no good, I thought, and rang the surgery for an emergency appointment. Our usual GP was away, but the colleague I saw had no hesitation in referring me straight back to hospital.

So, again I was making arrangements for Rita, but more easily this time because, during the previous year, we had moved into a comfortable apartment in a "retirement village". There was good support for her there, as well as several old friends not far away and family 20 miles away, so I was confident this time she would be all right on her own. Our friend Robert kindly drove me to the hospital.

I was admitted to the Emergency Assessment Unit and, somewhat to my surprise, placed in isolation due to my recent return from a "tropical" country. They needed to test for TB, HIV and a number of other potential diseases which may have been divulged to me, but I have forgotten which they were. Within a few days all these tests came back negative, but the isolation continued. This had the advantage of giving me a quiet private room, but with the downside that I had no access to a bath or shower for four days.

The reason I was in hospital was that the pneumonia had now infected both lungs and became much more problematic. The consultant, with whom I got on very well, refused to prescribe antibiotics because they had been so ineffective in South Africa. Before prescribing steroids (the only sensible alternative to antibiotics, he told me), he needed to know the exact cause of my pneumonia, not least because steroids are liable to cause unpleasant side effects and are not to be given lightly. Finding the precise cause of my illness became the problem. Based on the test results, the cause appeared to be neither bacterial nor viral. So, because I had a slightly raised eosinophil count, perhaps something was causing that. But none of the tests was in any way conclusive. "You are going to have to get better by yourself. That would be much the best solution." the consultant said, then added, "People do, you know!"

I had a CT scan, plus a bronchoscopy at the third attempt. The first two dates set were cancelled as patients with greater need than mine appeared on the scene. The bronchoscopy was eventually done on Thursday 14 May and was not a procedure I would wish on anyone! It was to be several days before the results would be available. With another weekend imminent when nothing would happen, and I could stand no more daytime TV nor read solidly all day any longer, I negotiated with the consultant to go home on the basis I would be better off there. He agreed on the understanding that, if my health deteriorated, I would return immediately to hospital and, in any case, I would go in the next Tuesday for another chest X-ray. As there was no available appointment for weeks ahead in his diary, I should then hunt for him on the wards to have a further review of my condition. That I happily agreed.

Surprisingly, on the Monday morning I felt significantly better, an improvement that was sustained on Tuesday when Robert drove me back to hospital. The X-ray confirmed an improvement compared with the one taken about a week earlier. So the next follow-up meeting with the consultant would not be for two weeks unless, of course, I deteriorated once more; but this didn't happen. That marked the end of it, pretty well. From then on I got steadily better. Later, the consultant sent me copies of letters he had written, including one to a colleague in a London hospital asking for her views on my condition, and describing it as a "devastating pneumonia slow to resolve". This surprised me. I had felt ill, but not devastatingly so!

In mid July, I returned to hospital for a lung function test, at which the technician said my lungs were working significantly better than the average for someone in good health and my age and height. I certainly felt better than I had all year. Against that, the consultant suspected that my immune system had been "compromised" by the pneumonia and prescribed several vaccinations to counteract possible problems in the future. His continuing interest was reassuring.

At last we come to the real purpose of this epilogue: to use my illness to demonstrate how well Rita had recovered from her multiple disabilities. In South Africa, during April, she looked after herself for five days. Back in England I was in hospital for nine days and she coped perfectly well – even walked a mile into town several times to shop for consumables and found her way home again. I had been more than concerned at leaving her alone, but I should have remembered, accepted and had faith in Adele's strictures to "keep pushing the boundaries". My two hospitalisations were unplanned "pushes at Rita's boundaries" and they showed how much more capable she was than I had thought. This may also be true of many long-term disabled stroke survivors. These may too easily become used to being dependent and having things done for them; routines may be too firmly established over months and years and then are never changed because no reason is seen to do so. It might be true that many disabled stroke survivors are capable of doing much more for themselves, were their boundaries given regular "pushes" to find out. And if so, they might find themselves living more rewarding lives.

Author's Note

This book is a "carer's eye view", written from the point of view of a full-time, untrained, amateur carer responsible for a badly disabled wife, rather than a first person account of "How I overcame my disabilities and regained a Life". It is more about how I found a way to overcome my wife's disabilities, regaining both our lives.

Soon after Rita had been transferred back to the local hospital from the neurosurgical unit, in May 2008, someone, I remember not who it was, suggested I start a journal to record Rita's and my daily life-after-stroke experiences. I might find it useful to have a record, they said, of what occurred and when. So I wrote page 1 of the journal on 18 May 2008 and it has continued until well into 2016. I am now halfway through volume 24. It is not a diary as such, completed each year, just one book follows another as each becomes full.

As a result, I now have a daily record covering eight years of what happened, who we met, why, what was agreed or decided, who said they would do what, how Rita behaved, how I felt about things and, for what it was worth, my state of mind. This record has enabled me, just as an example, to add up how many employees of the NHS, Social Services and other local authority departments, charities and other NGOs I have met, written to or telephoned in my mostly unsuccessful attempts during the first two years to organise treatment for Rita. The total number of people involved one way or another, to a greater or lesser extent, came to more than 70. I have a not-so-little list of them all! Many promises were made, designed to help Rita. I know when these promises were made and by whom. With some research later on in the journal, I can confirm that a great many of these promises were not kept. The negative nature of Part 1 is, regrettably, one of its most marked attributes. Almost everything seemed negative then, very negative compared with the relaxed and positive approach we enjoyed when overseas which is described in Part 2.

The journal has also confirmed to me what a fickle thing memory can be. Several times I have written short passages of the book from memory to avoid breaking into the flow of my thoughts, then gone back to the journal to check the validity of what I had written, only to find that my memory had been wrong. Some events actually had not happened in the order I remembered; things had been said that were recorded in the journal differently from how I recalled them. A few times I was even wrong about who said what and who was at a meeting. So there has been quite a lot of correction to be done because I have always taken the journal, written at the time, to be more reliable than memory. For any dispute there was between my memory and the journal's written word, the written record always won.

The journal was always an up-to-date record of events, being written the same day, or at the latest the day after, throughout eight years. This has enabled me to put this book together as a factual account of what happened during Rita's long rehabilitation period. I know, for example, that she only three times saw a physiotherapist during the first few months from being discharged home, who that physio was and the dates she worked with Rita. And that Rita did not see an occupational therapist once during the same time band. Perhaps unsurprisingly, my recordings of how I felt at the time differ considerably from my view now, looking back. At the time they were immediate and all-encompassing; now they have mellowed, especially in the light of what happened during the later years in South Africa. When I wrote down my thoughts in this story it was the way I was thinking at the time – which I now often find somewhat embarrassing.

My wife's history developed into a very different story from the way it began. The first draft was completed during 2009 to the summer of 2010 and was titled "If You're Going to Have a Stroke, Don't Have It Here", which is now the heading for Part 1. The first draft was long and included, in considerable detail, pretty well everything that happened to Rita and me during the first two-and-a-half years. It was a recording of how difficult things were (unnecessarily difficult was my opinion) when one had to take on a caring job at short notice which was long-term, very time-consuming, for which one had no training, no interest in and no aptitude for. Many people would make much better "voluntary" carers than I did. Just as an observation, I found it odd that paid carers must be trained for the job (in order to meet Health and Safety Regulations) before taking up the responsibility of looking after disabled people. However, it is assumed unpaid carers (usually family members) apparently can carry out the same work safely from the word go with no training at all. They are allowed to do so anyway; there is no legal requirement for any training whatever, as I understand things. With the best of intentions, untrained carers will make mistakes to the probable detriment of the patient.

I then did nothing with the book for more than two years, by which time it was clear that Rita, unexpectedly, was making a dramatic recovery that looked as though it could become almost complete. She was getting her old life back again, against all the prognoses from health and care professionals in the UK. But not, interestingly, against what the authors of the *National Stroke Strategy* and the *National Clinical Guideline for Stroke* had written. They appeared to have had a more positive view of what was possible than the professionals we had to interact with face-to-face in real life.

Getting my wife back, especially when she managed to lose her irrational behaviour and overcame her double incontinence, was wonderful enough, but the fact of her recovery excited my curiosity (I was trained as an R&D scientist, after all). *How,* and especially *why,* did she recover so well? These two questions developed in importance from the autumn of 2010 onwards – that really exciting time – while I explored rational and pragmatic reasons to answer them.

So the book's story became markedly more interesting and possibly useful to others. In the summer of 2013, I took up the writing project once more. The long first draft was cut down to less than half its original length and became Part 1. Part 2 was added as a description of *how* Rita recovered. Part 3 as an explanation of *why* she was able to regain a normal lifestyle together with a vastly improved quality of life – all of it made up of my own assessments of cause and effect, of course.

Please note that the book is not written as a day-to-day diary in chronological order. Instead, many of the chapters relate to specific subjects that can be followed from beginning to end on their own. In effect, these chapters are written in parallel with each other. If the book had been written as a day-to-day diary, different events would have been mixed together and become more than difficult to follow. With many of the chapters written "in parallel", the book can either be read from start to finish like a novel or individual chapters can be picked out if their subject matter is of particular interest. Many of the chapters stand alone as records of the course of single aspects of Rita's treatment or recovery. This does result in some repetition of events in order to "set the scene" at the beginning of some chapters, and some anecdotes and ideas are repeated two or three times (usually expressed differently) in those chapters in which they are relevant.

Inevitably, Rita's story is anecdotal. It concerns only *her* recovery and how it was achieved. When viewed scientifically as an exercise from which useful information can be gathered, it has the considerable disadvantage that the sample size is just one – Rita – not hundreds of stroke survivors. Possibly for this reason, my attempts to replicate her success, by persuading academics who have worked in the field of rehabilitation medicine for long periods of time to set up a pilot experiment, such as described in Appendix E, were unsuccessful. They were not interested in anecdotal stories.

This attitude was understandable, but a mistake. Many discoveries have been made as a result of one-off observations of events that did not meet expectations, or were not immediately explainable. As mentioned earlier, this idea is discussed by Nicholas Carr in the book *This Idea Must Die*, edited by John Brockman. An article "Get Lucky" was published in *New Scientist* for 22 August 2015. This discussed some of the considerable number of well-known inventions that have arisen from serendipity – the observation and following up of unexpected results – plus thinking outside the box. Maybe Rita and I were serendipitously lucky in finding a way to "cure" Rita's disabilities in Fish Hoek. It is evident that although Rita's story is anecdotal, it contains a number of indisputable facts that, together, suggest there could be ideas usefully transferable to other severely disabled stroke survivors.

Perhaps unusually, I am offering my sincere thanks to the books and documents listed in the Reference section. These educated and guided me through what was a brand new area of knowledge for me.

Thanks also to Mo, whose unfailing optimism and support helped Rita and me through a dismal period. It was a real sadness that Mo died before Rita's recovery was really beginning to show. She would have loved to have seen that. To three charities for their unflagging support, in alphabetical order they were Action for Family Carers, Headway and Success After Stroke. To the wonderful therapists and nurses in Fish Hoek who never even thought about giving up on Rita (as far as I know!), namely Adele, Estie, Shona, Jenny and Heather. We are so grateful to them. And not forgetting the 15 or more enthusiastic, black carers in South Africa who all gave Rita so much practical help and in so cheerful a manner over a period of several years.

Finally, I must offer my heartfelt apologies to my dear wife for recounting the many very private and embarrassing moments that she endured. They were not her fault but the result of the severe injury to her brain caused by the haemorrhage. This story would not have been a factual account of this dramatic episode in our lives had I been selective and left out some of the worst things with which we were afflicted during this long time.

References and Further Information

Brockman, John (ed) (2015). *This Idea Must Die: Scientific Ideas That are Blocking Progress*, Harper Perennial. ISBN: 978-0-06-237434-9.

Chown, Marcus (2013). *What a Wonderful World: One Man's Attempt to Explain the Big Stuff*, Faber & Faber, page 85. ISBN: 978-0-571-27839-8.

Doidge, Norman (2008). The Brain that Changes Itself: Stories of Personal Triumph from the Frontiers of Brain Science, Penguin Books. ISBN: 978-0-141-03887-2.

Headway (nd). *Rehabilitation after Brain Injury* (available online at https://www.headway.org.uk/about-brain-injury/individuals/rehabilitation-and-continuing-care/rehabilitation/).

Health, Department of (2007). *National Stroke Strategy*, Document No. 284536.

Holmes, Bob (2015). "Get Lucky (the history of inventions is full of chance finds)", *New Scientist*, Vol 227, No 3035, 22 August, pages 38–41. (http://www.sciencedirect.com/science/article/pii/S0262407915310332)

Marriott, Hugh (2009). *The Selfish Pig's Guide to Caring: How to Cope with the Emotional and Practical Aspects of Caring for Someone*, 5th ed, Piatkus. ISBN: 978-0-7499-2986-2.

Matthews, Jane (2007). *The Carer's Handbook: Essential Information and Support for All Those in a Caring Role*, 2nd rev ed, How To Books Ltd. ISBN: 978-1-84528-194-6.

Michelon, Pascale (2012). *Max Your Memory: The Complete Visual Programme*, DK Publications. ISBN: 978-1-4093-7455-8.

NICE (2013). *Stroke Rehabilitation in Adults*, Clinical Guideline [CG162], National Institute for Health and Care Excellence (available online at https://www.nice.org.uk/guidance/cg162).

PatientPlus (2013). *Cerebrovascular Event Rehabilitation,* (available online at http://patient.info/doctor/cerebrovascular-event-rehabilitation).

Powell, Trevor (2004). *Head Injury: A Practical Guide*, 2nd rev ed, Speechmark Publishing Ltd. ISBN: 978-0-86388-451-1.

Royal College of Physicians (2016). *National Clinical Guideline for Stroke*, 5th ed, Royal College of Physicians (available online at https://www.strokeaudit.org/SupportFiles/Documents/Guidelines/2016-National-Clinical-Guideline-for-Stroke-5t-(1).aspx). [Fifth edition published October 2016]

Taylor, Jill Bolte (2009). *My Stroke of Insight*, Hodder. ISBN: 978-0-340-9805007. Dr Taylor was carrying out postgraduate research on the brain when she suffered a subarachnoid haemorrhage herself. The story of her personal experience is fascinating, in comparison to Rita's.

Fish Hoek – Caring

Fish Hoek Home Nursing Services Trust
Website: www.fhhomenursing.com

"Fish Hoek Home Nursing is a non-profit organisation which has been serving the elderly within our community for the past 25 years. The care provided is a very viable alternative to retirement complexes, frail care or a post-operative step down facility. We assist people of all ages at home, including mothers and new-born babies. We have a Sister on call 24 hours a day to respond to emergency calls, to perform specific nursing procedures, to supervise all care given and to provide help and support to both patient and family. A care plan is designed specifically for each patient taking into consideration any special requirements they may have. We have a bank of very reliable carers, some of whom have been with us for 25 years, who not only help with all the activities of daily living, but will also provide a complete home service, including cooking, cleaning and laundry to ensure that all the needs of their patients are adequately catered for."

Fish Hoek – Occupational Therapy

Website: www.creativeot.co.za

Shona Saayman, the South African Occupational Therapist who helped Rita so well between 2012 and 2015, has been in practice since 1990, having graduated from the University of Cape Town with a BSc (OT) Hons.

Fish Hoek – Physiotherapy

The Wellspring Health Centre (AP Physio and Aquatic Specialists).
Address: 2 Longboat Street, Sun Valley, Cape Town 7975, South Africa
email: info@wellspringcentre.co.za
Telephone: +27 21 785 7200.
Website: www.wellspringcentre.co.za

"Adele Pudney Aquatic Physiotherapists is a physiotherapy practice consisting of a number of physiotherapists who work in close collaboration with other health care and allied practitioners at the Wellspring Centre in Cape Town.

Adele Pudney started her practice in 2006 in Fish Hoek. She has a keen interest in neuro-rehabilitation and treating chronic pain. The practice includes other physiotherapists, who each have a special interest in different areas of treatment.

All practitioners practice in a client-centred holistic manner, which takes the approach of tailor-making a treatment programme for each individual client according to their goals and life setting.

We believe that due to the brain's and body's characteristics of plasticity, we can always have a therapeutic effect on movement and function. We work closely with the client and family members in order to set achievable goals with functional outcomes. We use various treatment modalities and problem-solve according to many rehabilitation models and years of experience.

Our first goal is to explain to all involved that the treatment approach is a journey and the results that are achieved are dependent on the time and effort that is put in by the client. Education and empowerment form a big part of our treatment strategies and we deliver this to a level that is appropriate for each client.

We work closely with occupational therapists and speech therapists in order to get the most therapeutic benefit out of each treatment session. Using a multidisciplinary team approach is very helpful as each therapist has specific expertise that is needed to achieve a holistic treatment approach."